# Irradiation of Polymers

A symposium sponsored by
the Division of Industrial
and Engineering Chemistry
at the 151st Meeting of the
American Chemical Society,
Pittsburgh, Pa., March 29-30, 1966.

**Norbert Platzer,** *Symposium Chairman*

ADVANCES IN CHEMISTRY SERIES **66**

AMERICAN CHEMICAL SOCIETY

WASHINGTON, D.C.     1967

# Advances in Chemistry Series

**Robert F. Gould,** *Editor*

*Advisory Board*

AMERICAN CHEMICAL SOCIETY PUBLICATIONS

# FOREWORD

ADVANCES IN CHEMISTRY SERIES was founded in 1949 by the American Chemical Society as an outlet for symposia and collections of data in special areas of topical interest that could not be accommodated in the Society's journals. It provides a medium for symposia that would otherwise be fragmented, their papers distributed among several journals or not published at all. Papers are refereed critically according to ACS editorial standards and receive the careful attention and processing characteristic of ACS publications. Papers published in ADVANCES IN CHEMISTRY SERIES are original contributions not published elsewhere in whole or major part and include reports of research as well as reviews since symposia may embrace both types of presentation.

# CONTENTS

Preface ................................................................................. vii

### HIGH ENERGY RADIATION

1. Radiation Mechanics in Polymers.............................................. 1
   Arthur Charlesby, Physics Department, Royal Military College of Science, Shrivenham, Swindon, Wiltshire, England

2. Chemical Nature of the Reactive Species Produced in Polymers by Ionizing Radiations...................................... 22
   Adolphe Chapiro, Laboratoire de Chimie des Radiations, Centre National de la Recherche Scientifique, Bellevue, France

### CROSSLINKING VS. SCISSION

3. Reactive Intermediates in the Radiation Chemistry of Polyethylene ................................................................................. 31
   Malcolm Dole, Northwestern University, Evanston, Ill., and David M. Bodily, University of Arizona, Tucson, Ariz.

4. Irradiation of Hydrocarbon-Polymers in Nitrous Oxide Atmosphere ......................................................................... 44
   Yoichi Okada, Central Research Laboratory, Sumitomo Bakelite Co., Yokohama, Japan

5. Effects of Radiation on the Olefinic Groups in Polybutadiene    57
   W. W. Parkinson, Oak Ridge National Laboratory, Oak Ridge, Tenn., and W. C. Sears, University of Georgia, Athens, Ga.

6. The Effect of Ionizing Radiation on Ethylene-Alkyl Acrylate Copolymers ......................................................................... 71
   James E. Potts, Chester L. Purcell, and Outten J. Clinard, Union Carbide Corp., Bound Brook, N. J.

7. Transient Acceleration of Creep Rates of Polymers During High Intensity Irradiation..................................................... 79
   James B. Bell, Alan S. Michaels, Allan S. Hoffman, and Edward A. Mason, Massachusetts Institute of Technology, Cambridge, Mass.

8. Radiation Modification of Poly(ethylene oxide)...................... 113
   P. A. King, Union Carbide Corp., Tuxedo, N. Y.

9. Radiation Chemistry of Polyethylene Terephthalate................ 127
   D. T. Turner, Camille Dreyfus Laboratory, Research Triangle Institute, Durham, N. C.

10. Radiation Crosslinked Ionomers and Polyethylenes................. 139
   B. J. Lyons and C. R. Vaughn, Raychem Corp., Redwood City, Calif.

11. Radiation Crosslinking of Some New Ethylene Copolymers.... 156
   Rudolph Vermes, Allied Chemical Corp., Morristown, N. J., and Walter Brenner, New York University, Bronx, N. Y.

HOMOPOLYMERIZATION

12. Radiation-Induced Polymerization of Pure Liquid α-Methylstyrene .................................................................................... 170
   Donald J. Metz, Brookhaven National Laboratory, Upton, N. Y.

13. Gamma Radiation-Induced Polymerization of Some Vinyl Monomers in Emulsion Systems................................................ 184
   Gregor J. M. Ley, Dieter O. Hummel, and Christel Schneider, Universität Köln, Cologne, Germany

GRAFT-COPOLYMERIZATION

14. Reaction Rates and Physical Properties in the Radiation Graft-Copolymer System: Poly(vinyl chloride)-Styrene........ 203
   David E. Harmer, The Dow Chemical Co., Midland, Mich.

15. Radiation-Induced Graft Polymerization of Flexible Polyurethane Foam ........................................................................ 214
   Walter J. Skraba, Union Carbide Corp., Tuxedo, N. Y., and John W. Lynn, Union Carbide Corp., South Charleston, W. Va.

16. Radiation Grafting of Vinyl Monomers to Wool..................... 221
   Daniel Campbell, J. L. Williams, and Vivian Stannett, Camille Dreyfus Laboratory, Research Triangle Institute, Durham, N. C.

ULTRAVIOLET LIGHT RADIATION

17. Photolytic Degradation of Cellulose Triacetate...................... 240
   Catherine S. Hsia Chen, Stanley Jankowski, and Allen Brother, Celanese Corporation of America, Summit, N. J.

18. Free Radicals in Polyolefins Initiated with Ultraviolet and Ionizing Radiation ................................................................. 256
   Bengt Rånby and Peter Carstensen, The Royal Institute of Technology, Stockholm, Sweden

vi

# PREFACE

For the past 20 years, radiation chemistry has received considerable attention in polymer research. High energy radiation, as obtained from electron beams and x- or beta rays, initiates ionization and radical formation. It may cause either crosslinking or chain scission, depending on the chemical structure of the polymer and dose rate. In the presence of oxygen, peroxides may be formed. When they are trapped, ions, radicals, or peroxides can produce postirradiation reactions. High energy radiation may also be used to initiate polymerization or to engraft mono- or multifunctional monomers upon polymeric chains. Low energy radiation, such as ultraviolet light, is less penetrating and has been restricted to surface treatment.

For several years, crosslinking of polyethylene had been the only commercial process used in the polymer industry. Recently, other processes have gained importance, especially in the area of grafting. The Division of Industrial and Engineering Chemistry, recognizing the potential of polymer irradiation for industrial applications, held a two-day symposium on this subject during the 1966 spring meeting of the American Chemical Society in Pittsburgh. The participants were selected among the world experts in this field, well known through their books, publications, and patents. This volume contains the papers presented at that symposium.

When considering industrial use of polymer irradiation, the following four questions arise:

1. What are the advantages of irradiation?
2. Which properties can be improved by irradiation?
3. What kind of radiation source is preferred?
4. What does irradiation cost?

Most of these pertinent questions are answered in the chapters of the various authors. As a guideline, I shall attempt to discuss these questions briefly by referring to the different chapters and by filling in a few gaps, not covered by the authors.

## What Are the Advantages of Irradiation?

The major advantages are: (a) that the desired reactions can be carried out generally at lower temperatures than in operations employing chemical means, (b) that monomers can be polymerized free of catalyst contamination, (c) that crosslinking and grafting can be performed *in situ* on fabricated articles, and (d) that coatings can be applied in monomeric form, eliminating solvents.

New theories and findings on the formation of ionic species and radicals, which become trapped in the polymers, are discussed in the first two chapters, written by the two European authorities, Chapiro and Charlesby. The kinetics of crosslinking polyethylene is the subject of the American authority, Dole. A higher yield of crosslinking polyolefins was observed in the presence of nitrous oxide by the Japanese scientist, Okada.

Certain high polymers crosslink when irradiated whereas others degrade. This characteristic is related to the hydrogen which is bonded to the polymeric chain. Generally, polymers crosslink if all the carbon atoms of the main chain carry at least one hydrogen atom, but they degrade if tetrasubstituted carbons are present in the chain. This is probably caused by a larger steric hindrance which can be observed through a lower heat of polymerization than theoretically calculated and through a higher yield of recoverable monomer on pyrolysis. Crosslinking of ethylene-acrylate copolymers is the topic of Potts, and of polyethylene oxide is that of King, both with the Union Carbide Corp. Crosslinking of ionomers (Surlyn A) has been investigated by Lyons and Brenner, and of polyethylene terephthalate (Mylar) by Turner.

Gamma radiation-induced mass and emulsion polymerization of vinyl monomers has been studied by the American, Metz, and the German, Hummel.

Irradiating a polymer and adding a monomer may lead to the formation of a graft copolymer when irradiated. It causes the formation of free radicals in both the polymer and the monomer. Graft copolymerization is favored over homopolymerization of the added monomer if the $G_R$ value (free radicals per 100 e.v.) of the polymer is significantly higher than the $G_R$ value of the monomer. Homopolymerization predominates if the $G_R$ value of the monomer is larger than that of the polymer. Poly (vinyl chloride), for example, has a high $G_R$ value and is well suited as a backbone for grafting, whereas polystyrene has a low $G_R$ value. Grafting 10 to 20% styrene upon poly (vinyl chloride) and the resulting increase in density, tensile strength, and flexural strength are discussed by Harmer of the Dow Chemical Co. Polystyrene, which is unsuitable as a backbone, can be made susceptible to grafting by incorporating rubber.

Allyl methacrylate and allyl acrylate are difunctional monomers, triallyl phosphate is a trifunctional monomer, and polyethylene glycol dimethacrylate is a polyfunctional monomer. All these lead to crosslinked graft copolymers.

Grafting vinyl monomers to flexible polyurethane foam is the subject of Skraba's chapter, and to wool is that of Stannett.

## Which Properties Can Be Improved by Irradiation?

Increasing heat resistance and strength, reducing stress cracking, and lowering permeability are a few of the advantages obtainable through gamma or electron irradiation. Surface improvements, such as weather resistance, hardening, dyeability, or destaticizing, are obtainable through ultraviolet light treatment.

Prestressed irradiated polyethylene film and tubing shrink when heated above the crystalline melting temperature and form tight covers over the enclosed object. Irradiated polyethylene film is used for food wrapping and for protecting metal parts and equipment during prolonged storage. Its sale is expected to rise from 1965's $8 million to $20 million by 1970. Heat-shrinkable tubing and tape are used for electrical insulation and moisture protection. Irradiated polyethylene bottles may be sterilized at 135°C. Swelling of polymers by gas generation during irradiation has been observed by Hoffman and Bell, who report on this phenomenon.

Impregnating wood with monomers, such as methyl methacrylate, hydroxyethyl methacrylate, or vinyl acetate, and polymerizing it by irradiation results in increased hardness, higher strength, and better form stability. For instance, the hardness of pine can increase by 700% and oak made as hard as teak by irradiation. Considerable research is being devoted to the graft- and homopolymerization of various monomers on sheet paper and on paper-making fibers. This enhances bulkiness, resilience, acid resistance, and tensile strength of paper—all properties in demand for applications such as grocery bags.

The properties of impact polystyrene can be improved by simultaneous grafting and crosslinking upon rubber. Changing *cis*-polybutadiene into *trans*-polybutadiene and eliminating the 1,2-vinyl configuration through radiation are discussed by Parkinson.

Chloromethylstyrene has been grafted to polypropylene fiber to facilitate dyeing. Since moisture pickup is improved at the same time, ironing the textile product is also easier. Preirradiation of polyamide and polyester fibers at a dose of 0.5 to 1.5 megarads, followed by grafting of methacrylic acid to the surface, also increases wetting and dye acceptance and reduces static. Styrene monomer is grafted in commercial operation to the surface of Teflon and Kel-F sheets and films to make them bondable, dyeable, and printable. There, a dose of 1.75 megarads is required. The surfaces of vinyl tiles are hardened by grafting acrylonitrile and glycol mono- and diacrylates at a dose rate of 0.4 to 1.5 megarads.

## What Kind of Irradiation Source Is Preferred?

Radioactive isotopes appear practical when considerable depth of treatment is required. For upgrading the physical properties of the polymer, an electron accelerator may be used. For surface treatment, an electron accelerator, x-ray machine, or ultraviolet light can be employed, depending on the depth of treatment desired.

Radioactive sources of commercial interest are γ- and β-ray emitters. The choice of sources has narrowed down to roughly three elements—cobalt-60, strontium-90, and cesium-137—as a result of their useful characteristics, reasonably long half-life, availability, and cost.

### Radioactive Isotopes

| | Element | | |
|---|---|---|---|
| | Cobalt | Strontium | Cesium |
| Atomic weight | 60 | 90 | 137 |
| γ-rays, m.e.v. | 1.17, 1.33 | | 0.66[a] |
| β-rays, m.e.v. | 0.306 | 0.61, 2.18[b] | 0.51(95%), 1.17(5%) |
| Mr/hr. output/curie at 1 ft. | 14,400 | | 3750 |
| Curies in 1/8 x 1/8 inch source | 5 | | 1.45 |
| Half life, years | 5.27 | 28 | 33 |

[a] 0.66 m.e.v. gamma from $Ba^{137}$.
[b] 2.18 m.e.v. beta from $Y^{90}$.

Cobalt-60 is made by exposing ordinary inexpensive cobalt in an atomic reactor. Strontium-90 is a fission product in nuclear power plants and has a higher beta radiation than cobalt-60. Cesium-137 is a fission product found in all nuclear reactors and must be removed from time to time to maintain efficiency. Evidently large quantities of strontium-90 and cesium-137 will be available in the year to come.

Electron accelerators are available for producing electron beams with energies ranging from 10 k.e.v. to 10 m.e.v. and overlapping into the area of x-rays and γ-rays. There are two general types of electron beam machines: the direct and the indirect. In the direct, such as the Van de Graaff, the resonant transformer, and the Dynamitron, the high voltage is applied directly between the anode and the cathode of the accelerator tube. The accelerator tube is essentially the same in all three, and they differ only in the manner in which the high voltage is generated. In the Van de Graaff accelerator, the high voltage is generated by electrons carried on a rapidly moving insulated belt. In the resonant transformer, the high voltage is generated by a parallel circuit in its secondary which resonates at 180-cycle frequency fed to the primary. In the Dynamitron, the high voltage is generated by a set of cascaded rectifiers coupled to a 300-kc. RF-oscillator.

The insulated core transformer is another direct electron beam machine. It is similar to a three-phase power transformer in that a core and coils are used. One insulated core transformer will drive three accelerator tubes, which allows great flexibility and good power utilization. The Linac (linear accelerator) is an indirect electron beam machine. There, power is generated externally in a microwave oscillator at 3 kilomegacycles, and the accelerator tube takes the form of a circular copper wave guide. The advantage of this machine is that high voltage is not required and therefore insulation problems are not as severe as in the direct machines, and, in addition, rather higher powers can be generated.

A radiation dose of 1 kw. could irradiate about 795 pounds per hour of any material to a dose level of 1 Mrad at 100% efficiency. The power efficiency of the different machines varies from a low of 15% for a Van de Graaff accelerator or resonant transformer to 90% for an insulating core transformer. On the other hand, the Van de Graaff accelerator, being a d.c. machine, can be precisely controlled and adjusted, which is important for research and development. The resonant transformer, Dynamitron, and ICT are less precise, but they have lower operating costs and higher output power, making them more suitable for production purposes.

The use to which the machine will be put has a bearing on its choice. If it is used for sheets, films, or surface treatment, where only modest penetration, is called for, a low voltage machine, such as the ICT, is suitable. If greater penetration is necessary, a higher voltage machine is needed, and the choice is between the resonant transformer and the Dynamitron. For surface treatment, an ultraviolet light might be sufficient. This is created when an electric arc passes between electrodes separated by gas or vapor. There are two main classes of arcs: open, such as the carbon arc, and closed as the various vapor lamps.

### Types of Ultraviolet Radiation Sources

| UV Source | Max. Power, Kw. | Efficiency (UV and Visible), % | Spectrum Range, A. |
|---|---|---|---|
| Plasma arc | 250 | 30 | 1500– 3500 [a] |
| Tungsten filament | 10 | 15 | 4000– 7000 [b] |
| Mercury xenon tube | 5 | 40 | 4000– 7000 [b] |
| Carbon arc | 25 | 10 | 5000–15,000 [b] |

[a] Controlled within spectrum range by gas or gas mixture.
[b] Not controllable within spectrum range.

The plasma arc is a recent development, with a potential of high intensity and efficiency. By using photosensitizers, visible light or laser beams may also be employed.

The effect of ultraviolet light on polymers is discussed in two chapters by Chen and Rånby.

### What Does Irradiation Cost?

Cobalt-60 now costs $1 per curie or roughly $70,000 per kilowatt produced while electron accelerators are now between $5000 and $10,000 per kilowatt output. The price of a plasma arc is $1000 to $1500 per kilowatt. It is expected that, in the future, cobalt-60 may be reduced to as low as 20 cents per curie. This is still about $13,000 per kilowatt, and the cost of electron accelerators and ultraviolet sources may also be reduced. Shielding for isotope sources, which are gamma emitters, is considerably more expensive than for electron accelerators and ultraviolet sources.

The cost of polymer irradiation depends on the type of polymer, formulation, and shape of the fabricated polymer. Upgrading polymers by electron beam radiation costs about 1 to 4 cents per pound. Some of this cost can be equalized through material saving in view of property improvement. Surface treatment might be as low as 0.1 to 0.2 cents per pound.

For polymerizing monomers into commodity resins, cost of irradiation would have to be reduced to the cost of catalyst in order to compete economically with the present commercial polymerization processes. For engrafting monomers to finished articles, the cost can be higher, especially when solvents are eliminated.

This book is not intended to give a complete survey of polymer irradiation. For this, we have to refer to such excellent texts as "Atomic Radiation of Polymers" by Charlesby and "Radiation Chemistry of Polymeric Systems" by Chapiro. Since these books were issued in 1961 and 1962, more experimental research has been done and more theories have been developed by these authors, who are also the authors of the first two chapters of this volume. New trends have been discovered, and more light has been shed on polymer irradiation by the authors of the following 18 chapters. Thanks to their work and efforts, polymer irradiation is making inroads into the plastic and related industries.

It is a privilege to express the division's and my deepest appreciation to all of those who made the symposium and this book possible.

NORBERT A. J. PLATZER

Springfield, Mass.
April 1966.

xii

# Radiation Mechanisms in Polymers

ARTHUR CHARLESBY

Physics Department, Royal Military College of Science, Shrivenham, Swindon, Wiltshire, England

*Investigating polymers irradiated under various conditions provides information on many of the processes occurring between initial energy absorption and final physical and chemical change. Among factors which can modify these reactions are the type of radiation, presence of oxygen and of additives, degree of crystallinity, and presence of solvent. Reactions may also be affected by nonlocalization of absorbed energy, energy transfer, electron trapping and recapture, and abstraction by high and low energy hydrogen atoms. Several new techniques are available to study these intermediate states. Radiation treatment of polymers can be used to investigate crystal morphology, reinforcement, and electrical properties. Many of these results are applicable to radiobiology.*

I n the early 1950's, considerable interest was shown in the potential use of high energy radiation to initiate polymerization or to modify polymers by such processes as crosslinking and degradation (*3, 4, 5*). The ability to initiate useful chemical reactions in the solid state by a readily controllable source was only one of the factors which encouraged industrial studies. I cannot help feeling that the prevailing atmosphere of awe engendered by the revelation of tremendous energy concealed in the nucleus must have influenced the decision of some research directors to enter this apparently virgin field. This resulted in a mass of parallel research programs, often in fields where it could be shown, even with the limited knowledge then available, that applications at an economic cost were extremely unlikely. Nevertheless some radiation processes have been developed successfully on a commercial basis but usually only in specific areas such as solid state reactions where no simple chemical alternative is readily available. It is to be hoped that further successful applications will emerge from the present intensive investigations into graft polymerization and solid state polymerization; these are not discussed further in this review.

By far the most interesting application to date is the ability to crosslink polymers in the solid state, and much research has been devoted to studying the reactions involved. The initial physical process of energy absorption and the final chemical change—formation of crosslinks—can be readily determined. However, there is still considerable doubt as to the intermediate reactions, and this problem offers an appropriate start of this review.

### Ionization and Excitation

By analogy with the reactions in gases, it is usually assumed that the first reactions following absorption of energy from the incident beam are ionization and excitation and that these occur at random throughout the specimen. (Account may have to be taken of the varied binding energies of electrons in different shells, but this is usually ignored.) How far can we assume that ionization and excitation occur at random? The average energy lost by an incident fast electron per collision is roughly 100 e.v. The uncertainty in time corresponding to this energy change is immediately deduced from the uncertainty principle:

$$\Delta t \sim h/\Delta E \sim 4 \times 10^{-17} \text{ sec.}$$

For an electron moving close to the speed of light, this corresponds to an uncertainty in position of about 120 A., far greater than the individual electron orbit. We may therefore envisage the energy as being deposited over a relatively large volume and only later being directed toward a specific electron within it. If the nature of the chemical bonds within this volume is heterogeneous, some selectivity can appear subsequently. For example, if radicals are present, owing to prior irradiation, these may be the preferred site. We might then expect to see a change in reaction processes when the radical concentration is one per volume of $\frac{4}{3}\pi(120)^3$ A.$^3$ (equals $1.4 \times 10^{17}$ per cc.). If $(\Delta t)(\Delta E) \sim \hbar$, the corresponding concentration is $2 \times 10^{19}$ per cc. In fact, the radical concentration in many irradiated polymers, as determined by electron spin resonance, does reach a maximum in this range. This agreement may, however, be fortuitous, and alternative suggestions need to be examined.

Next we must consider the precise meaning to be attached to the term "ionization" in the condensed phase. Unlike the situation in an irradiated gas, the electron liberated by ionization of a molecule loses energy rapidly by colliding with other molecules and may have insufficient kinetic energy to escape the field of its parent ion. In this case we may justifiably speak of a superexcited state not to be found in gases.

The critical escape distance, a, beyond which the electron can be considered free—*i.e.*, outside the influence of its parent ion—can be estimated:

$$e^2/\bar{\epsilon}a = \tfrac{1}{2}kT$$

when $\bar{\epsilon}$ is the effective dielectric constant, allowing for a lower value in the immediate vicinity of the ion. In the case of water a is only a few Angstroms, but in organics, with a bulk dielectric of about 2, the critical distance becomes 50A. One can therefore expect that only a small fraction of the ejected electrons can truly escape and eventually produce ionic reactions. The rest will be recaptured by the parent ions to give highly excited molecules and eventually lead to radical reactions.

In conformity with this view, there is considerable evidence that in many organic systems, G values for radical production (resulting from excitation) run to about 3 to 5 whereas the G values for ion formation are down by a factor of 10 or more (*11, 13*).

In radiation-induced ionic polymerization conducted in the presence of fine powders ($ZnO$, $SiO_2$, etc.) much higher G values for initiation have been reported, but it now appears that they are caused by chain transfer reactions (*8, 10, 25*), giving a higher number of molecular chains than were initiated by radiation. Again the presence of $N_2O$ acting as an electron scavenger is reported (*21*) to yield apparently high values of G (ion) up to 3. This would imply a high ionic contribution to many radiation-induced reactions, for which there is little evidence. However, it can be argued that the concentration of the scavenger is in fact sufficiently high to capture some of these super-excited electrons which would otherwise return to their parent ions after a lengthy journey in the neighborhood, to give excited states and eventually radical reactions (*1, 24*). However, this cannot be the complete story since we find with paraffins irradiated in the presence of $N_2O$ an increase in radical production and crosslinking density which can be determined by the reaction of such radicals with iodine (Table I).

### Mechanisms of Crosslinking

Considerable disagreement still prevails as to the mechanism of crosslinking in polymers. Is it an ionic or a radical process? While the author admits the existence of some ionic species (as revealed by ESR at low temperature and by radiation-induced conductivity), his present view is that the ionic contribution to crosslinking in solids and liquids is only minor. This attitude is based *inter alia* on the following evidence.

Crosslinking can occur readily in dilute aqueous polymer solutions when there is little likelihood that two polymer ion molecules will be in the correct position for linking during the short life of the ion.

Table I.   Irradiation of Cyclohexane in the Presence
of $N_2O$ and Iodine[a]

| $[N_2O]$, mM | $[I_2]$, mM | $G(R_2)$ | $\Delta G(R_2)$ | $G(-I)$ | $\Delta G(I)$ |
|---|---|---|---|---|---|
| 0 | 0 | 1.63 | | | |
| 15–130 | 0 | 2.48 | 0.85 | — | — |
| 0 | 0.59 | 0.3 | 0 | 5.1 | 1.8 |
| 100 | 0.59 | 0.3 | | 6.9 | |
| 0 | 0.89 | 0.3 | 0 | 5.1 | 1.7 |
| 100 | 0.89 | 0.3 | | 6.8 | |
| 0 | 6.22 | 0.3 | 0 | 5.5 | 1.8 |
| 100 | 6.22 | 0.3 | | 7.3 | |

[a] In the absence of iodine, $N_2O$ increases crosslinking; $\Delta(C_{12}H_{22}) = 0.85$. Iodine can scavenge the cyclohexyl radicals, leading to dimer formation (except a residual 0.3 dimer) and produce the iodide; $G(R_2)$ decreases from 1.63 to 0.3, and iodine is lost. In the presence of $N_2O$ there is a greater loss of iodine, corresponding to the larger amount of dimer which would otherwise be formed; $2 \times 0.85 \sim 1.7$ to 1.8.

Polymer radicals can be observed in irradiated solid polymer (ESR) and in aqueous solutions (pulse radiolysis), in concentrations comparable with the eventual crosslinking density.

Low concentrations of radical scavengers can greatly reduce the density of crosslinking of liquid polymers although most radicals will be formed some distance from a scavenger. For a solid polymer much higher concentrations are needed, but crosslink densities can still be approximately halved.

If we assume that crosslinking is primarily caused by the reaction between two polymer radicals, we must still explain how they come sufficiently close together to react. Here we must choose between two alternatives:

• The two radicals are formed in close proximity; at the low doses required for gelation this implies that each pair is the consequence of a single ionization or excitation.

• Radicals are formed at random and migrate until they find a partner.

Neither of these explanations is entirely satisfactory. In particular the former would not allow for significant radiation protection by small concentrations of additive; in fact, the gelation dose can be doubled by only 1% of additive in solid polymer and considerably less in liquid polymer. The second explanation would lead to almost complete protection since the additive concentration vastly exceeds the polymer radical concentration, and radicals would react with the additive before meeting another radical. In practice partial protection is observed.

The explanation which seems at present most feasible is as follows. Following each excitation-ionization, a polymer radical and a hydrogen atom are formed. Some of these hydrogen atoms (which are released with considerable kinetic energy) abstract in the immediate vicinity, yielding secondary polymer radicals. Pairs of adjacent radicals (formed one by radiation, the other by abstraction) can then crosslink readily, with the minimum chance of interference by other molecules. If hydrogen does not abstract in the first few collisions, it becomes thermalized and can then travel long distances and suffer numerous collisions before abstracting a second hydrogen, to give a second polymer radical. Protection against such dispersed radicals (but not initially adjacent pairs) is readily achieved at low additive concentration—*e.g.*, by reaction of additive with a polymer radical or by trapping of thermalized hydrogen before it abstracts.

This explanation for crosslinking, though attractive, is still far from proved—for example, additives should influence hydrogen yield as should radicals trapped in the solid phase. One no longer expects the density of crosslinking to remain proportional to dose. Neither of these predictions is adequately confirmed. We also must account for the mobility of polymer radicals, even in solid polymer. One method of transfer is hydrogen addition to radicals, and hydrogen abstraction from polymer, this process being accelerated by the presence of hydrogen gas in the system. ESR results (*18*) show that the radical concentration in polyethylene decays more rapidly in the presence of hydrogen. Crosslinking occurs most readily in the amorphous regions between polymer crystallites (where the chains can move into a suitable spatial arrangement), so we may visualize a slow migration of trapped radicals from within the crystallite into the amorphous regions. This is revealed by a reduction with time after radiation in the asymmetry of ESR signals from radicals in stretched polyethylene. The larger the crystal, the slower should be the rate of radical arrival at the crystal surface; this is confirmed by the more rapid decay rate of radical concentration in the low density polyethylenes.

### Influence of Type of Radiation

Further insight into radiation mechanisms can be obtained by comparing different types of radiation, in particular alpha radiation, gamma (or fast electron) radiation, and ultraviolet light. Their effects are also important in such varied fields as space materials and radiological protection.

Alpha radiation differs from gamma or electron radiation primarily in the much denser distribution of reactive entities along the alpha particle track; with ultraviolet light at $254m\mu$, often requiring the presence of a sensitizer, one is dealing primarily with excitation and not ionization.

In this short review it is perhaps sufficient to indicate that in organic materials the primary processes and products of alpha and gamma radiation are usually fairly similar. However, major differences occur in the presence of so-called protecting additives, which are far less effective in the case of alphas. This is to be expected from the high concentration of radicals built up in the dense alpha track, far higher than in gamma or electron spurs. From the data on the effect of radical scavengers on the final product, the diameter of the alpha track can be estimated.

Both alpha and gamma radiation destroy crystallinity in polyethylene but only at high doses (2). This is surprising since the energy released within the narrow track of each alpha particle as it passes through a polymer corresponds to a rise in temperature of over $10^4$ °C., even after allowing for the energy lost to ionization and excitation. This local heating dissipates outwards from the initial track with a velocity equal to that of sound in the medium so that the high temperature is retained for an appreciable time. Yet there is little evidence of local melting and loss of crystallinity in polyethylene within this time. Lengthy heating to temperatures only a few degrees above the melting point of the irradiated material is far more effective in causing loss of crystallinity. This observation throws a surprising light on the thermal spike concept used in investigating irradiated materials.

### trans-Vinylene Unsaturation

A second important reaction observed in irradiated polyethylene and certain other polymers as well as paraffins is the formation of trans-vinylene. This product is far less influenced by such factors as temperature or radical scavengers than is crosslinking, and it is therefore often assumed to be formed directly by a "molecular" process—i.e., molecular detachment of hydrogen. Even this simple explanation cannot be fully sustained. Long after radiation has ceased, the trans-vinylene concentration continues to rise or fall, whether the specimen is exposed to oxygen or not. This behavior may possibly be correlated with the reaction of trapped alkyl and allylic radicals, which, being slightly mobile, can add to trans-vinylene or each other over a period of days.

Apart from this behavior, the concentration of trans-vinylene increases with dose, at first linearly but then tends to a limiting value which depends on the type of radiation (7). This limit is possibly caused by the capture by trans-vinylene of the thermalized hydrogen atoms released elsewhere by radiation. From the limiting concentration of unsaturation the number of collisions made by each thermalized hydrogen atom before it abstracts can be deduced; this lies in the range $10^3$ to $10^4$.

Furthermore the limiting trans-vinylene concentration is greatly affected if oxygen is present during—but not after—irradiation. The concentration of oxygen is inadequate to ensure that one molecule is likely to be immediately present at most potential sites of molecular detachment and so would not be able to influence a simple reaction of this type. Hence, we are forced to seek alternative explanations—for example, oxygen can be expected to act as an effective electron trap and may therefore interfere even with simple reactions by hindering the recapture of superexcited electrons.

So far I have confined my remarks to some aspects of radiation mechanisms in polymers. However, the use of radiation as a scientific tool has grown and is yielding valuable information in various fields, including polymer structure and radiation physics of polymers, and the results of this work are impinging on the vastly complex problems of radiobiology. It therefore seems appropriate to give a few selected samples of these techniques.

### Crystal Morphology

Our views on the arrangement of molecules in a partially crystalline polymer have been greatly affected by the studies of Keller and others, largely based on electron microscopy. Under suitable conditions, large single crystals of polyethylene can be grown, and it appears that each polymer molecule is folded back and forth to give a series of parallel chains, connected top and bottom alternatively by loops, somewhat like a firecracker. This model can be conveniently analyzed by subjecting such crystals to radiation, which produces crosslinking and eventually insolubility. It can be shown theoretically that for a random distribution of crosslinks, the radiation dose required for incipient gelation corresponds to one crosslink unit (0.5 crosslink) per weight average molecule. Internal links—*i.e.*, links between different units in the same molecule —are ineffective for gelation and must be ignored.

With large single crystals of polyethylene, the gelation dose is some 10 times greater than for the same polymer grown under conventional conditions (*14*). This is not caused by any inherent difference in the effect of radiation since both the radical concentration (deduced from ESR measurements) and hydrogen production are similar. We must therefore assume that most of the links produced in the single crystal are internal links which do not influence solubility. This is understandable in a crystal where each molecule folds backward on itself.

As high doses these internal links would be expected to produce looped structures, with a marked effect on viscosity. No such effect is observed. To explain this, we must assume that the radicals, trapped in the crystalline regions, migrate to the surface where the molecular loops are found (corresponding to some extent to the old amorphous regions), where they form internal links enclosing only a few units; these would have only a small effect on polymer viscosity.

If, during growth, the single crystals are under some pressure, the gelation dose can be greatly decreased. This means that a higher percentage of the links are formed between separate molecules. Our model allows for this since growth under pressure would bring the surfaces of adjacent crystals closer and result in an interleaving of the surface loops.

### Reinforcement

Increases in such mechanical properties as elastic modulus and tensile strength are obtained if fine particles—e.g., carbon black—are incorporated in elastomers before vulcanizing or crosslinking. The nature of this reinforcement is not yet adequately understood. Radiation offers a particularly suitable way to investigate the cause of this reinforcement since it obviates many of the difficulties of chemical cure involving the incorporation of chemical agents and thermal treatment. At the same time the degree of the reaction can be readily controlled in a reproducible and quantitative way, merely by altering the radiation dose.

Young's modulus in an irradiated nonfilled elastomer increases uniformly with dose—i.e., with density of crosslinks. If a fine powder filler is incorporated, a much higher modulus is obtained at the same dose (16). From this we may infer that the density of crosslinks is increased by the formation of additional links between elastomer and filler. However, this can be shown not to be the case. Using mixtures of low molecular weight silicones or squalene (as a model for rubber), with carbon black or silica powder, and irradiating to the same dose as for high molecular elastomers, does not give any evidence for major attachment between the two constituents. (This method avoids the difficulty of extracting filler from a polymer network, where extraction is hindered by the network as well as by the hypothetical filler-elastomer bond.) Again it is claimed that ESR shows evidence for radicals in carbon blacks and that these radicals link with those formed on elastomer molecules to provide a strong chemical bond. We also reject this interpretation. In our view the increase in modulus is caused by the physical presence, within each network loop, of small particles which reduce the maximum extension of which each network chain is capable merely by their physical presence within the available volume.

A lengthy series of measurements with silicone gums, incorporating varying concentrations of a series of fillers, and exposed to a range of doses, shows that Young's modulus $E$ is approximately proportional to filler concentration $c$ and to radiation dose $r$. The effectiveness of a filler as a reinforcing agent can therefore be represented at least approximately by the ratio $E/cr$. Our results show that $E/cr$ is determined primarily

by filler size and only to a small extent by its nature (carbon black, reinforcing or nonreinforcing; silica, surface-treated or not). Of course, it is
important to ensure good dispersion of the filler (Figure 1). Other
factors which play a role are filler-filler interactions (mainly at low ex-

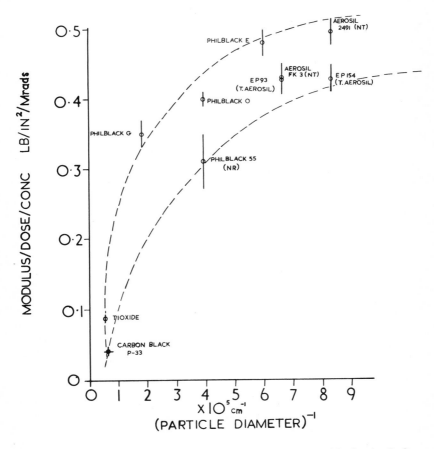

Figure 1.   *Reinforcement of silicone gums by carbon blacks (including
non-reinforcing NR), silica powder (both surface-treated T and untreated
NT), and titanium dioxide. The increase in modulus per unit dose and
filler concentration depends on filler particle size.*

tensions) and chemical reactions between filler and reactive end groups
in the elastomer, but these are usually of minor importance.
    The presence of filler does not greatly affect the maximum elongation
at break of the elastomer; hence, the increase in tensile strength is largely
caused by the higher Young's modulus at the same extension.

## Thermoluminescence

Many polymers, after irradiation at low temperature, give off light when allowed to warm. This phenomenon of thermoluminescence depends not only on the chemical structure but also on crystal morphology. In polyethylene, for example, peaks in the thermoluminescence glow curve correspond, respectively, to the crystalline and the amorphous regions (9, 19, 22) (Figure 2).

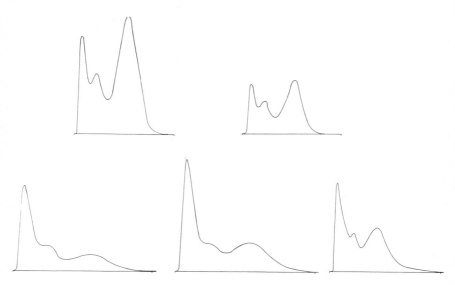

*Figure 2. Glow curves of various polyethylenes with different ratios of crystallinity–amorphous components. Temperature rises from left to right. Peaks α, β, γ, where α is caused by crystalline component, and γ by amorphous component.*

We are in fact dealing with traps for the electron ejected during ionization, these traps being related to the polymer itself. On warming, these electrons are released and then captured by luminescent centers, which must be some impurity or structural modification associated with the polymer. Thus the temperature at which the electron is released relates to crystal morphology while the spectrum of thermoluminescence (which is closely related to the fluorescence and phosphorescence spectra) provides information on these impurities or polymer chemical modifications. The method is extremely sensitive to even minute concentrations of these luminescent impurities, some of which can be washed out and reappear in the solvent. Our tentative analysis indicates rather surprisingly that they contain aromatic residues (Figures 3 and 4). Further work is proceeding, but it is already shown that in several ways

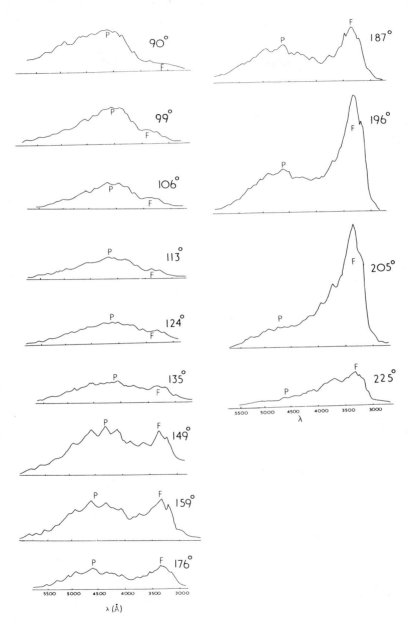

*Figure 3.   Thermoluminescence in polyethylene.   The spectrum com-*
*prises both fluorescent (F) and phosphorescent (P) components.   Contri-*
*bution of P falls as the temperature rises owing to competitive, non-*
*radiative processes.   Polyethylene alkathene 20, no $O_2$, dose 0.8 Mrad,*
*heating rate 2.7°/min.   Temperature in °K.   Intensities not to same scale.*

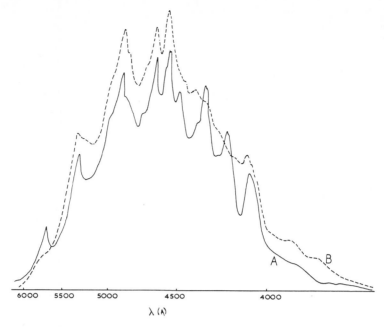

Figure 4.   Effect of oxidation on phosphorescent spectrum.   A:
Polyethylene milled for 30 min. at 120°C. B: Initial polyethylene.
Note several new peaks owing to oxidation.   Other peaks are
unaffected.

radiation can be used as a sensitive technique for studying polymer
structure and morphology (17, 20).

### Polymers in Solution

**Radioprotection.** The processes of crosslinking and degradation observed in polymers irradiated in the pure state can also be observed
in polymers irradiated in solution. The presence of a solvent can intervene in the reaction in several ways; thus it allows increased polymer
mobility, and some of the radiolytic products of the solvent may react
with the polymer or with the polymer radicals, etc. The polymer–water
system is of particular interest in that it provides a simple model for
some radiobiological systems and can be analyzed far more readily.

In certain water-soluble polymers such as polyvinylpyrrolidone,
the minimum dose required for gel formation shows a curious dependence on concentration. As this is reduced to about 1%, the gelation
dose decreases in spite of the fact that the polymer molecules are further
apart. This is ascribed to the higher contribution made to polymer radi-

cal formation by the radiolytic products of water (indirect effect). A similar effect is observed in many biological systems where increased lethality is observed as the concentration of the biological component is decreased.

At lower concentrations the gelation dose increases sharply until no network is formed, even at the highest doses. This competing effect is ascribed to internal linking—links occur between different monomers in the same chain but are ineffective for network formation.

Systems such as these are extremely valuable for measuring radiation protection by various additives. The increased gelation dose is a direct measure of this protection and can be used to compare the effects of polymer concentration, additive concentration, oxygen, pH, etc. In this way a table of protecting effectiveness of additives can be prepared. It is highly significant that over a wide range of compounds for which such tests have been carried out, the most effective are those containing the sulfhydryl group. These compounds are similar to, or closely related to, those most effective for radiobiological protection (6, 15).

To follow up this line of research we have recourse to two new techniques. The first—pulse radiolysis—measures the change in optical absorption over a range of visible and ultraviolet wavelengths of polymeric or biological solution subjected to short, intense pulses of radiation from a linear accelerator (Figure 5). The short-lived spectrum of the polymer radical can be readily traced as can its subsequent decay as these radicals react and disappear (12). This gives a direct measure of the reaction rate. An extension of this work relates to the influence on these spectra of the presence of traces of a protecting agent within the solution (Figure 6). Here we see most directly and vividly the manner in which these additives intervene in these radiation-induced reactions.

The second new technique envisages the use of ESR to detect these radicals. This technique has been used to study a number of polymers irradiated in the solid state. Applying it to polymers irradiated in water is difficult because of the extremely high absorption of electromagnetic radiation at these frequencies. We have therefore designed a new type of spectrometer which is capable of detecting radicals in the presence of large excess of water and obtained spectra from such irradiated systems. This technique shows considerable promise for investigating radiation effects in polymeric and biological aqueous solutions.

### Extension to Radiobiological Systems

Although the precise mechanisms of radiation-induced changes in polymers are not yet fully agreed upon, much of the information already gathered is in a form which can be readily analyzed quantitatively. We can therefore ask whether any of the main conclusions already reached

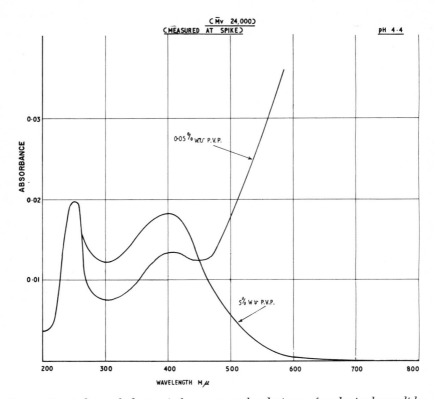

*Figure 5. Pulse radiolysis of deoxygenated solutions of polyvinylpyrrolidone showing peaks at 250 and 400 m$\mu$, and a broad absorption ascribed to electrons up to 700 m$\mu$ in low concentration solution*

are applicable to the far more complex systems studied in radiobiology. The answer to this important question is very much in the affirmative. Thus we can usefully extend our ideas into the more difficult problems of cell structure and radiation damage and analyze, on the basis of our knowledge of polymer radiation, some aspects of the behavior of model biological systems exposed to radiation. In particular we can differentiate between the radiation physical and chemical events and those which are specifically biological in nature. In this way we can relieve the radiobiologist of many of his problems and set up a sound framework within which he can further develop his specifically biological ideas.

The following reactions are among those which seem to show the same relationship as between polymeric and biological macromolecules.

The sensitivity of enzymes at various temperatures follows closely that measured in some polymers. Thus we need not propound abstruse biological explanations for this behavior, which can be readily explained on purely physical lines.

Many biological systems show an increased sensitivity to radiation in the presence of oxygen. This again is observed in polymers, where the chemical reactions can be more readily followed.

Radiation protectors can increase the dose needed to produce a certain degree of damage in a biological system. The same additives also protect polymers—*e.g.*, by reducing crosslinking—and this to an extent which can be readily determined.

The mechanisms of protection by these compounds have been evaluated for irradiated polymers. Many so-called protectors contain sulfhydryl groups and appear to operate by replacing or capturing the hydrogen atom lost by irradiating the macromolecule. It appears most reasonable to assume that the same mechanism often occurs in biological systems.

Only a limited degree of protection can be achieved, even with high concentrations of protecting additive. The results obtained with polymers account readily for this limit.

With most solid polymers the $G$ values for radical production, as determined by ESR, lie in the range 2 to 5. With biological macromolecules irradiated in the solid state comparable $G$ values are obtained.

Following irradiation at low temperatures, the ESR spectrum of polymers shows changes in radical structure, ascribed to the movement of electrons and radicals to other and more stable sites. The behavior of many dried biological macromolecules is similar although a detailed interpretation may be more difficult.

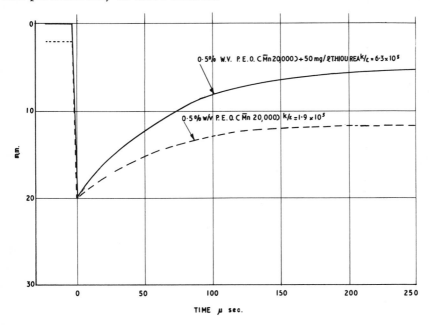

*Figure 6.   Effect of thiourea on decay of radicals in aqueous solutions of polyethylene oxide. Time after pulse in $\mu sec$. Broken line is decay in PEO radicals. Solid line is decay when thiourea is present. Dose about 5000 rads.*

In the presence of water, polymers reveal a greater sensitivity to radiation. This increase has been shown to be caused by the indirect effect of radiation—*i.e.*, the radiolytic products of water react with and form new radicals in the dissolved polymer. This indirect effect is also present in aqueous biological systems. The usual ESR techniques do not enable such radicals to be readily revealed because of the high absorption of water, but other techniques using radical scavengers reveal their presence.

These similarities encourage us to assume that the initial physical and chemical effects following exposure to radiation are inherently similar in simple macromolecules such as polymers and in the far more complex biological systems. The pathological changes are then the consequence of these physical and chemical events, whose nature we can already surmise, at least in general terms. However, there appear to be several serious objections to this basic assumption; two major difficulties relate to the great radiation sensitivity of many biological systems and to the effect of different forms of radiation.

### Radiation Sensitivity

To produce marked changes in most polymeric materials requires roughly one chemical change per molecule. Since a dose of $r$ rads deposits an average of $0.625 \times 10^{14} \ rM/6.02 \times 10^{23} = 1.04 \times 10^{-10} \ rM$ e.v. per molecule of molecular weight $M$, and 100 e.v. produces $G$ chemical changes (with $G$ between 1 and 5 in all but exceptional cases), the dose needed to achieve such changes (with $M \sim 10^6$, $G \sim 2$) is:

$$r = (100/G)(0.96 \times 10^{10}/M) \sim 500,000 \text{ rads}$$

This is roughly the order of dose needed to modify most polymeric materials. At much lower doses, say $10^5$ rads, most molecules will be unaffected. In biological systems similar $G$ values are in fact observed by ESR techniques, and the molecular weights usually reported are no greater. Yet effective doses involved in radiobiology are frequently much smaller and can be as low as a few hundred rads. We are therefore driven to seek an alternative explanation. Among others, the following possibilities may be advanced.

• The mechanism of radiation damage is quite different from the simple type of radical reaction envisaged—*e.g.*, a chain reaction *via* hydrogen bonds.

• Major damage results from the radiolytic products of water; experiments with aqueous solutions of polymer reveal such effects but could hardly increase the damage by much more than a factor of about 10.

• One modified chemical group in any one of a number of macromolecules is sufficient to cause serious pathological damage to the whole cell.

• The molecular weight of the macromolecule or structure involved is in fact larger than the values previously quoted for such molecules.

It is satisfying to find recent reports that unfractured DNA molecules from *E. coli* have molecular weights of about $2 \times 10^9$.

## Effect of Radiation Type

The second difficulty arises from the greater sensitivity of biological systems to radiation of high LET (high ionization density along the particle track). This is notably the case for alpha and neutron radiations (*via* ejected protons), where the relative biological effect (RBE) may be higher by a factor of up to 10 than for the same dose of gamma or fast electron radiation. For simple polymers the RBE of alphas is usually equal to 1 or less.

To explain this difference, it is usually assumed that several adjacent "hits" are needed to inactivate a biological molecule. The dense alpha track, of radius about 15 A., and with about one ionization per Angstrom along the track, would be far more effective in scoring multiple hits on a molecule than would the same number of ionizations (or excitations) scattered at random throughout the sample, as results from gamma or fast electron radiation. Evidence for this multihit process is provided by the shape of survival-dose curves, which show a shoulder at low doses. This conclusion militates against the possibility that the vulnerable molecule is of molecular weight $10^6$ or less since the chance of multiple hits with randomly distributed ionizations becomes extremely small at low doses. The argument can be pursued along more quantitative lines.

A dose of $r$ rads of gamma or electron radiation achieves a random "hit" density of $0.625 \times 10^{12} \, Gr\rho$ per cc. ($G$ hits per 100 e.v., density of material $\rho \sim 1$). A target volume $v$ cc. therefore receives an average number of hits:

$$m = 0.625 \times 10^{12} \, Gr \, (\rho v)$$

For a random distribution, the fractions of target volumes hit 0 or 1 times are $\exp(-m)$ and $m \exp(-m)$, and for 50% damaged by multiple hits following exposure to $r_{50}$ rads;

$$(1+m) \exp(-m) = 0.5; \qquad m = 1.7$$

The mass of the target volume, and its molecular weight, $M$, are

$$\rho v = (1.7/0.625 \times 10^{12})(1/Gr_{50})$$

$$M = 6.02 \times 10^{23} \, \rho v = 1.6 \times 10^{12}/Gr_{50}$$

For $G \sim 2$ and $r_{50} \sim 500$ rads, $M = 1.6 \times 10^9$ while for $G \sim 2$, $r_{50} = 50{,}000$ rads, $M \sim 1.6 \times 10^7$.

The average distance between hits is about 1200 and 250 A. (These can hardly be considered adjacent hits.)

Turning now to alpha radiation, the track density is such that almost any overlap with a macromolecule results in multiple hits. For 2-m.e.v. alpha particles, a dose of $r$ rads requires a flux of only $4 \times 10^4$ $r$ particles per sq. cm., and with a track radius $a = 15$A., the total area covered is only $2.8 \times 10^{-9}$ $r$ per sq. cm. For 50% of target molecules to be hit at the doses envisaged each must have a larger area.

Let us now consider several possible models for the target molecule. If it consists of a sphere of radius $b$A., the target area is $\pi(a+b)^2$, and for a 50% probability of a hit

$$0.5 = \exp(-\pi \overline{a+b^2} \times 4 \times 10^4 \, r_{50});$$

hence, $a + b = 2.4 \times 10^{-3}/r_{50}^{1/2}$ cm.

Since $b >> a$, the volume and molecular weight of the target

$$v = 5.8 \times 10^{-8} \, r^{-3/2} \text{ cc.}$$

$$M = 35 \times 10^{15} \, \rho r_{50}^{-3/2}$$

With $r_{50} = 500$ rads, $M \sim 3 \times 10^{12}$, while with $r = 50{,}000$ rads, $M \sim 3 \times 10^9$.

These high molecular weights cannot be reconciled with those derived from the gamma and electron data, even allowing for a high RBE factor; hence, the spherical target model must be rejected.

As a second model we may consider a hollow sphere, with wall thickness $t$. A similar calculation leads to the following results:

$$v = 7.3 \times 10^{-5} t/r_{50}$$

$$M = 4.4 \times 10^{19} \, t\rho/r_{50}$$

Since $t$ cannot be much less than 10A.,

$$M \sim 9 \times 10^9 \ (r_{50} = 500 \text{ rads})$$

$$M \sim 9 \times 10^7 \ (r_{50} = 50{,}000 \text{ rads})$$

These values are comparable with, but still somewhat higher than, those deduced for electron and gamma radiation.

A third model involves an elongated cylinder, length $l$, radius $b$. The cross-section is now $\frac{1}{2}l(2a+2b)$, the factor $\frac{1}{2}$ owing to the possible orientation of the target relative to the alpha particle. Then by the same argument

$$l(a+b) = 0.7/4 \times 10^4 \, r_{50}$$

A minimum value of the diameter $2b$ is about 10A. Then

$$l \sim 80/r_{50}$$

$$v \sim 6 \times 10^{-13}/r_{50}$$

$$M \sim 3.6 \times 10^{11} \, \rho/r_{50}$$

Thus if $r_{50} = 500$ rads, $M \sim 0.7 \times 10^{9}$ while $r_{50} = 50,000$ leads to $M \sim 0.7 \times 10^{7}$. These values can be made to correspond to the electron and gamma molecular weights if we assume an RBE $\sim 2.4$. A much higher value of $b$ is no longer acceptable.

Many alternative models have been examined, but they rarely meet the requirements of high sensitivity to radiation, inactivation by multiple hits, and comparable effects with densely and sparsely ionizing radiation, with a small but significant RBE effect.

Therefore, starting with our past knowledge of polymer radiation and a few simple biological data, we can select workable models for radiobiological systems, giving approximate molecular weights and shapes. That the cylindrical model is at best a vast oversimplification and possibly fallacious, I would be the first to agree. But we can already definitely exclude certain models which might otherwise appear equally acceptable.

### Reactivity Transfer

Although the initial energy deposition in an irradiated organic may occur at random, the first chemical change is nonrandom—even at liquid nitrogen temperature, when radical mobility is absent. This can be shown in various proteins whose ESR spectra fall into two distinct patterns (23). The symmetrical patterns occur in non-sulfur-containing proteins such as gelatin, salmine, zein, and silk. On the other hand non-symmetrical patterns are found in sulfur-containing proteins with cystine or cysteine residues. When cystine with an S—S bond is present, an ion is formed on this bond (BSA, trypsin, RNase, DNase). If the S is present only in sulfhydryl form (as in reduced glutathione), an S ion can still be formed: $SH^- + SH \rightarrow SS^- + H_2$. Both these reactions occur at liquid nitrogen temperature, indicating some form of nonrandom localization or migration. Other radicals are also seen, but these are stable at this low temperature.

This is confirmed by the observation that the second type of non-symmetrical pattern is obtained when a nonsulfur protein is freeze-dried with cysteamine—the ion migrates to the S.

The amount of S ion formed depends on pH, being more stable at higher pH. It can also be influenced by $Fe^{3+}$, which reacts with and reduces the ion concentration.

On warming, further reactions occur. The S ion causes bond scission and the formation of —$CH_2S\cdot$ radicals. Other radicals (such as glycine residue, —CO—CH—NH—) also change, with a transfer to the sulfydryl group. This would appear to represent one form of radiation protection. Similar results can be expected in irradiated organic polymers containing sulfur.

### Conclusions

In presenting this survey I have had to omit completely many aspects of possible relevance—for example, radiation-induced conductivity. Others have been glossed over or left for others to discuss. I have deliberately chosen to present the more controversial aspects of the subject, in the hope of stimulating thought and discussion. I am reminded of the professor who, at the end of a tedious, lengthy, and difficult course, addressed his students immediately before their examination. "Now that you have listened to all my lectures, I must confess that half of what I told you is wrong; furthermore, I don't know which half." If my score of successful remarks is equally high, I shall be more than gratified.

### Literature Cited

(1)  Blackburn, R., Charlesby, A., *Nature* **210,** 1036 (1966).
(2)  Blackburn, R., Charlesby, A., Woods, R. J., *European Polymer J.* **1,** 161 (1965).
(3)  Bovey, F. A., "Effects of Ionizing Radiation on Natural and Synthetic High Polymers," Interscience, New York, 1958.
(4)  Chapiro, A., "Radiation Chemistry of Polymeric Systems," Interscience, New York, 1962.
(5)  Charlesby, A., "Atomic Radiation and Polymers," Pergamon Press, London, 1960.
(6)  Charlesby, A., Garrett, P., Kopp, P. M., *Intern. J. Radiation Biol.* **5,** 439 (1964).
(7)  Charlesby, A., Gould, A. R., Ledbury, K. J., *Proc. Roy. Soc. (London)* **A277,** 348 (1964).
(8)  Charlesby, A., Morris, J., *Proc. Roy. Soc. (London)* **A273,** 389 (1963); **A281,** 392 (1964).
(9)  Charlesby, A., Partridge, R. H., *Proc. Roy. Soc. (London)* **A271,** 170, 188 (1963); **A283,** 312, 329 (1965).
(10) Dalton, F. L., *Polymer (London)* **6,** 1 (1965); **7,** 107 (1966).
(11) Davison, W. H. T., Pinner, S. H., Worrall, R., *Chem. Ind. (London)* **33,** 1274 (1957).
(12) Ebert, M., ed., Proceedings of Pulse Radiolysis Conference, North Holland, 1966.
(13) Freeman, G. R., Fayad, R. J. M., *J. Chem. Phys.* **43,** 86 (1965).
(14) Kawai, T., Keller, A., Charlesby, A., Ormerod, M. G., *Phil. Mag.* **10,** 799 (1964); **12,** 657 (1965).
(15) Kopp, P. M., Charlesby, A., *Intern. J. Radiation Biol.* **5,** 521 (1962); **7,** 173 (1963).
(16) Morris, J., Charlesby, A., *J. Polymer Sci.,* in press.

(17) Nikolskiĭ, V. G., Tochin, V. A., Buben, N. Ya., *Fiz. Tverd, Tela* **5**, 2248 (1963); *Dokl. Akad. Nauk SSSR* **134**, 147, 1466 (1962).
(18) Ormerod, M. G., *Phil. Mag.* **12**, 118 (1965).
(19) Partridge, R. H., *J. Polymer Sci.* **A3**, 2817 (1965).
(20) Partridge, R. H., Charlesby, A., *Polymer Letters* **1**, 439 (1963).
(21) Scholes, G., Simic, M., *Nature* **202**, 895 (1964).
(22) Singh, B. B., Charlesby, A., *Photochem. Photobiol.* **5**, 63 (1966).
(23) Singh, B. B., Ormerod, M. G., *Nature* **206**, 1314 (1965); *Biochem. Biophys. Acta* **109**, 204 (1965).
(24) Swallow, A. J., Land, E., Keene, J. P., Ebert, M., *J. Am. Chem. Soc.* **87**, 5284 (1965).
(25) Worrall, R., Charlesby, A., *J. Appl. Radiation Isotopes* **6**, 8 (1958).

RECEIVED April 27, 1966.

# 2

# Chemical Nature of the Reactive Species Produced in Polymers by Ionizing Radiations

ADOLPHE CHAPIRO

Laboratoire de Chimie des Radiations, Centre National de la Recherche Scientifique, Bellevue, France

*Three types of reactive species are formed under irradiation and may become trapped in polymers: ionic species, radicals, and peroxides. Little is known about the role of ions in the chemical transformations in irradiated polymers. Long-lasting ions arise, as demonstrated by radiation-induced conductivity, and may become involved in postirradiation effects. The presence of trapped radicals is well-established in irradiated polymers, but certain problems remain unsolved concerning their fate and particularly the migration of free valencies. Stable peroxides are produced whenever polymers are irradiated in the presence of oxygen. Both radicals and peroxides can initiate postirradiation grafting, and the various active centers can lead to different kinetic features.*

Irradiation provides a powerful method for modifying polymers, and radiation-initiated processes such as crosslinking and graft copolymerization have attracted considerable interest in past years. Although only a few irradiation processes are currently used in industry, it seems most likely that this field will grow and expand actively in the not-too-distant future.

The basic mechanisms of radiation-initiated transformations in polymers are far from being completely understood. Most reactions are commonly interpreted on the basis of free radical processes, but other species—e.g., ions, and other reactive intermediates—may play a significant role. A better understanding of the basic reactions occurring in irradiated polymers is required, and this would undoubtedly spur further developments and industrial applications. This paper is devoted to a survey of the different species found in irradiated polymers. Attention is primarily focused on intermediates which may be responsible for further chemical transformations, such as crosslinking and grafting.

### Primary Events

The primary interaction of radiation with matter leads to the formation of positive ions and excited molecules. Thus, in a medium constituted of molecules of a substance AB, the primary radiation-chemical events can be written:

$$AB \leadsto AB^+ + e \tag{1}$$

$$AB \leadsto AB^* \tag{2}$$

The electrons ejected in processes such as Reaction 1 usually carry enough kinetic energy to enable them to ionize and excite many more molecules, AB. Ultimately, the electrons having lost most of their energy become "thermalized" and may then either attach to a neutral molecule:

$$AB + e \longrightarrow AB^- \ (\text{or } A^\cdot + B^-) \tag{3}$$

or else recombine with a positive ion:

$$AB^+ + e \longrightarrow AB^{**} \tag{4}$$

The excited molecules formed in Reactions 2 and 4 may dissociate to form radicals:

$$AB^* \longrightarrow A^\cdot + B^\cdot \tag{5}$$

It follows that irradiating any substance (including a polymer) will lead to the formation of ions and free radicals, and these are responsible for most of the observed chemical changes. If the irradiated substance is a solid, these reactive intermediates often remain trapped for a considerable time after irradiation and cause further chemical transformations, the so-called "aftereffects."

Oxygen plays a major role in radiation-induced processes. If it is either present during irradiation or admitted to the substance after irradiation, another type of reactive species may arise—a peroxide. Peroxides are usually fairly stable at moderate temperatures and accumulate in the system to a certain extent. They are easily decomposed at elevated temperatures; moreover, they are selectively decomposed on further irradiation.

### Ionic Species

Little information is available on the role played by ions in the ultimate transformations occurring in irradiated polymers, although this matter has given rise to numerous speculations. Most ionic reaction mechanisms which have been suggested are based on extrapolating from the known behavior of ionic fragments in the mass spectrometer. Thus, a condensation process similar to the one observed with methane in the mass spectrometer

$$CH_3^+ + CH_4 \longrightarrow C_2H_5^+ + H_2 \tag{6}$$

has been suggested for the crosslinking of polyethylene (4)

$$\overset{|}{C}H^+ + \overset{|}{C}H_2 \quad {}^+\overset{|}{C}-\overset{|}{C}H + H_2 \tag{7}$$

Alternatively, the well-known proton transfer process:

$$CH_4^+ + CH_4 \longrightarrow CH_5^+ + CH_3 \cdot \tag{8}$$

could also account for the crosslinking of polyethylene *via* the following sequence of reactions (4):

PROTON TRANSFER

$$\overset{|}{C}H_2^+ + \overset{|}{C}H_2 \longrightarrow \overset{|}{C}H \cdot + \overset{|}{C}H_3^+ \tag{9}$$

NEUTRALIZATION

$$\overset{|}{C}H \cdot + \overset{|}{C}H_3^+ + e \longrightarrow \overset{|}{C}H \cdot + \overset{|}{C}H \cdot + H_2 \tag{10}$$

This would lead to the formation of two polymeric radicals in close vicinity, and these would almost certainly recombine to form a crosslink:

$$\overset{|}{C}H \cdot + \overset{|}{C}H \cdot \longrightarrow \overset{|}{C}H-\overset{|}{C}H \tag{11}$$

The weak point of a theory based on such mechanisms is the fact that Reactions 6 and 8 are known to occur only in the gas phase at the low pressure existing in the mass spectrometer, and no direct evidence is available to show that such processes also occur in a condensed state and could involve polymer molecules.

However, ionic species are undoubtedly present in irradiated polymers and persist for a considerable time after irradiation. This is demonstrated by the radiation-induced conductivity observed in most plastic insulators and by the slow decay of this conductivity, which may still be noticeable several months after irradiation (7).

Detailed studies of this effect, coupled with an investigation of the chemical transformations occurring in irradiated polymers, are lacking.

Work along these lines could give a better understanding of the role
played by ions in the radiation chemistry of polymers. The fact that ions
can induce chemical reactions in irradiated organic solids is clearly demonstrated by the polymerization of certain crystalline monomers which
are known to polymerize only when treated with ionic catalysts (3).

### Free Radicals

Free radicals are produced in the radiolysis of all organic molecules,
and in the case of solids they remain trapped in the substance after irradiation. Electron spin resonance (ESR) has been widely used to detect
and study radicals in irradiated polymers. Usually, in a polymer subjected to ionizing radiations *in vacuo*, free radicals accumulate until a
limiting concentration is reached, beyond which the number of radicals
remains independent of dose. Such a relationship, which was established
by ESR measurements for numerous polymers, is also obtained in studies
of the kinetics of graft copolymerization initiated by trapped radicals.
Figure 1 shows the influence of preirradiation dose *in vacuo* on the rate
of subsequent grafting of methyl methacrylate onto poly(vinyl chloride)
(5). A limiting grafting ratio is reached after a total dose of approximately 1 megarad, which presumably corresponds to the limiting concentration of trapped radicals in the system.

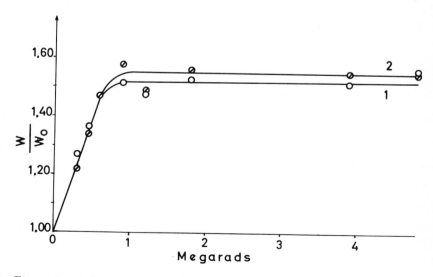

*Figure 1.    Influence of preirradiation dose of poly (vinyl chloride) films
in vacuo on the extent of grafting observed after heating in methyl methacrylate at 50°C. for 1 hr. (Curve 1) and 2 hrs. (Curve 2) (5)*

The actual value of the limiting concentration of trapped radicals depends strongly on the physical state of the polymer since this determines the mobility of the radicals in the medium. Thus, no significant amount of trapped radicals is found in elastomers irradiated at room temperature whereas large concentrations of the order of $10^{19}$ spins per cc. can be observed in glassy or crystalline polymers.

The combination of two radicals to form a crosslink raises a number of problems, some of which have not yet been satisfactorily solved. If the radicals are produced in pairs, such as by Reactions 9 and 10 or by a "hot" hydrogen atom mechanism (4), they would combine almost instantaneously at ordinary temperatures, and these radicals could hardly be responsible for long-lasting ESR signals. On the other hand, radicals distributed at random in a solid polymer are stable and can meet only if they are able to migrate over long distances in the solid. Physical migration—e.g., by molecular diffusion—seems unlikely in view of the low diffusion rates of macromolecules in a polymeric medium. Therefore, several chemical processes leading to effective migration of radical sites have been suggested. The simplest "chemical" migration via hydrogen atom transfer (Reaction 12) is a slow process at room temperature since

$$\overset{A}{\underset{|}{C}}H\cdot + \overset{B}{\underset{|}{C}}H_2 \longrightarrow \overset{A}{\underset{|}{C}}H_2 + \overset{B}{\underset{|}{C}}H\cdot \qquad (12)$$

this reaction requires an activation energy of ca. 10 kcal. per mole for aliphatic hydrocarbons. More recently it has been established that hydrogen (deuterium) molecules exchange with irradiated polyethylene, and the following reactions have been suggested (6, 12).

$$\overset{|}{\underset{|}{C}}H\cdot + D_2 \longrightarrow \overset{|}{\underset{|}{C}}HD + D\cdot \qquad (13)$$

$$D\cdot + \overset{|}{\underset{|}{C}}H_2 \longrightarrow \overset{|}{\underset{|}{C}}H\cdot + DH \qquad (14)$$

It was further found that the trapped radicals in polyethylene decayed more rapidly in a hydrogen atmosphere. The migration of the free valencies was therefore explained on the basis of a process similar to Reactions 13 and 14, assuming an exchange reaction involving the hydrogen which results from the radiolysis of the polymer. However, Reaction 13 is endothermic and therefore unlikely to occur at room temperature.

Other gases—e.g., NO, $N_2O$, etc.—were found to affect crosslinking yields, but the mechanism of their action is not clear (9, 10).

Thus, it appears that several processes which may play a major role in radiation-induced crosslinking, such as migration of free valencies and hydrogen exchange, cannot be accounted for by simple free radical reactions. An alternative explanation could be found in a chemical process involving the long-lasting ionic species which are present in irradiated polymers and which could simultaneously lead to hydrogen exchange and free radical migration. However, any specific reaction which one could imagine for a process of this type would be highly speculative in character at the present time.

### Peroxides

If a polymer is irradiated in the presence of oxygen, the free radicals produced are rapidly converted into peroxidic radicals (Reaction 15).

$$R^{\cdot} + O_2 \longrightarrow RO_2^{\cdot} \tag{15}$$

These may remain trapped for some time in the system and are easily detected by their ESR signal. Their ultimate fate depends to some extent on the nature of the irradiated substance and also on several physical parameters of the experiment, such as temperature, dose rate, and total dose. The two main reactions involving peroxidic radicals are:

Hydrogen Atom Abstraction

$$RO_2^{\cdot} + R'H \longrightarrow RO_2H + R' \tag{16}$$

which may lead to a chain peroxidation process, since $R'^{\cdot}$ will be rapidly converted into $R'O_2^{\cdot}$ by Reaction 15.

Recombination

$$RO_2^{\cdot} + RO_2^{\cdot} \longrightarrow ROOR + O_2 \tag{17}$$

These two reactions compete. Reaction 16 requires a significant activation energy and will therefore be favored at elevated temperatures and in polymers containing labile(tertiary) hydrogens. It will also occur at low doses when the concentration of $RO_2^{\cdot}$ is too small to make mutual combination likely. This reaction is actually responsible for the well-known autoxidation process, which can be initiated in certain polymers by fairly low doses of radiation.

Conversely, Reaction 17 will take place chiefly at low temperatures and high doses and will primarily apply to linear, nonsubstituted polymers.

The two products formed in Reactions 16 and 17—*i.e.*, hydroperoxides and diperoxides, respectively—exhibit different properties, and this makes it possible to assign a reaction mechanism to a given peroxidation process if one can establish the nature of the resulting peroxide. Thus, hydroperoxides are usually less stable to heat than diperoxides.

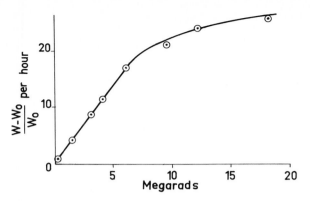

*Figure 2. Influence of preirradiation dose of poly-
ethylene films in air on the rate of grafting observed
on heating at 135°C. in acrylonitrile (2)*

The concentration of hydroperoxides can often be determined by infrared
analysis or by chemical titration. Diperoxides are more difficult to detect
experimentally. If both substituents of the peroxide are polymeric radicals, P, the corresponding peroxide POOP can actually be considered
as an oxygen bridge between two macromolecules and should therefore
behave like a crosslink:

$$\}{-}O{-}O{-}\{$$

Such structures have been characterized in air-irradiated polyethylene by the resulting change in mechanical properties of the polymer
at moderate temperatures (*1*). At elevated temperatures these links
break, and this further demonstrates their peroxidic character.

Another difference between hydroperoxides and diperoxides becomes
apparent when the peroxidized polymer is used to initiate graft copolymerization. The thermal breakdown of a diperoxide, POOP, leads
to two polymeric fragments, PO·, which in the presence of a monomer
will give rise to two grafted branches whereas a hydroperoxide POOH
will give under similar conditions one grafted branch and one molecule
of homopolymer resulting from chain initiation by the OH· radical. This
behavior is best illustrated by comparing the graft copolymerizations
initiated by radiation-peroxidized polyethylene and polypropylene (*2*).
The former polymer contains peroxides which are extremely stable at
room temperature and keep their activity for grafting for periods exceeding one year. Furthermore, when used to initiate grafting, this polymer
yields only small amounts of homopolymer. In contrast, polypropylene,
preirradiated in air, initiates graft copolymerization at room temperature
and leads to the formation of considerable amounts of homopolymer. In
addition, polypropylene is much more susceptible to peroxidation by low

radiation doses than polyethylene, which suggests that in this polymer
hydroperoxides are formed by a chain reaction *via* hydrogen atom abstraction (Reaction 16), a view supported by the presence of tertiary
hydrogens in the monomer unit of this compound.

When irradiation is carried out at higher temperatures (60°C.),
polyethylene may also become peroxidized by a chain reaction leading
to hydroperoxides (*11*).

For low radiation doses, peroxides accumulate almost linearly with
dose. However, after a certain dose has been reached, their concentration
tends to level off. This conclusion can be derived from the observed
change in the rate of graft copolymerization initiated by polymers subjected to increasing doses of preirradiation in air. Figure 2 illustrates
this effect in the case of grafting acrylonitrile onto polyethylene (*2*).
The drop in the yield of peroxide production presumably results from
the efficient radiation-induced decomposition of these peroxides. Peroxides are known to decompose under free radical attack, and selective
destruction of peroxides under irradiation has been established experimentally (*8*). This decomposition can become autocatalytic, and sometimes the concentration of peroxides may reach a maximum at a certain
dose and decrease on further irradiation. Such an effect was observed
in the case of poly(vinyl chloride). Figure 3 shows the influence of
preirradiation dose on the grafting ratio obtained with poly(vinyl chlo-

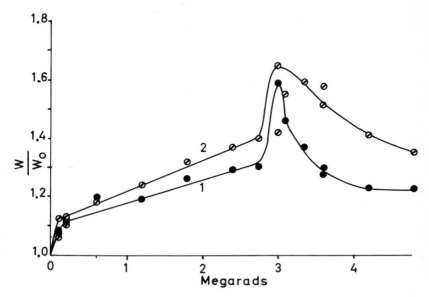

*Figure 3.   Influence of preirradiation dose of poly (vinyl chloride) films in
air on the extent of grafting observed after heating in acrylonitrile at 80°C.
for 1 hr. (Curve 1) and 2 hrs. (Curve 2) (5)*

ride) films after 1 and 2 hours' heating at 80°C. (5). The sudden increase in grafting rate observed after 3 megarads presumably results from an autocatalytic destruction of the peroxides. Beyond 3.5 megarads the rate slowly decreases with dose. The rate of grafting rises sharply after fairly low doses and increases only slowly on further irradiation. It is believed that this effect follows from a contribution of trapped radicals to the reaction since the initial grafting occurs rapidly during the time required to swell the film.

### Conclusions

Our knowledge of the concepts which can be used to interpret the mechanisms of the chemical transformations occurring in irradiated polymers is still rudimentary, and many problems remain unsolved. More efforts should be directed toward experiments which could give more detailed information on the nature and the fate of the primary species resulting from the radiolysis of polymers. Electrical conductivity measurements coupled with the study of chemical changes occurring during and after irradiation could provide interesting data on the role played by ions, a field which remains practically unexplored.

### Literature Cited

(1) Chapiro, A., *J. Chim. Phys.* **52**, 246 (1955).
(2) Chapiro, A., *J. Polymer Sci.* **34**, 439 (1959); **48**, 109 (1960).
(3) Chapiro, A., "Effets Chimie et Biologique Radiations," M. Haissinsky, ed., 10ᵉ série, Masson et Cie, Paris, 1966.
(4) Chapiro, A., "Radiation Chemistry of Polymeric Systems," Interscience, New York, 1962.
(5) Chapiro, A., Mankowski, Z., *European Polymer J.* **2**, 163 (1966).
(6) Dole, M., Cracco, F., *J. Phys. Chem.* **66**, 193 (1962).
(7) Fowler, J. F., *Proc. Roy. Soc. (London)* **A236**, 464 (1956).
(8) Krongauz, V. A., Bagdasaryan, Kh. S., *Dokl. Akad. Nauk. SSSR* **114**, 829 (1957); *Zh. Fiz. Khim.* **32**, 1863 (1958).
(9) Lyons, B. J., Dole, M., *J. Phys. Chem.* **68**, 526 (1964).
(10) Okada, Y., *J. Appl. Polymer Sci.* **7**, 695, 703, 1153 (1963); **8**, 467 (1964).
(11) Sack, H., *J. Polymer Sci.* **34**, 434 (1959).
(12) Varshavskii, Ya. M., Vasilev, G. Ya., Karpov, V. L., Lazurkin, Yu. S., Petrov, I. Ya., *Dokl. Akad. Nauk SSSR* **118**, 315 (1958).

RECEIVED April 4, 1966.

# Reactive Intermediates in the Radiation Chemistry of Polyethylene

MALCOLM DOLE

Northwestern University, Evanston, Ill.

DAVID M. BODILY

University of Arizona, Tucson, Ariz.

*The types and reactions postulated for reactive intermediates in the radiation chemistry of polyethylene are reviewed. Ultraviolet spectroscopy is an important tool in complementing data obtained from electron spin resonance studies. Finally, the kinetics of growth and decay of the allyl and polyenyl free radicals as inferred from ultraviolet spectra are discussed.*

R eactive intermediates in the radiation chemistry of polyethylene have been postulated to be positive ions of various types, trapped electrons, electronically excited groups, alkyl and allyl type free radicals, diffusible species such as atomic hydrogen, or the methyl radical, and so on. To this list we should like to add negative ions, carbanions. The electron must always be considered to be present, trapped, or otherwise when positive ions exist, but it has not yet been identified in polyethylene as a chemically reactive intermediate as has the hydrated electron in water, although the postulate of trapped electrons in irradiated polyethylene has been invoked by Partridge (33) working with Charlesby to explain their luminescence decay curves.

## Ionic Intermediates

**Positive Ion.** Many ion-molecule reactions have been suggested to explain unsaturation and crosslinking in polyethylene. The subject has recently been reviewed by the author (10). However, there has been practically no direct evidence of ion-molecule reactions. The author (10) proposed that production of *trans*-vinylene unsaturation in polyethylene may occur by means of Reaction 1

$$-\overset{+}{C}H_2-CH_2- \rightarrow H_2 + -CH^+=CH- \quad (trans) \qquad (1)$$

because of the small effect of temperature or phase on $G(t-Vl)$ and because Reaction 1 is exothermic (Table I). $G(t-Vl)$ is the number of *trans*-vinylene groups produced per 100 e.v. of energy absorbed. However, the production of molecular hydrogen and the vinylene group might equally well be independent of temperature and phase if the reactive intermediate were an electronically excited species, $-CH_2CH_2{}^*-$. There are other processes, of course, which give rise to hydrogen, as discussed below.

**Table I. Some Postulated Ion-Molecule Reactions (10)**

|  | *Reaction* | *e.v.* |
|---|---|---|
| (1) | $-CH_2CH_2{}^+- \rightarrow H_2 + -CH=\overset{+}{C}H-$ | $-0.105$ *(cis)* |
|  |  | $-0.145$ *(trans)* |
| (2) | $-CH_2{}^+- + -CH_2- \rightarrow -\overset{+}{C}H_3- + -CH-$ | $0$ |
| (3) | $-CH_2CH=CH_2 + -CH_2CH^+=CH_2 \rightarrow -CHCH=CH_2$ |  |
|  | $\quad + -CH_2\overset{+}{C}HCH_3$ | $+0.25$ |
| (4) | $-CH_2\overset{+}{C}HCH_3 + -CH_2CH=CH_2 \rightarrow$ |  |
|  | $\quad -CH_2CHCH_2\overset{+}{C}HCH_2-$ | $-0.61$ |
|  | $\qquad\quad \mid$ |  |
|  | $\qquad\quad CH_3$ |  |

Inasmuch as the production of *trans*-vinylene unsaturation is one of the important processes occurring during the γ-ray irradiation of polyethylene, it is interesting to compare $G(t-Vl)$ in polyethylene with $G(Vl)$ values in other substances. Data are presented in Table II where $G(Vl)$ represents a monoene group, whether cis or trans.

**Table II.  G Values for Production of Unsaturation
at Room Temperature**

| *Substance* | *Phase* | $G(t-Vl)$ | $G(Vl)$ | *Ref.* |
|---|---|---|---|---|
| Linear polyethylene | Solid | 2.4 |  | (10, 15) |
| Low density polyethylene | Solid | 1.7 |  | (15) |
| n-Hexane | Liquid | 1.2 |  | (9) |
| Cyclohexane | Liquid |  | 3.2 | (21) |
| Dioxane | Liquid |  | ~0 | (26, 35) |

The results of Table II are interesting from several standpoints. In the first place the vinylene groups in polyethylene (PE) are all trans, as would be expected because the trans-configuration can be formed with fewer chain rearrangements in the solid than the cis. However, in cyclo-hexane all of the vinylene groups must be cis, yet the yield is quite high. This may partly be the result of the liquid state of the sample, although Hamashima, Reddy, and Burton (20) have shown that $G(H_2)$ for cyclohexane, which is equal to the high value of 6.0, is independent of temperature from $-60°$ to $+25°C$. (melting point of cyclohexane is 6.5°C.). More recent determinations of $G(H_2)$ from liquid cyclohexane have yielded the values 5.55 (16) and 5.3 (38). This constancy of $G(H_2)$ with temperature is in contrast to polyethylene, whose $G(H_2)$ rises from 4.01 at 100°C. to 5.4 above the melting point at 140°C. (22). If $G(H_2)$ is constant with change of phase, $G(Vl)$ of cyclohexane is probably also constant or nearly so. The fact that the double-bond yield from cyclohexane is high and that dioxene has not been observed in the radiolysis of dioxane (26, 35), a geometrically similar molecule, is inter-esting but not surprising when it is remembered that organic chemists find it most difficult to make dioxene and that the free radical shown be-low is undoubtedly stabilized by resonance of the electrons of the lone

pair on the oxygen atom with the unpaired electron of the free radical group. The dimer formed by recombination of the free radicals in dioxane is chemically equivalent to practically all of the hydrogen liberated; hence, material balance requires that little, if any, dioxene be formed. As far as the major events in dioxane are concerned, it does not seem necessary to invoke ion-molecule reactions to explain the chemical effects observed. There is some ring degradation, however, as indicated by the significant value of $G(C_2H_4)$ equal to 0.50 and of $G(CO)$ equal to 0.23. These compounds probably arise from the decomposition of the energy-rich dioxane formed on recapturing the electron by the positive ion, as suggested by Llabador and Adloff (26).

In the case of cyclohexane ion-molecule reactions may contribute to some of the radiolysis products, but we believe (for reasons given below) that in this case also the ion-molecule yields are small if not completely negligible. The radiological behavior of dioxane shows that when a reactive intermediate is more stable, in this case the $C_4H_7O_2 \cdot$ free radical, it will form and react in preference to other possible intermediates.

Possibly the most convincing evidence for positive ion-molecule reactions in polymers is the high rate of decay of vinyl unsaturation during the radiolysis of polyethylene, as recently discussed by Dole, Fallgatter, and Katsuura (13). The ideas of these authors with respect to the carbonium ion mechanism for vinyl decay by means of a dimerization reaction were largely suggested by the mechanisms proposed by Collinson, Dainton, and Walker (5) for vinyl decay (polymerization) in the radiolysis of n-hexa-1-decene, Reactions 3 and 4 of Table I.

Although the ion-molecule theory of Libby (25) for the crosslinking mechanism in polyethylene is extremely attractive, there is no solid evidence to date that crosslinking occurs other than by free radical recombination. Inasmuch as the $G$ value for producing free ions in a liquid n-paraffinic hydrocarbon is only about 0.1 as found by several workers [see Williams (39) for a review] one would not expect ion-molecule reactions to be important in the radiation chemistry of polyethylene unless a chain reaction is possible, the ions and electrons become stabilized in some way, or there are reactive scavengers present that can react with the electrons or positive ions before the positive ions recapture the electrons (38). A double bond, such as a vinyl or vinylene group, represents a location where a positive charge could become slightly stabilized because the ionization potential of a saturated paraffinic chain, 10.55 e.v., is about 1.3 e.v. higher than that of an olefinic vinyl group (9.24 e.v.) [gas phase data from Field and Franklin (18)]. In a system such as n-hexa-1-decene which was investigated by Collinson, Dainton, and Walker (5), the $G$ values for vinyl group decay were so high that chain reactions must have been caused by irradiation. Under these conditions ion-molecule reactions can become important. The $G$ value for total possible ions is estimated to be about 3 (1).

Another example of a significant ion-molecule reaction which can occur during radiolysis is the proton scavenging by ammonia in the γ-ray radiolysis of liquid cyclohexane as studied by Williams (38). In this case $NH_4^+$ is formed at a rate that can compete with the rate of geminate recombination of the ions. An analogous reaction in the case of pure polyethylene (or of pure cyclohexane) is Reaction 2 of Table I. For such a reaction to occur it is necessary that the methylene groups in polyethylene have a high proton affinity, but the proton affinity, which is high in the case of methane, is less in ethane and and still less in propane. Derwish et al. (8) could find no evidence for the ion $C_3H_9^+$ in the mass spectrum of propane even at the high pressure of 0.12 torr in the ionization chamber of the mass spectrometer. Thus it seems unlikely that Reaction 2 of Table I can occur to any significant extent in either polyethylene or cyclohexane.

**Negative Ions and Trapped Electrons.** At the present time we can only speculate on the nature of electron traps in irradiated polyethylene. Partridge (*33*) suggests that electrons are trapped between molecular chains because luminescence in irradiated polyethylene occurs in the temperature intervals where mechanical losses occur. For large doses, free radicals, $R \cdot$, are abundant enough to be significant in trapping electrons. The reaction:

$$R \cdot + e^- \rightarrow R \colon^-$$

to form a carbanion is exothermic to the extent of about 1 e.v. or more, as judged by analogy with the electron affinity of the methyl free radical, $CH_3 \cdot$, which is $1.08 \pm 0.4$ e.v. (*30*). Because of polarization of the surrounding medium, the electron affinity may be even greater than the gas-phase value given above. Williams (*39*) has estimated the polarization energy of an electron in a hydrocarbon of static dielectric constant equal to 2 and in a cavity of radius 4.7A. to be 0.38 e.v.

At present there is no definite evidence that carbanions, $R \colon^-$, or trapped electrons enter into specific chemical reactions during the irradiation of polyethylene.

### Diffusible Intermediates

**Atomic Hydrogen.** Although there is much evidence for reactions produced by "hot" hydrogen atoms and by hydrogen atoms which have become "thermalized" by collisions with the matrix atoms, hydrogen atoms as such have never been observed in irradiated polyethylene even at temperatures as low as $-195°C$. Inasmuch as the ESR spectrum of atomic hydrogen is a doublet with the large separation of 508 gauss, hydrogen atoms should be readily detectable if they exist. They have been seen in irradiated ice at liquid hydrogen temperatures, but they recombine at measurable rates when the ice is warmed to $20°K$. or higher (*19*). Nevertheless, we know that atomic hydrogen must exist if only momentarily because free radicals such as $R \cdot$ have been shown to cause the exchange of deuterium between $D_2$ and polyethylene at room temperature after the irradiation, presumably by a chain reaction of the type (*12*):

$$R \cdot + D_2 \rightarrow RD + D \cdot$$
$$D \cdot + RH \rightarrow R \cdot + HD$$

Further results of Dole and Cracco (*12*) indicated that the deuterium atoms of the above reactions did not diffuse far through the polyethylene before abstracting a hydrogen atom from the polyethylene chain.

**Methyl Radicals.** Yoshida and Rånby (*41*) have recently shown by ESR measurements that the methyl free radical is produced in polypropylene by irradiation with ultraviolet light at liquid nitrogen temperature but decays at that temperature. The reaction is slow at −196°C., which suggests that all other hydrocarbon free radicals of larger molecular weight than the methyl free radical can be frozen in and immobilized at that temperature.

The mechanism of the decay reaction of the methyl free radicals at −196° is not known; however, the γ-ray irradiation of polypropylene at −196°C. produces only methane and no ethane (*36*), as demonstrated by gas analysis after warming to room temperature after irradiation. It may be that the methyl free radicals abstract hydrogen atoms on warming to room temperature or that "hot" methyl radicals are produced during the radiolysis with sufficient excess energy to abstract hydrogen atoms at liquid nitrogen temperature.

### Aliphatic Free Radicals

**Alkyl Free Radicals.** The primary alkyl free radical, $RCH_2 \cdot$, has been postulated to exist in gamma-irradiated polyethylene (*23*), but its presence has never been unambiguously demonstrated. If all the $\alpha$ and $\beta$ protons interacted equally with the unpaired electron, the primary alkyl free radical ESR spectrum should consist of five lines, in contrast to those of the secondary and tertiary alkyl radicals whose ESR spectra should consist of six and eight lines, respectively (the latter calculated for the tertiary free radical in polypropylene). The existence of the secondary

free radical, $—CH_2\dot{C}HCH_2—$, has been well documented in polyethylene by several workers (*23, 24, 37*), while the tertiary alkyl free radical,

$$—CH_2\dot{C}—CH_2—,$$
$$\quad\quad\; |$$
$$\quad\quad CH_3$$

is believed to be formed initially during the low temperature γ-ray irradiation of polypropylene (*28*) but is converted (*27*) to other types of free radicals on heating above 263°K., probably to the

allyl type radical, $—CH_2C\dot{C}H{=}C—CH_2—.$
$$\qquad\qquad\qquad\quad | \qquad\quad |$$
$$\qquad\qquad\qquad CH_3 \quad\; CH_3$$

**Methylene Free Radicals.** As suggested by my associate, G. G. A.

Böhm, the methylene free radical, $—CH_2\dot{C}CH_2—$, may be produced momentarily in polyethylene by eliminating molecular hydrogen during the irradiation. This process could replace or exist in addition to that represented by Equation 1. Such a biradical (or Lewis acid) would not be expected to be stable but could revert to the vinylene group

—CH=CHCH$_2$— or —CH$_2$CH=CH— by the intrachain migration of a single hydrogen atom or to a crosslink —CH$_2$CHCH$_2$— by the interchain migration of a single hydrogen atom, followed by coupling of the two secondary free radicals so produced. The latter is equivalent to the reaction observed in the methane radiolysis at 77°K. in which ethane is formed by the insertion of CH$_2$ into CH$_4$ (*2*).

**Allyl Free Radicals.** Ayscough and Evans (*3*) have recently studied, by ESR measurements, the types of allylic free radicals produced by gamma-irradiation of several monomeric olefins. In irradiated polyethylene the allyl free radical is quite stable, persisting for several months at room temperature (*31*). The presence of these allyl free radicals is most noticeable in the case of high density polyethylene, and this type of free radical is undoubtedly the cause of the slow oxidation of polyethylene at room temperature, which lasts for 40 or more days after irradiation (*10*). Williams and Dole (*40*) could observe little if any oxidation of low density polyethylene when it was exposed to air after irradiation. By oxidation we mean formation of carbonyl groups as detected by infrared absorption studies at 1725 cm$^{-1}$. Parenthetically, it should be noted that adding an oxygen molecule to a free radical produces initially another type of free radical, a peroxy free radical, but in this paper we shall not discuss free radicals of this or any other types except those of hydrocarbons.

**Polyenyl Free Radicals.** As the number, $n$, of conjugated double bonds in the polyenyl free radical, —ĊH(—CH=CH)$_n$—, increases, the ESR signals merge to a singlet, thus making it impossible to identify and measure quantitatively the type and concentration of the individual polyenyl free radicals present. However, in the case of polyethylene irradiated to high doses at room temperature, relatively stable polyenes of the structure —CH$_2$(—CH=CH)$_n$—CH$_2$—with $n$ values as high as 5, and reactive polyenyl free radicals of the structure —ĊH(CH=CH)$_n$—CH$_2$— with $n$ also as high as 5 can be separately recognized and studied by ultraviolet spectroscopy (*17*). By observing the ultraviolet absorption bands at liquid nitrogen temperature, the spectra become considerably sharper, and the broad diene band, for example, breaks up into three well-resolved peaks (*11*). By irradiation at liquid nitrogen temperature, however, the production of polyenes and polyenyl free radicals with $n$ greater than 3 is considerably reduced.

Up to now we have been able to observe 13 separate absorption bands in the ultraviolet region of the spectrum between 220 and 400 m$\mu$. The shift in the $\lambda_{max}$ of polyenyl free radicals to longer wavelengths with increasing $n$ would be expected to be linear with $n$, similar to the increase of $\lambda_{max}$ with $n$ in the case of the symmetrical odd-atom polymethine cyanine dyes studied by Brooker (4). On the other hand, the $\lambda_{max}$ of the even-atom polyene chains tends to converge with increasing $n$. Platt (34) has discussed this behavior and shown that the convergence occurs in systems in which one ground state resonance structure is strongly stabilized compared with other possible structures. The difference between linear as compared with convergent behavior has greatly aided us in assigning the ultraviolet absorption bands summarized in Table III.

### Table III.   Assignment of Ultraviolet Absorption Bands in Irradiated Polyethylene (11)

| Polyenes | | Polyenyl Free Radicals | |
|---|---|---|---|
| Name | $\lambda_{max}$, $m\mu$ | Name | $\lambda_{max}$, $m\mu$ |
| Diene | 229, 236, 245 | Allyl | 258 |
| Triene | 264, 275, 288 | Dienyl | 285 |
| Tetraene | 310 | Trienyl | 323 |
| Pentaene | 340 | Tetraenyl | 359 |
|  |  | Pentaenyl | 396 |

**Kinetics of the Allyl Free Radical Growth.** Bodily and Dole (11) were able to demonstrate that during irradiation at liquid nitrogen temperature few allyl free radicals were formed, but most of them were created on warming to room temperature after $\gamma$-ray irradiation at $-196°C$. Evidence for this behavior was obtained by measuring the ultraviolet absorption spectra under several different conditions as illustrated in Figure 1, where Curve 1 is the ultraviolet spectrum taken at liquid nitrogen temperature after irradiation in vacuum to 421 Mrad. There is a small peak at 258 m$\mu$ which we believe is caused by the allyl free radical. On heating to room temperature Curve 2 was obtained. After standing at room temperature for 42 hours in a vacuum, Curve 4 was taken. The intensity of the absorption band had decreased, indicating that the allyl radical concentration had decreased on standing at room temperature. On cooling to $-196°C.$, however, the 258-m$\mu$ band sharpened considerably, as shown by Curve 3. Since the intensity at 258 m$\mu$ of Curve 3 is much greater than that of Curve 1, the allyl concentration must have grown considerably on the first warming to room temperature. It also must have decreased somewhat on standing at room temperature, but not enough to fall to the initial allyl free radical concentration shown by Curve 1.

As other workers have shown (6, 27, 32), the concentration of the allyl free radical decreases on exposure to ultraviolet light at liquid

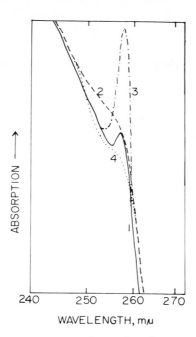

*Figure 1. Ultraviolet absorption spectra of Marlex–5003 polyethylene irradiated to 421 Mrad at liquid nitrogen temperature in vacuo. Curve 1: spectrum taken at liquid nitrogen temperature (lnt) after irradiation. Curve 2: spectrum taken at room temperature immediately after warming to room temperature (rt). Curve 4: spectrum taken at rt after standing for 46 hours at rt in vacuo. Curve 3: spectrum taken at lnt after the 46 hours at rt*

nitrogen temperature. The ultraviolet absorption spectra demonstrate this nicely (Figure 2, where all the spectra were taken at liquid nitrogen temperature). Gurve 1 is similar to Curve 3 of Figure 1. Curve 2 represents the ultraviolet spectrum after an irradiation with ultraviolet light at $-196°C$. The allyl peak has almost completely disappeared. On heating to room temperature and then cooling again to $-196°C.$, the allyl concentration was restored to its initial value (Curve 3).

The exact mechanism by which ultraviolet light eliminates the allyl free radical and heating restores it is not known, but the following

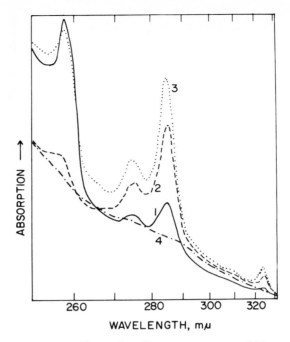

*Figure 2. Ultraviolet absorption spectra of Mar-
lex–5003 polyethylene all taken at liquid nitrogen temperature (lnt). Irradiation at lnt for 20
minutes in an electron beam. Curve 1: after 16
hours storage at room temperature in vacuo.
Curve 2: after irradiation at lnt with ultraviolet
light for 37 minutes. Curve 3: after 2.5 hours
storage at rt in vacuo. Curve 4: after exposure
to air at rt*

mechanism can be suggested. This is in line with the suggestion of
others (27) and is discussed more fully by Dole and Bodily (11).

HEATING

$$—CH_2\dot{C}HCH_2CH{=}CH— \xrightarrow{\text{Heating}} —CH_2CH_2\dot{C}HCH{=}CH—$$

(or perhaps the hydrogen migration is intermolecular rather than intra-
molecular).

ULTRAVIOLET IRRADIATION

$$—CH_2CH_2\dot{C}HCH{=}CH— + h\nu \longrightarrow —CH_2CH_2\dot{C}HCH{=}CH^*—$$
$$—CH_2CH_2\dot{C}HCH{=}CH^*— \longrightarrow —CH_2\dot{C}HCH_2CH{=}CH—$$

Another possibility involves the migration of electrons instead of a
hydrogen atom, as suggested by the work of Moorthy and Weiss (29).

who found that the yellow color of gamma-irradiated $6M$ sulfuric acid glasses can be bleached by visible light at liquid nitrogen temperature and then restored by heating to $120°K$. The cycle can be repeated many times with only a small loss of spectral intensity on each cycle. Moorthy and Weiss explain these phenomena in terms of an electron migration:

$$\begin{array}{c} SO_4^- \, (H_2O) \\ \text{Yellow} \\ \text{color} \end{array} \xrightarrow[\text{Heating}]{\text{Bleaching}} SO_4^{2-} \, (H_2O)^+$$

This reversible transformation was also followed by ESR measurements. A line at 3288 $G$, which Moorthy and Weiss attributed to the $SO_4^-$ radical ion, disappeared on bleaching and reappeared on heating. A line at 3217.5 $G$ behaved oppositely and is part of a spectrum owing probably to the trapped positive hole $H_2O^+$. An analogous but unlikely cycle in polyethylene would be:

$$-CH_2CHCH_2\dot{C}HCH{=}CHCH_2- \xrightarrow[\text{Heating}]{\text{Bleaching}}$$

$$-CH_2\overset{=}{C}HCH_2\overset{+}{C}HCH{=}CHCH_2-$$

However, these reactions do not agree with the ESR spectra observed by Ohnishi *et al.* (*32*). Another possibility involving carbonium ion migration is:

$$-CH_2\overset{+}{C}HCH_2\dot{C}HCH{=}CHCH_2- \xrightarrow[\text{Heating}]{h\nu}$$

$$-CH_2\dot{C}HCH_2\overset{+}{C}HCH{=}CHCH_2-$$

This reversible cycle would agree with both the ESR and ultraviolet absorption data. However, it seems unlikely that a positive ion could persist for days and undergo the above transformation without any change in its abundance.

In addition to explaining the allyl free radical transformation, we have to consider mechanisms for growth of the dienyl and trienyl free radicals both on irradiation with ultraviolet light and on warming to room temperature. Polyene groups on absorption of ultraviolet light could become free radicals on liberation of hydrogen atoms or migration of hydrogen atoms to other groups:

$$-CH_2(-CH{=}CH)_nCH_2- + h\nu \rightarrow -\dot{C}H(-CH{=}CH)_nCH_2- + H$$

On heating, migration of a hydrogen atom, alpha to a polyene group, to an alkyl free radical site would also convert a polyene to a polyenyl free radical, a transformation similar to transformation of the allyl free radical described above:

$$-CH_2(-CH{=}CH)_nCH_2- + R\cdot \rightarrow$$

$$RH + -\dot{C}H(-CH{=}CH)_nCH_2-$$

Evidence for the "hydrogen hopping" mechanism proposed by the author (*14*) in 1953 seems to be accumulating.

**Air Oxidation of Free Radicals.** Curve 4 of Figure 2 represents the absorption spectrum after admitting air to the ultraviolet absorption cell. The bands at 258, 285, and 323 m$\mu$ which we believe to be caused by the allyl, dienyl, and trienyl free radicals, respectively, were completely eliminated by the oxidation.

**Kinetics of Growth of Dienyl and Trienyl Free Radicals.** In contrast to the allyl free radical, the dienyl and trienyl free radicals grow both on irradiation with ultraviolet light at liquid nitrogen temperature and with warming to room temperatures as mentioned above. The failure of these groups to decay on ultraviolet irradiation in contrast to the allyl free radical may be simply an artifact owing to the type of ultraviolet light used for the irradiation. If the intensity of the latter were weak at 285 and 323 m$\mu$, the dienyl and trienyl free radicals would not absorb and hence would not decay. Experiments to resolve this uncertainty have not yet been performed.

## Conclusions

One of the most pressing problems in the radiation chemistry of high polymers is to obtain definite proof of one or the other of the mechanisms proposed for the interconversion of alkyl and allyl free radicals. Such information might also be of great help in understanding other effects produced by irradiating high polymers.

## Acknowledgment

Thanks are due to Lloyd M. Cooke, Union Carbide Corp., and James A. Reid, Phillips Petroleum Co., for gifts of polyethylene samples.

## Literature Cited

(1) Allen, A. O., Hummel, A., *Discussions Faraday Soc.* **36**, 95 (1963).
(2) Ausloos, P., Rebbert, R. E., Lias, S. G., *J. Chem. Phys.* **42**, 540 (1965).
(3) Ayscough, P. B., Evans, H. E., *Trans. Faraday Soc.* **60**, 801 (1964).
(4) Brooker, L. G. S., *Rev. Mod. Phys.* **14**, 275 (1942).
(5) Collinson, E., Dainton, F. S., Walker, D. C., *Trans. Faraday Soc.* **57**, 1732 (1961).
(6) Deffner, C. U., *Kolloid Z.* **201**, 65 (1965).
(7) *Ibid.*, p. 863.
(8) Derwish, G. A. W., Galli, A., Giardini-Guidom, A., Volpi, G. G., *J. Chem. Phys.* **41**, 2998 (1964).
(9) Dewhurst, H. A., *J. Phys. Chem.* **62**, 15 (1958).
(10) Dole, M., "Mechanisms of Chemical Effects in Irradiated Polymers," in "Crystalline Olefin Polymers," Chap. 16. R. A. V. Raff and K. W. Doak, eds., Vol. I, Interscience, New York, 1965.

(11) Dole, M., Bodily, D. M., Third International Conference on Radiation Research, Cortina d'Ampezzo, Italy, June 1966; *J. Chem. Phys.* **45**, 1428, 1433 (1966).
(12) Dole, M., Cracco, F., *J. Phys. Chem.* **66**, 193 (1962).
(13) Dole, M., Fallgatter, M. B., Katsuura, K., *J. Phys. Chem.* **70**, 62 (1966).
(14) Dole, M., Keeling, C. D., *J. Am. Chem. Soc.* **75**, 6082 (1953).
(15) Dole, M., Milner, D. C., Williams, Ffrancon, *J. Am. Chem. Soc.* **80**, 1580 (1958).
(16) Dyne, P. J., Stone, J. A., *Can. J. Chem.* **39**, 2381 (1961).
(17) Fallgatter, M. B., Dole, M., *J. Phys. Chem.* **68**, 1988 (1964).
(18) Field, F. H., Franklin, J. L., "Electron Impact Phenomena," Academic Press, New York, 1957.
(19) Flournoy, J. M., Baum, L. H., Siegel, S., *J. Chem. Phys.* **36**, 2229 (1962).
(20) Hamashima, M., Reddy, M. P., Burton, M., *J. Phys. Chem.* **62**, 246 (1953).
(21) Ho, S. K., Freeman, G. R., *J. Phys. Chem.* **68**, 2189 (1964).
(22) Kang, H. Y., Saito, O., Dole, M., *J. Am. Chem. Soc.* **89**, 1980 (1967).
(23) Lawton, E. J., Balwit, J. S., Powell, R. S., *J. Chem. Phys.* **33**, 395, 405 (1960).
(24) Libby, D., Ormerod, M. G., *Phys. Chem. Solids* **18**, 316 (1961).
(25) Libby, W. F., *J. Chem. Phys.* **35**, 1714 (1961).
(26) Llabador, Y., Adloff, J. P., *J. Chem. Phys.* **61**, 681 (1964).
(27) Milinchuk, V. K., Pshezhetskiĭ, S. Ya., *Dokl. Akad. Nauk SSSR* **152**, 665 (1963).
(28) Milinchuk, V. K., Pshezhetskiĭ, S. Ya., *Polymer Sci. USSR* **26**, 733 (1964).
(29) Moorthy, P. N., Weiss, J. J., *J. Chem. Phys.* **42**, 3127 (1965).
(30) National Bureau of Standards, "Preliminary Report on Thermodynamic Properties of Selected Light Elements and Some Related Compounds," Rept. **8628** (Jan. 1, 1965).
(31) Ohnishi, S., Sugimoto, S., Nitta, I., *J. Chem. Phys.* **37**, 1283 (1962).
(32) *Ibid.*, **39**, 2647 (1963).
(33) Partridge, R. H., *J. Polymer Sci.* **3A**, 2817 (1965).
(34) Platt, J. R., *J. Chem. Phys.* **25**, 80 (1956).
(35) Rojo, E. A., Hentz, R. R., *J. Phys. Chem.* **69**, 3024 (1965).
(36) Schnabel, W., Dole, M., *Ibid.*, **67**, 295 (1963).
(37) Smaller, B., Matheson, M. S., *J. Chem. Phys.* **28**, 1169 (1958).
(38) Williams, Ffrancon, *J. Am. Chem. Soc.* **86**, 3954 (1964).
(39) Williams, Ffrancon, Polymer Preprints, Division of Polymer Chemistry, ACS, Vol. **7** (1), 47 (1966).
(40) Williams, Ffrancon, Dole, M., *J. Am. Chem. Soc.* **81**, 2919 (1959).
(41) Yoshida, H., Rånby, B., *J. Polymer Sci.* **B2**, 1155 (1964).

RECEIVED May 6, 1966. Work supported in part by the U. S. Atomic Energy Commission, AEC C00–1088–17. Facilities made available by the Advanced Research Projects Agency, Department of Defense, through the Northwestern University Materials Research Center.

# 4

# Irradiation of Hydrocarbon
# Polymers in Nitrous Oxide Atmosphere

YOICHI OKADA

Central Research Laboratory, Sumitomo Bakelite Co., Ltd., Yokohama, Japan

*Polyethylene, polypropylene, and polyisobutylene were ir-
radiated by γ-rays from a cobalt-60 source in an atmosphere
of nitrous oxide ($N_2O$). Polyethylene and polypropylene
irradiated in $N_2O$ give a higher yield of crosslinks than when
irradiated in vacuo. On the other hand, nitrous oxide reduces the amount of radiation degradation of polyisobutylene. The effect of nitrous oxide on the three polymers
increases monotonically with the gas pressure in an irradiation ampoule. The disappearance of nitrous oxide and the
formation of water and nitrogen indicate a dehydrogenation
process from the hydrocarbon polymer chains. $G(-N_2O)$ is
on the order of $10^3$. This large value suggests energy transfer.*

The yield of radiation-crosslinking of polyethylene was considered to
be highest in a vacuum atmosphere and to be reduced in the presence
of any gas like air. However, recently we presented evidence (3, 4, 6, 8)
that polyethylene irradiated with γ-rays in an atmosphere of nitrous
oxide ($N_2O$) gives higher yields of crosslinks and unsaturation (*trans*-
vinylene) than polyethylene irradiated *in vacuo*.

Nitrous oxide reduces the amount of radiation degradation of polyisobutylene (5), though this is a typical polymer which degrades under
radiation.

In this paper a similar experiment on polypropylene and the effects
of nitrous oxide on these three types of polymer are compared and discussed in detail.

## Effects of Nitrous Oxide on Crosslinking and Degradation

**Polyethylene.** In order to obtain the degree of crosslinking, the irradiated film was extracted with hot xylene, and the sol fraction, S,

was plotted (6) according to Charlesby's form as shown in Figure 1:

$$S + S^{1/2} = p_0/q_0 + 1/q_0u_1r$$

$p_0$ = probability of main chain scission; $q_0$ = probability of formation of a crosslinked unit; $u_1$ = number average degree of polymerization

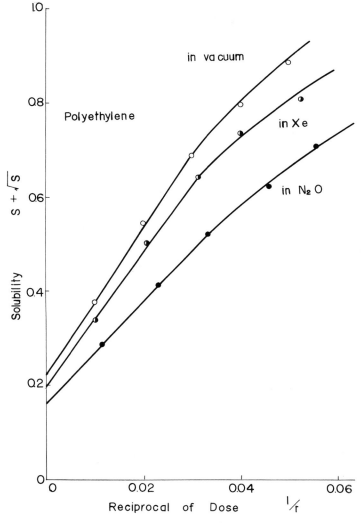

Journal of Applied Polymer Science

*Figure 1.   Sol fraction and dose (6)*

$N_2O$ 600 mm. Hg, Xe 4000 mm. Hg 0.3 mm. thick film (low density)
Charlesby's form of sol fraction $S + S^{1/2} = p_0/q_0 + 1/q_0u_1r$

In Figure 1, the effect of xenon gas is also shown. From the initial slope of the curve, the probability of crosslinking is calculated to increase by 44% in the presence of nitrous oxide at 600 mm. of Hg as compared with that *in vacuo.*

Infrared analysis (6) of irradiated film showed an increase in the yield of *trans*-vinylene unsaturation (Figure 2). The calculation from the

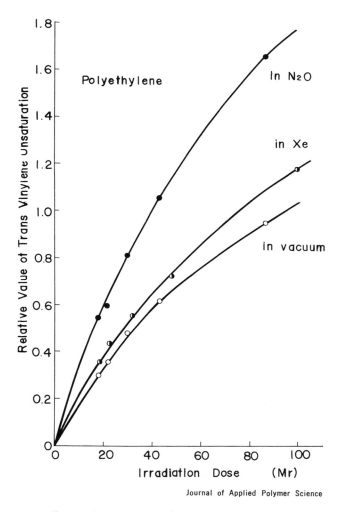

*Figure 2.    trans-Vinylene  unsaturation*  (6)

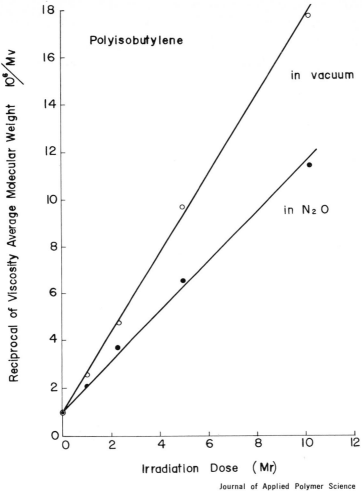

Figure 3. Degradation vs. dose (5)

*Block of Vistanex MML–100*       $N_2O$. *600 mm. Hg*

initial slope of the curve gives the increment caused by nitrous oxide as 87%. The formation of *trans*-vinylene, in the case of polyethylene, is a notable chemical change under radiation *in vacuo*. These results are compared in Table I with those of a xenon atmosphere.

### Table I. Increment of Polyethylene (%)

|  | $N_2O$ (600 mm.) | Xe (4000 mm.) |
|---|---|---|
| Crosslinks | +44 | +10 |
| Unsaturation | +87 | +19 |

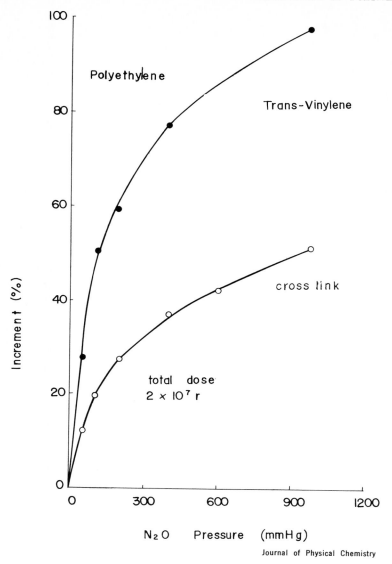

Figure 4.   Effect of $N_2O$ pressure (PE) (7)

From Charlesby's equation          $\dfrac{\Delta q_0}{q_0} = \Delta \left( \dfrac{1}{S + S^{1/2}} \right) \Big/ \dfrac{1}{S + S^{1/2}}$

**Polyisobutylene.**  The solution viscosity of an irradiated polyiso-butylene block was measured in $CCl_4$ at 30°C. to determine the degree of degradation (5). The variation of viscosity-average molecular weight, $Mv$, with the dose, $r$, is shown in Figure 3. Nitrous oxide reduced the amount of degradation to 63% of that *in vacuo.* Infrared analysis of the irradiated specimen indicates that the formation of vinylidene unsaturation is also reduced to about 90% at a pressure of 350 mm.; the vinylidene formation is a typical change under radiation in the case of polyisobutylene. At 350 mm., the degradation becomes about 85% of that *in vacuo.*

## Effects of $N_2O$ Pressure

**Polyethylene.** The variations of crosslinks and of unsaturation with the gas pressure (7) are shown in Figure 4. Here each curve gives increments of yield which are shown as values relative to that *in vacuo.* The general shape of the curves, monotonically increasing with the gas pressure, seems to be natural since the gas concentration in the polymer solid should increase with pressure. The increment of unsaturation is nearly twice that of crosslinks.

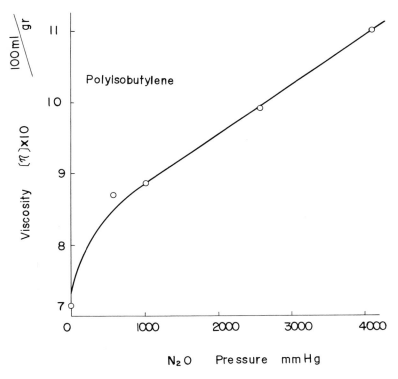

*Figure 5.   Effect of $N_2O$ pressure (PIB)*

*Solution viscosity in $CCl_4$ at 30°C.*                     *Dose rate: 5.9 × 10⁵ r/hr.*

*Total dose: 5 × 10⁶ r*

**Polyisobutylene.** The viscosity of irradiated polyisobutylene is plotted against $N_2O$ pressure in Figure 5. The curve increases monotonically with increasing pressure. If nitrous oxide is effective in reducing the amount of degradation, the behavior of the curve seems to be reasonable since the gas concentration in the polymer solid should increase with the gas pressure.

**Polypropylene.** A similar study on polypropylene is interesting because polypropylene has a molecular structure intermediate between polyethylene and polyisobutylene. An atactic polypropylene specimen was prepared by ether extraction and irradiated in a nitrous oxide atmosphere. The changes in gel fraction (insoluble in hot xylene) as a function of $N_2O$ pressure are shown in Figure 6. Gel formation (crosslinking) of polypropylene is also promoted in the presence of nitrous oxide.

### Material Balance of Nitrous Oxide

**Polyethylene.** To determine the role of nitrous oxide during irradiation, the material balance of nitrous oxide was measured (7). A known

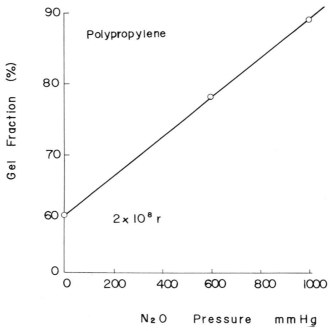

*Figure 6.   Effect of $N_2O$ pressure (PP)*

*Atactic polypropylene (porous block)*
*Gel fraction; insoluble in 100°C. xylene (3 days)*

amount of nitrous oxide was enclosed in an ampoule with a quantity
of polymer specimen before irradiation, and the gas remaining in the
ampoule after irradiation was analyzed by fractional distillation and
mass spectrometry.

### Table II.  Material Balance of $N_2O$ (PE) (7)

| Expt. No. | Film, grams | $G(-N_2O)$ | Loss of $N_2O$, moles $\times 10^4$ | Formation of $N_2$, moles $\times 10^4$ | Formation of $H_2O$, moles $\times 10^4$ |
|---|---|---|---|---|---|
| 1 | 0 | 10 > | 9.98 | — | — |
| 2 | 18.0 | 1710 | 6.95 | 7.37 | 6.83 |
| 3 | 20.0 | 2280 | 11.4 | 11.0 | 10.8 |

As shown in Table II, in the presence of polymer, the enclosed nitrous oxide is completely consumed during irradiation. In the place of
nitrous oxide, nitrogen and water are formed. The yield of nitrogen or
water corresponds stoichiometrically to the loss of nitrous oxide. A large
*G* value, about 2000, is given for the disappearance of nitrous oxide. Esti-
mation of the *G* value is based on the assumption that the available
energy for the consumption is only that absorbed directly by the gas
dissolved in the polymer solid. The *G* values for the formation of water
and nitrogen should be equal to 2000. Moreover, the summation of the
amount of the excess formation of crosslinks and unsaturation becomes
stoichiometrically almost equal to the loss of nitrous oxide, as shown in
Table III. The equation of material balance of nitrous oxide, therefore,
should be written as follows:

$$N_2O \overset{2H}{\rightarrow} N_2 + H_2O$$

Here 2H does not mean an evolved hydrogen. In the absence of
polymer, nitrous oxide decomposes at a low *G* value.

### Table III.  Amount of Excess Formation (PE) [a]

$$- \Delta N_2O = \Delta \text{ crosslinks} + \Delta \text{ unsaturation}$$

| | |
|---|---|
| Loss of $N_2O$ | 11.4 |
| Excess formation of crosslinks | 4.8 |
| Excess formation of unsaturation | 7.3 |

[a] Mole $\times 10^4$

**Polyisobutylene and Polypropylene.** In a similar way, the material
balance of nitrous oxide in the case of polyisobutylene was measured
as shown in Table IV. In this case, whereas the enclosed nitrous oxide
is not completely consumed during irradiation, the consumption proceeds

at a high $G$ value, and water and nitrogen are formed at an equal rate. The loss of nitrous oxide and the yields of water and nitrogen are stoichiometrically equal in the range of experimental error. The equation of material balance of nitrous oxide is the same as in the case of polyethylene. In the case of polypropylene, a similar measurement was not carried out. However, many water droplets formed on the inner wall of ampoule after irradiation. The formation of nitrogen and water was reported by Dole (2).

### Table IV. Material Balance of $N_2O$ (PIB)[a]

$$N_2O \overset{2H}{\rightarrow} N_2 + H_2O$$

| Expt. No. | $N_2O$, Moles $\times 10^4$ | | $G(-N_2O)$ | Loss of $N_2O$, Moles $\times 10^4$ | Formation of $N_2$, Moles $\times 10^4$ | Formation of $H_2O$, Moles $\times 10^4$ |
|---|---|---|---|---|---|---|
| | Initial | Final | | | | |
| 1 | 11.0 | 2.6 | 1040 | 8.4 | 9.2 | 8.1 |
| 2 | 11.0 | 2.3 | 1110 | 8.8 | 9.6 | 7.6 |

[a] cf. PIB 4 grams. Total dose. $2 \times 10^8$ r.

### Discussion

The behavior of nitrous oxide during irradiation seems quite unusual. Whereas, as an irradiation atmosphere, 18 types of well-known inorganic gases and 4 types of saturated hydrocarbon gases were tested previously, the species which evidently showed such a singular effect were limited to nitrous oxide and xenon. In the work reported here, three types of polymers having different types of molecular structure were examined, but examination showed many points of similarity in the behavior of nitrous oxide.

Nitrous oxide disappears at a high rate in the cases of both polyethylene and polyisobutylene, but no chemical addition to the polymer chain can proceed because the nitrous oxide changes simply to nitrogen and water during irradiation in the polymer solid phase. This behavior of nitrous oxide differs entirely from that of oxygen, chlorine, sulfur dioxide, etc., as an atmosphere during irradiation. In the case of these latter gases, the irradiated polymer should be oxidized, chlorinated, or sulfonated.

Since nitrous oxide is one of the most soluble inorganic gases in the polymer solid, under our experimental conditions nitrous oxide can be regarded not only as an atmosphere but as a small additive in the polymer solid. In the polymer solid, especially in its amorphous region, nitrous oxide apparently dissolves homogeneously and disperses molecularly. At 600 mm. of Hg, in the case of polyethylene, the weight concentration is calculated as 0.1 to 0.2%. The gas solubility in polypropylene or polyisobutylene must be approximately equal to that in polyethylene since all of these are supposed to be hydrocarbon liquids.

Little radiation energy should be absorbed directly by the dissolved gas because the gas forms only a small weight fraction in the solid. Accordingly, the $G$ value for the disappearance of nitrous oxide becomes extremely large (on the order of $10^3$) if it is calculated on the assumption that the reaction of dissolved nitrous oxide is caused only by the energy absorbed directly. The energy absorbed directly, in other words, must be insufficient to consume almost all of the dissolved gas. The high $G$ value can be readily accounted for by assuming energy transfer from the polymer chain to the dissolved gas molecule. Moreover, if most of the nitrous oxide molecules are efficiently excited owing to the energy transfer, it is not strange that a notable chemical change is induced in the polymer solid, though the concentration may be low. On the other hand, it may be possible also that most of the nitrous oxide molecules become efficiently reactive by capturing the thermalized electron in the polymer solid. In the case of a xenon atmosphere, which shows an effect similar to $N_2O$, electron capture should be impossible. If both nitrous oxide and xenon react with the polymer in a similar mechanism, the energy transfer theory would be favorable. In the case of polyethylene, the formation of crosslinks and unsaturation is nothing but a dehydrogeneation from the polymer. The formation of crosslinks and unsaturation should be an indication that two hydrogen atoms are abstracted from the polymer chains by the excited nitrous oxide in the vicinity.

EXCESS FORMATION OF CROSSLINKS

EXCESS FORMATION OF UNSATURATION

These schemes satisfy the fact that the summation of $G$ values for the excess formation of crosslinks and unsaturation becomes almost equal to the $G$ value for the disappearance of nitrous oxide. In addition, they conveniently account for the fact that the energy transferred to the dis-

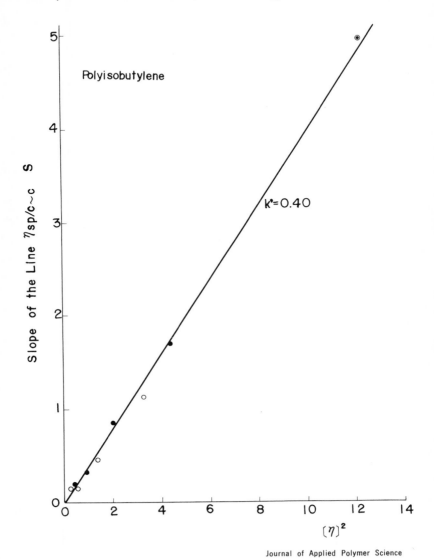

Figure 7.   Degree of branching (PIB) I (5)

○ In vacuo
● In N₂O, 600 mm.
Huggins' equation
$\eta_{sp}/c = [\eta] + k'[\eta]^2 c$
k'. Huggins' constant

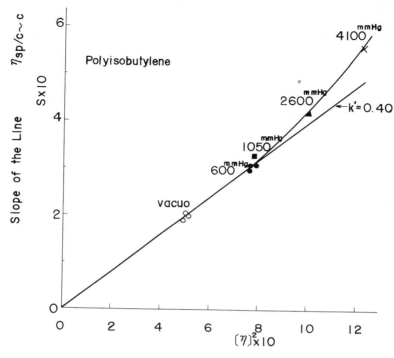

*Figure 8.    Degree of branching (PIB) II*

High pressure of $N_2O$
1050, 2600, and 4100 mm. Hg

solved nitrous oxide is relatively low and insufficient to induce directly any chemical change of polymer like crosslinking.

In the case of polyisobutylene, it is still difficult to explain clearly the role of nitrous oxide. There is no convincing evidence whether nitrous oxide protects the polymer chain against scission or induces crosslinking to increase the molecular weight of the polymer. Such crosslinking corresponds in appearance to the inhibition of degradation. If the mechanism developed for polyethylene is applied directly to the case of polyisobutylene, the dissolved nitrous oxide becomes reactive by energy transfer, two hydrogen atoms are abstracted from polymer chains in the vicinity, and thereafter a crosslinking between these polymer chains is induced. In this case, the polymer chain increases not only in molecular weight but in degree of branching because crosslinking and main chain scission occur simultaneously. The change in degree of branching can be estimated to some extent by Huggins' plot (*1*) as shown in Figures 7 and 8. As shown in Figure 7, at only 600 mm. of Hg of nitrous oxide, no deviation from a straight line ($k' = 0.40$) can be observed. At high pressure, as shown in Figure 8, a little deviation can be detected. This may indicate that the degree of branching increases in the presence of nitrous oxide. However, the idea (5, 7) that nitrous oxide protects the polymer chain against scission through an energy transfer process from the polymer chain to nitrous oxide still cannot be ruled out. In this case, energy of high level sufficient for chain scission must be transferred. The decrease in the formation of vinylidene unsaturation may indicate a decrease in chain scission.

From industry's viewpoint, the action of nitrous oxide should be useful to cut down the dose required for the crosslinking of polyethylene or polypropylene and to keep polyisobutylene from degradation. However, it is a question whether the complexity of processing caused by using nitrous oxide would pay economically.

### Acknowledgment

The author thanks A. Amemiya, University of Tokyo, and his group for many helpful discussions and suggestions during this work. Thanks are also given to T. Ito for his assistance in the experimental work.

### Literature Cited

(1)  Huggins, M. L., *J. Am. Chem. Soc.* **64,** 2716 (1942).
(2)  Kondo, M., Dole, M., *J. Phys. Chem.* **70,** 883 (1966).
(3)  Okada, Y., *J. Appl. Polymer Sci.* **7,** 695 (1963).
(4)  *Ibid.,* p. 703.
(5)  *Ibid.,* p. 1791.
(6)  *Ibid.,* **8,** 467 (1964).
(7)  Okada, Y., *J. Phys. Chem.* **68,** 2120 (1964).
(8)  Okada, Y., Amemiya, A., *J. Polymer Sci.* **50,** S22 (1961).

RECEIVED February 7, 1966.

# Effects of Radiation on the Olefinic Groups in Polybutadiene

W. W. PARKINSON

Reactor Chemistry Division, Oak Ridge National Laboratory, Oak Ridge, Tenn.

W. C. SEARS

Department of Physics and Astronomy, University of Georgia, Athens, Ga.

*Olefinic groups, present in high concentration in polybutadiene, change rapidly when exposed to ionizing radiation. Concentration changes of olefinic groups in four polybutadienes resulting from gamma and reactor irradiation were measured by infrared absorption spectra. The four types, irradiated in vacuum as x-ray-cured thin films were 92% cis-1,4, crystalline 95% trans-1,4, amorphous 73% trans-1,4, and an amorphous 71% side vinyl 1,2 polymer. The cis-vinylene groups were destroyed at a rate (G value) of −15 groups per 100 e.v., with the rate of conversion to the trans isomer proceeding at G = ~ 7. The trans-vinylene and side vinyl groups were destroyed in the polymers containing appreciable concentrations of them in apparent first-order processes. Their high reaction rates indicate efficient energy or charge transfer to the olefinic groups or possibly chain reactions.*

R adiation-induced crosslinking and scission profoundly affect the mechanical properties of polymers. These processes, then, are of primary interest in studying the effect of radiation on plastics and elastomers. On the other hand, Dole and others (5, 7) pointed out some years ago that the olefinic groups in polyethylene decrease rapidly during irradiation, and they suggested that these groups are involved in endlinking and crosslinking reactions. Whether or not there is participation in crosslinking reactions, any process which occurs at a high rate during irradiation deserves attention since it may offer an alternative mode of disposing of radiation energy which might otherwise produce crosslinking and changes in mechanical properties.

Olefinic groups in high concentration make up the molecular structure of the chemically simple hydrocarbon, polybutadiene. Moreover, several polybutadienes are available and in commercial use, containing a high fraction of the olefin groups in any one of three isomeric forms. These forms are cis, trans, and side vinyl as shown below. Consequently,

cis                              trans                    side vinyl

polybutadiene and the radiation-induced changes in its olefin groups are most appropriate subjects for study in considering the action of radiation on polymers.

Golub, in a recent series of papers (11, 12), showed that the olefin groups in high cis-polybutadiene decreased rapidly under irradiation (G = −7.9) along with undergoing conversion to the trans form at a similar rate (G = −7.2). (G or G value is the number of molecular groups altered per 100 e.v. absorbed.) Much greater rates of disappearance of unsaturated groups were reported by Kuzminsky and co-workers (16), who reported G values for double bond disappearance in excess of −2000. The objective of this investigation was to determine conversion reactions among the isomeric forms of the olefinic groups and to measure net changes in the over-all concentration of all unsaturated groups.

### Experimental

**Materials and Methods.** The isomeric compositions of the four polybutadienes used are listed in Table I. Samples were prepared for infrared measurement from solutions of the polymer without further purification. Most films were cast from carbon disulfide solutions on mercury or on glass plates, but a few films were cast from hexane solutions to determine whether or not the solvent affected the radiation-induced behavior. No difference was observed for films cast from the different solvents. The films were cured by exposure to x-rays in vacuum. (Doses were below the level producing detectable radiation effects.) They were then mounted on aluminum frames for infrared measurements. The thicknesses of the films were controlled for desirable absorbance ranges and varied from $0.6 \times 10^{-3}$ to $2 \times 10^{-3}$ cm. After measuring the infrared spectrum with a Perkin-Elmer 221 infrared spectrophotometer, the mounted films were evacuated to 3 microns and sealed in glass or quartz tubes (quartz tubes only were used for reactor irradiations).

The specimens were irradiated in either $^{60}$Co gamma sources or in a nuclear reactor. (The reactor was a natural-uranium, graphite-moderated, air-cooled type having a high ratio of fast neutrons to gamma photons. The thermal neutron flux was $8 \times 10^{11}$ n/sq. cm.-sec. and the fast neutron flux about 10% of this value.) The $^{60}$Co facilities had dose rates of $0.4 \times 10^6$ to $4 \times 10^6$ rads per hour (no effect of dose rate was noted). Irradiations were carried out at room temperature with water cooling (about 22°C.) and at 110°C. without cooling. Specimens irradiated in the reactor were water-cooled and were exposed to a dose rate of about $2 \times 10^6$ rads per hour, of which about 75% came from fast neutrons. After irradiating the specimens, their spectra were recorded first with the specimens in helium to avoid oxidation, then with the specimens in air to indicate spectral effects from the helium cell.

**Calculations.** The spectrum of a typical high *cis*-1,4 polymer sample is shown before and after irradiation in Figure 1 and that of a *trans*-1,4 polymer film in Figure 2. The significant infrared bands are listed in Table II for all of the polybutadienes, with the assignments to the various modes of molecular oscillation as developed by Binder (2). The bands used to estimate quantitative changes in the olefin groups were those at 740 cm.$^{-1}$ for the cis isomer, 967 cm.$^{-1}$ for the trans isomer, and 910 cm.$^{-1}$

### Table I.    Composition of Polybutadiene Sample Material

| Polymer Type | cis-Vinylene Content | | trans-Vinylene Content | | Side Vinyl Content | |
|---|---|---|---|---|---|---|
| | Moles/ liter[a] | Fraction olefin groups | Moles/ liter[a] | Fraction olefin groups | Moles/ liter[a] | Fraction olefin groups |
| High *cis*-1,4[b] | 15.3 | 0.92 | 0.55 | 0.03 | 0.75 | 0.05 |
| High *trans*-1,4[b] | 0.1 | 0.006 | 17.1 | 0.954 | 0.72 | 0.04 |
| Amorphous trans (emulsion)[c] | 0.2 | 0.012 | 11.8 | 0.733 | 4.1 | 0.256 |
| Side vinyl (sodium, 1-2)[c] | 0.2 | 0.013 | 4.3 | 0.278 | 11.0 | 0.710 |

[a] In moles of $C=C$ per liter of polymer.
[b] Supplied by D. C. Smith, Phillips Petroleum Co., Bartlesville, Okla.
[c] Supplied by J. L. Binder, Firestone Tire and Rubber Co., Akron, Ohio.

for the side vinyl group. Although most of the spectra showed the $C=C$ stretching bands at 1640 and/or 1660 cm.$^{-1}$, these bands could not be used to determine the over-all loss in unsaturation since they are weak or absent in the trans isomer. Instead, over-all changes in unsaturation were calculated from the summation of changes in each type of olefin group.

The complex spectral structure from 750 to 650 cm.$^{-1}$ was resolved mathematically by Binder into a series of overlapping bands of the theoretical Lorentz shape (3). It was shown that only the band at 740 cm.$^{-1}$ originated in the *cis*-olefin group. However, measurements on

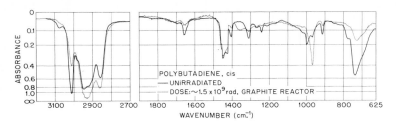

*Figure 1.   Spectra of high cis-1,4-polybutadiene*

solutions of simple *cis*-olefins showed that the characteristic band frequency and the molar absorptivity varied among the different olefins. Furthermore, the molar absorptivity was not constant above moderate concentrations (departed from the Beer-Lambert law) (9, 19). Therefore, to determine the concentration of *cis*-vinylene groups, the integrated band area or intensity at 740 cm.$^{-1}$ was used instead of the molar absorptivity. Ramsay (20) has shown that the integrated absorption intensity, $A \equiv \int_{\nu_1}^{\nu_2} \alpha d\nu$, is

$$A = \frac{\pi}{2cl} \, \Delta\nu_{\frac{1}{2}} \log_e \left( \frac{I_0}{I} \right)_{\nu_0} \tag{1}$$

where $\alpha$ is the molar absorptivity being integrated over the wave number limits of the band $\nu_1$ and $\nu_2$, $c$ is the concentration of the absorbing group in moles per liter, $l$ is the thickness of sample in centimeters, $\Delta\nu_{\frac{1}{2}}$ is the band width in cm.$^{-1}$ at half maximum absorbance, and $(I_0/I)\nu_0$ is the ratio of incident to transmitted intensity at the frequency of maximum absorption, $\nu_0$. To minimize contribution from the overlapping structure at frequencies below 740 cm.$^{-1}$, only the high frequency side of the 740-cm.$^{-1}$ band was used to estimate the band width.

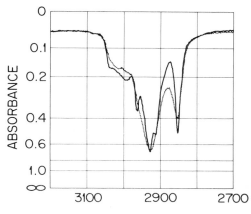

*Figure 2.   Spectra*

To determine the concentration of *cis*-vinylene groups in irradiated specimens, the original *cis*-polybutadiene itself was used as a standard, and a value for $A$ (assumed independent of concentration) was determined from $\Delta\nu_{\frac{1}{2}}$ and $\log_e (I_0/I)_{\nu_0}$ of unirradiated specimens. The total concentration of unsaturation was accepted (*15*) as 100% of theoretical and the density as 0.90 gram per cc. The cis concentration was obtained by subtracting from the total unsaturation the *trans*-vinylene and vinyl contents determined from the calibration curves developed as described below. The value of $A$ so determined was $2.67 \times 10^3$ liters/mole-sq. cm.

To use the absorbance of the band at 967 cm.$^{-1}$ to determine *trans*-vinylene groups in the high cis-polymer, it was necessary first to correct for the overlap from the wing of the *cis*-vinylene band at 998 cm.$^{-1}$

### Table II.   Infrared Absorption Bands in Polybutadiene

| Band Wave No., cm.$^{-1}$ | Origin |
|---|---|
| 3077 | C—H stretch, $CH_2$=CH—, vinyl group |
| 3012 | C—H stretch, —CH=CH—, *cis* |
| 2990 to 2840 | C—H stretch, —$CH_2$— and other groups |
| 1660 | C=C stretch, —CH=CH—, *cis* |
| 1640 | C=C stretch, $CH_2$=CH—, vinyl |
| 1055 | Crystalline, —CH=CH—, *trans* |
| 998 | ?, —CH=CH—, *cis* |
| 995 | C—H, out-of-plane bend, $CH_2$=CH—, vinyl |
| 967 | C—H, out-of-plane bend, —CH=CH—, *trans* |
| 910 | C—$H_2$, out-of-plane bend, $CH_2$=CH—, vinyl |
| 775 | Crystalline, —CH=CH—, *trans* |
| 740 | C—H, out-of-plane bend, —CH=CH—, *cis* |
| 710 to 650 | ?, cyclic structures |

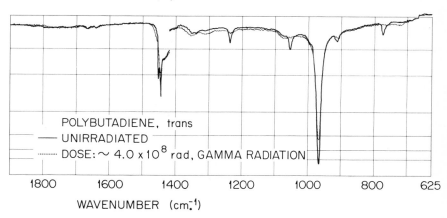

POLYBUTADIENE, trans
—— UNIRRADIATED
········ DOSE: ~ 4.0 x 10$^8$ rad, GAMMA RADIATION

WAVENUMBER (cm.$^{-1}$)

*of high* trans-1,4-polybutadiene

(Figure 1). The absorbance at 967 cm.$^{-1}$ contributed by this wing was calculated in unirradiated specimens from the Lorentz band shape equation and the intensity and half-maximum band width of the 998-cm.$^{-1}$ band. In irradiated specimens the growth of the 967-cm.$^{-1}$ band and overlap from this band on that at 998 cm.$^{-1}$ precluded the use of this procedure. For these specimens, the absorbance at 967 cm.$^{-1}$ was corrected for overlap from the 998-cm.$^{-1}$ band according to the following equation: $A_{967} = H_{967} - H_{740}(W'_{967}/H'_{740})$ in which $A_{967}$ is the corrected absorbance, $H_{967}$ is the uncorrected absorbance of the band at 967 cm.$^{-1}$, $H_{740}$ is the absorbance of the irradiated specimen at 740 cm.$^{-1}$, $W'_{967}$ is the calculated absorbance at 967 cm.$^{-1}$ of the wing of the cis band at 998 cm.$^{-1}$ in the unirradiated specimens, and $H'_{740}$ is the absorbance in the cis band at 740 cm.$^{-1}$ in these specimens.

As reported by others (*21*, *23*) molar absorptivities at 910 and 967 cm.$^{-1}$ determined from solutions of low-molecular-weight terminal and *trans*-olefins were found to be inapplicable to the emulsion and sodium polybutadienes. However, the unirradiated polymers themselves could be used to calculate molar absorptivities and calibration curves by using simultaneous equations of the form: $A_{fn}/l_n = a_f c_{in}$, in which $A_{fn}$ is the absorbance of specimen $n$ of thickness $l_n$ at the band frequency $f$ characteristic of the olefin species $i$, $a_f$ is the molar absorptivity at $f$, and $c_{in}$ is the concentration of the olefin species in the specimen. The concentration terms were reduced to the concentration of two olefin species by subtracting from the total concentration of olefin groups the concentration of cis species, which was low enough to be estimated with adequate accuracy using approximate absorptivities from low molecular weight olefins. The total concentration of olefin groups was calculated from the densities and the known fraction of the theoretical unsaturation present in the two types of polybutadiene—i.e., 97% for the emulsion (*15*), 94% for the sodium polybutadiene (*4*), and density 0.89 gram per cc. for both.

To obtain the absorbances at 910 and 967 cm.$^{-1}$, it was necessary to correct the observed band intensities for the overlapping of adjacent bands. The band at 910 cm.$^{-1}$ for the vinyl group was corrected for the absorbance from the wing of the 967-cm.$^{-1}$ *trans*-vinylene band, and the latter band was corrected for the vinyl band at 995 cm.$^{-1}$. The Lorentz band shape equation was used to calculate the absorbance in the wings, and in the thicker specimens, successive approximations were necessary. This treatment gave the four equations below, which yielded the concentrations of trans and vinyl groups for the emulsion and sodium polybutadienes listed in Table I. Implicit in these equations is the assumption that the absorptivities are independent of concentration.

$$797 = a_{910}\, c_{v_1}$$
$$351 = a_{967}\, (15.3 - c_{v_1})$$
$$290 = a_{910}\, c_{v_2}$$
$$1000 = a_{967}\, (15.8 - c_{v_2})$$

Concentrations are expressed in moles of olefin groups per liter and absorptivities in liters per mole-cm. The concentration of the side vinyl group in the sodium polymer is $c_{v_1}$ and for the *trans*-vinylene group, $15.3 - c_{v_1}$; similarly for the emulsion polymer, $c_{v_2}$ is vinyl, and $15.8 - c_{v_2}$ is trans concentration. Solving these equations gave molar absorptivities and concentrations from which calibration curves were constructed, relating corrected absorbance at 910 and 967 cm.$^{-1}$ to concentration of side vinyl and trans groups, respectively.

The trans calibration curve, derived from amorphous polymers, was unsuitable for the high *trans*-1,4 polymer, which was crystalline and which showed a molar absorptivity much higher than that indicated by the curve. High *trans*-1,4 polymer is reported to undergo a first-order transition to an amorphous state at 76°C. by Moraglio *et al.* (*18*) as indicated by x-ray and calorimetric measurements. Dainton *et al.* (*6*) reported this transition at 44°C. from calorimetric measurements. We found in this study that the crystalline bands at 775 and 1055 cm.$^{-1}$ disappear in high *trans*-1,4 polymer progressively from 46° to 71°C. As described below, radiation appeared to produce a similar decrease in crystallinity and rendered inapplicable the calibration curves or molar absorptivities derived from both the amorphous trans and the crystalline high trans polymer.

### Results

Typical irradiation-caused changes in the infrared spectra of polybutadiene are shown by the broken lines in Figures 1 and 2, for high cis and high trans polymers, respectively. The outstanding change is the reduced concentration of olefin groups, shown for the cis polymer by decreases in band intensities at 740 and 3012 cm.$^{-1}$ and for the trans by a decrease in the 967-cm.$^{-1}$ band. However, in the cis specimens (Figure 1) there is a rapid increase in intensity in the band at 967 cm.$^{-1}$ resulting from isomerization of the cis groups, as Golub has described (*12*).

In the high *trans*-1,4 polymers (Figure 2) an additional change is the destruction of the crystallinity bands at 775 and 1055 cm.$^{-1}$. Since the absorbance showed a different dependence on concentration in the crystalline and amorphous (emulsion and sodium) polymers, this reduction in crystallinity precluded determinations of radiation yields in the high *trans*-1,4 specimens. However, maximum and minimum limits could be set on the yields by using the molar absorptivity of the crystalline polymer for the maximum and the calibration curve derived from the amorphous polymers for the minimum.

In all spectra, there was a decrease in intensity in the side vinyl band at 910 cm.$^{-1}$. This decrease was most rapid in the mixed polymers which contained an appreciable fraction of the olefin groups in this form. In polymers with low concentrations of vinyl groups (high cis and high trans polymers) the rate of disappearance of vinyl isomers appeared to be low until the total unsaturation had been reduced to about half its initial value. This behavior is depicted in Figure 3, which shows the

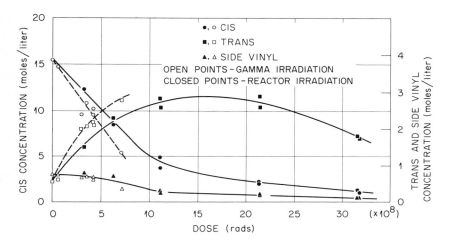

*Figure 3.    Concentration of olefin groups in irradiated cis-polybutadiene*

concentration of each type of olefin group as a function of dose for the high cis polymer.

At moderate doses the decrease of *cis*-vinylene groups, shown in Figure 3, follows a linear plot for zero-order decay better than a semilogarithmic plot of first-order kinetics. *trans*-Vinylene groups are produced at a rate which decreases as the cis concentration declines at higher doses. In the dose range of 1 to 2 × 10$^9$ rads, when the cis concentration has been reduced to less than one-third its original value, the concentration of trans groups reaches a maximum and then decreases as the rate of destruction exceeds the rate of formation.

The differences in slopes for reactor and gamma irradiations shown in Figure 3 are real rather than the result of inaccurate dose measurement since hydrogen production was observed to be greater in the reactor (*14*). Radiation yields are presented as initial G values in Table III, along with yields and reaction rates for the other types of polybutadiene. Irradiations without cooling, at 110°C., permitted the determination of activation energies, which are also listed in Table III.

The rates of disappearance of both the *trans*-vinylene and side vinyl groups in the amorphous *trans* (emulsion) and in the side vinyl (sodium) polymers decreased with increasing dose according to first-order kinetics. The changes in concentration of these olefin groups are shown on a semilogarithmic plot for the amorphous trans polymer in Figure 4, which is typical of both this and the side vinyl polymer. As in the case of the *cis*-1,4 polymer, the slopes for specimens irradiated in the mixed neutron-gamma field of the reactor were lower than those for specimens exposed to gamma radiation alone. These differences are shown in the first-order reaction rate constants listed in Table III.

## Discussion

The linear portions of the curves for *cis*-vinylene concentration (Figure 3) give G values of −15 for cis destruction by gamma radiation and −12 by the reactor field. The value for gamma radiation is in reasonable agreement with that observed by Golub (*12*) if his yield for loss of unsaturation is combined with his isomerization yield (G = −7.9 + −7.2 = −15.1). Golub also found a greater decrease in unsaturation (G = −13.6) for electron irradiation in a stream of nitrogen. He attributed the difference in rates of destruction to electron capture by the oxygen impurity in the nitrogen, resulting in longer lifetimes for ionized species and increased yields.

Initial yields for conversion to the *trans*-vinylene isomer can be derived by adding to the apparent yield the rate of destruction calculated from the initial concentration of *trans*-vinylene groups and the first-order rate constants determined for the amorphous trans polymer. The initial yield of *trans*-vinylene groups is 6.8 for gamma radiation and 4.4 for the reactor. The value for gamma radiation is similar to Golub's value of 7.2 for both gamma and electrons.

The activation energies for the high *cis*-1,4 polymer were 3.7 kcal. per mole for *cis*-vinylene destruction and 1.5 for *trans*-vinylene production. The difference in these values indicates a fundamental difference in the reaction mechanisms involved in the two processes. As explained below, the most probable product formed in the reaction of a cis group is a cyclic structure which would entail reorientation of several chain segments of the polymer molecule. On the other hand, the conversion of the cis to the trans isomer requires the movement of fewer chain segments following the radiation-excitation of a cis group, a process involving no thermal activation energy.

The destruction of *trans*-vinylene groups in the crystalline high trans polymer had upper and lower G values of 22 and 11. There was little or

**Table III.   Radiation Yields and**

| | | Type |
| --- | --- | --- |
| | | High cis-1,4 |

Reaction constants and yields

cis Groups

| | | |
| --- | --- | --- |
| Initial yield | $G_o$, groups/100 e.v. | $-15.2 \pm 0.8$ |
| Activation energy | $E$, kcal./mole | 3.7 |
| Reactor yield | $G_o$, groups/100 e.v. | $-12$ |

trans Groups

| | | |
| --- | --- | --- |
| Rate constant | $k$, g/e.v. | — |
| Initial yield | $G_o$, groups/100 e.v. | $+6.8$ |
| Activation energy | $E$, kcal./mole | $1.5 \pm 0.3$ |
| Reactor yield | $G_o$, groups/100 e.v. | $+4.4$ |
| Reactor rate constant | $k$, g/e.v. | — |

Side vinyl groups

| | | |
| --- | --- | --- |
| Rate constant | $k$, g/e.v. | 0 to 1.4 |
| Initial yield | $G_o$, groups/100 e.v. | 0 |
| Activation energy | $E$, kcal./mole | — |
| Reactor rate constant | $k$, g/e.v. | — |

Net change, all groups (gamma radiation)

| | | |
| --- | --- | --- |
| Initial yield | $G_o$, groups/100 e.v. | $-8.4$ |

no generation of a distinct *cis*-vinylene band at 740 cm.$^{-1}$, and it can be concluded only that cis production was less than $G = 1$. In the amorphous trans polymer, even thick samples showed little development of a cis band, and the upper limit of the cis yield was $G = 0.5$. Apparently, in the solid state, the decrease in olefin groups of all types is so rapid and the spectral interference from cyclic structures is such that the isomerization of trans to cis groups [described by Golub (*11, 12*) in the solid as well as liquid state] is quite difficult to observe.

In the amorphous *trans*- and the side vinyl polybutadienes, the first-order reaction rate constants (Table III) give high initial yields ($G_o$) for olefin disappearance when the initial concentration is inserted in the rate equation: $kD = \ln(C_o/C_D)$, where $k$ = rate constant, $C_o$ = initial concentration, and $C_D$ = concentration after dose $D$. The activation energies for the disappearance of both these olefinic species range from 3.4 to 4.0 kcal. per mole, not very different from the activation energy observed for cis disappearance.

**Reaction Rate Constants**

*of Polybutadiene*

| High trans-1,4 | Amorphous trans (emulsion) | Side vinyl (sodium) |
|---|---|---|
| $<+1.0$ | $<+0.5$ | 0 |
| — | — | — |
| — | — | — |
| $(1.4 \text{ to } 3.3) \times 10^{-23}$ | $2.2 \times 10^{-23}$ | $2.4 \times 10^{-23}$ |
| —11 to —22 | —19 | —7 |
| — | 3.4 | 4.0 |
| — | — | — |
| — | $0.9 \times 10^{-23}$ | $\sim 1 \times 10^{-23}$ |
| $0.5 \times 10^{-23}$ | $4.3 \times 10^{-23}$ | $5.4 \times 10^{-23}$ |
| —0.2 | —12 | —40 |
| — | 3.8 | 3.9 |
| — | $1.6 \times 10^{-23}$ | $\sim 1 \times 10^{-23}$ |
| —11 to —22 | —31 | —47 |

The high yields suggest that there is efficient transfer of excitation energy or of charge to the olefin groups of all types (*17*). The ionization and excitation energies of the olefin groups relative to those of the alkane moiety make these transfer processes possible (*8, 11*). Additional evidence for an energy or charge transfer process is the protection of the side vinyl group in the high *cis*-1,4-polybutadiene.

An energy or charge transfer mechanism is also consistent with the reduced yields observed in the nuclear reactor, where most of the dose was imparted by fast neutrons. The neutrons produce recoil ions having an average linear energy transfer (LET) of 3 e.v. per A. As in the case of the gamma photons, the energy of these recoil ions is not deposited homogeneously in the irradiated material. Instead interactions with the absorbing material occur at discrete points to give limited regions containing high concentrations of excited or ionized molecules. These regions are termed "spurs" and in water, according to Ganguly and Magee (*10*) are about 20 A. in diameter and result from the deposition of 50 to 60 e.v.

of energy. If these values for water are applicable to hydrocarbons, the average LET of the recoil ions from fast neutrons is seen to give over-lapping spurs. At the high $G$ values prevailing (Table III), the olefin groups will be depleted in the limited volume of a spur, and energy or charge transfer to these groups will be decreased during the later stages of the lifetime of a spur. If there are competing processes involving the

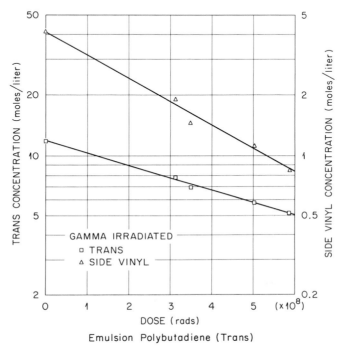

Figure 4. Concentration of olefin groups in irradiated amorphous trans-polybutadiene

excited or charged species, such as collisional deactivation or ion recom-bination, these may proceed unaffected by the depletion. Then under the condition of overlapping spurs, depletion could be appreciable, and a significantly larger fraction of the radiation energy could be dissipated by deactivation or neutralization. Other processes based on charge transfer competing with recombination can also explain the lower yields at high LET (14).

The first-order rate constants for terminal vinyl groups and for trans-vinylene groups in linear polyethylene were observed by Dole and Wil-liams (8) to be 20 to 30 times higher than our corresponding rates in the amorphous trans- and vinyl polybutadienes (Table III). On the other hand, the initial yields were lower than our $G_0$ values because of the lower concentrations of the olefin groups in polyethylene. These results can be rationalized on the basis of an energy transfer mechanism if we assume that energy transfer is more efficient in the largely crystalline matrix of polyethylene, to account for the higher rate constants in polyethylene. However, the yields per unit radiation dose are reduced in polyethylene because the low concentration of olefin groups lets competitive deactivation processes dissipate a larger fraction of the total radiation energy.

By far the dominant process in the irradiation of polybutadiene of all isomeric configurations is the loss of unsaturation. In high cis polymer the net loss of unsaturation ($G = 8.4$) exceeds the conversion to the trans form ($G_o = 6.8$). In the *trans-* and vinyl polybutadienes initial yields for destruction of olefin groups range from 18 to 40. Attempts were made to verify this large reduction in unsaturation by chemical means. Polybutadiene film was treated with bromine vapor, and changes in weight and the infrared spectrum were measured periodically. The rate of bromine addition to the double bond appeared to depend on swelling of the specimen, which varied nonuniformly with time and from one specimen to the next. Furthermore, the double bonds were not completely saturated by this method, even after lengthy exposures and severe deterioration of the specimens. We felt that the possibility of bromine-substitution reactions rendered such determinations of total unsaturation inaccurate.

A question of primary importance is the nature of the product formed through the consumption of these unsaturated groups at such high rates. The yield of hydrogen is low ($G = 0.4$ to $0.5$) (*14*) so that radiation-generation of unsaturation does not add to the problem seriously. But crosslinking reactions, a logical consumer of unsaturation, have been reported to show yields of only $G = 3.6$ for both high *cis-* (*13*) and emulsion (*24*) polybutadienes. Golub (*11*) suggested that the olefin groups are destroyed in the formation of cyclic structures, and indeed such groups have been observed in irradiated polyethylene by Dole (*7*) and by Sears (*22*). These groups have infrared bands in the 900- to 1050-cm.$^{-1}$ region, where the olefin groups also absorb. Apparently, the rapid changes in the olefinic bands obscure the appearance of new bands from the cyclic structures.

It is also possible that conjugated unsaturated groups could be formed in polybutadiene, but these groups also have bands near the olefin bands (983- to 994-cm.$^{-1}$). Conjugated groups cannot develop, however, through migration of double bonds. Golub's irradiation of

polybutadiene deuterated in the 2,3 positions showed that $C\!=\!\overset{\displaystyle H}{\underset{\displaystyle |}{C}}\!-$ bend-ing vibrations did not appear (*12*). He concluded that mechanisms involving the allyl radical as an intermediate could not be important in cyclization, crosslinking, or migration of double bonds. Instead, energy or charge transfer processes leading to formation of cyclic structures seem to be indicated. With the high yields of olefin destruction, certainly, short-chain reactions, either ion- or radical-initiated, cannot be ignored.

## Acknowledgment

The authors express their appreciation to O. Sisman for his interest in and support of the work and to W. K. Kirkland for his careful measurement of most of the infrared spectra.

## Literature Cited

(1)  Binder, J. L., *Anal. Chem.* **26**, 1877 (1954).
(2)  Binder, J. L., *J. Polymer Sci.* **A1**, 47 (1963).
(3)  *Ibid.*, **A3**, 1587 (1965).
(4)  Binder, J. L., private communication.
(5)  Chapiro, A., *J. Chem. Phys.* **52**, 246 (1955).
(6)  Dainton, F. S., Evans, D. M., Hoare, F. E., Melia, T. P., *Polymer* **3**, 263 (1963).
(7)  Dole, M., Milner, D. C., Williams, T. F., *J. Am. Chem. Soc.* **80**, 1580 (1958).
(8)  Dole, M., Williams, T. F., *Discussions Faraday Soc.* **27**, 74 (1959).
(9)  Francis, S. A., *J. Chem. Phys.* **19**, 942 (1951); **18**, 861 (1950).
(10)  Ganguly, A. K., Magee , J. L., *J. Chem. Phys.* **25**, 129 (1956).
(11)  Golub, M. A., *J. Am. Chem. Soc.* **82**, 5093 (1960); **81**, 54 (1959).
(12)  Golub, M. A., *J. Phys. Chem.* **69**, 2639 (1965).
(13)  Jankowski, B., Kroh, J., *J. Appl. Polymer Sci.* **9**, 1363 (1965).
(14)  Keyser, R. M., Oak Ridge National Laboratory, unpublished work.
(15)  Kirk, R. E., Othmer, D. F., "Encyclopedia of Chemical Technology," Vol. 11, 1st ed., p. 836, Interscience, New York, 1953.
(16)  Kuzminsky, A. S., *et al.*, *Proc. Intern. Conf. Peaceful Uses Atomic Energy (Geneva)* **29**, 258 (1958).
(17)  Lorquet, J. C., Elkomoss, S. G., Magee, J. L., *J. Chem. Phys.* **37**, 1991 (1962).
(18)  Moraglio, G., Polizzotti, G., Danusso, F., *Europ. Polymer J.* **1**, 183 (1965).
(19)  Parkinson, W. W., Sears, W. C., to be published.
(20)  Ramsay, D. A., *J. Am. Chem. Soc.* **74**, 72 (1952).
(21)  Richardson, W. S., Sacher, A., *J. Polymer Sci.* **10**, 353 (1953).
(22)  Sears, W. C., *J. Polymer Sci.* **A2**, 2455 (1964).
(23)  Silas, R. S., Yates, J., Thornton, V., *Anal. Chem.* **31**, 529 (1959).
(24)  Witt, E., *J. Polymer Sci.* **41**, 507 (1959).

RECEIVED July 11, 1966. Research sponsored by the U.S. Atomic Energy Commission at Oak Ridge National Laboratory under contract with the Union Carbide Corp.

# 6

# The Effect of Ionizing Radiation
# on Ethylene-Alkyl Acrylate Copolymers

JAMES E. POTTS, CHESTER L. PURCELL, and OUTTEN J. CLINARD

Polymer Research and Development, Plastics Division,
Union Carbide Corp., Bound Brook, N. J.

*Ionizing radiation crosslinks ethylene-alkyl acrylate copoly-
mers and as a result increases tensile strength, impact
strength, and stress crack resistance and permits the product
to be used above the crystalline melting point in certain
applications. Preformed tubing after crosslinking is readily
oriented to give clear, glossy, strong, heat-shrinkable film.
Copolymers containing above 15% alkyl acrylate, rein-
forced with carbon black and crosslinked, are flexible over
a wide temperature range. Copolymers containing above
25% alkyl acrylate exhibit the properties of rubber gum
stock and can be crosslinked to give elastic products having
the low permanent set characteristics of vulcanized rubber.*

This paper is concerned with the effect of ionizing radiation on the
physical and mechanical properties of copolymers of ethylene with
alkyl acrylates, such as ethyl acrylate, butyl acrylate, and 2-ethylhexyl
acrylate (1, 2, 3). These polymers are made by the free radical copolymerization of ethylene under high pressure with alkyl esters of
acrylic acid (9). They are more flexible than polyethylene and because
of the polar nature of the comonomer, they are more compatible with
fillers and with other polymers than is polyethylene.

Because of their lower level of crystallinity these copolymers soften
at lower temperatures than polyethylene. Table I compares the torsional
stiffness at various temperatures of an 18% ethyl acrylate–82% ethylene
copolymer with that of a 21,000 molecular weight, 0.918 density polyethylene made by high pressure polymerization (Bakelite DYNH, Union
Carbide Corp.).

An exhaustive discussion of the effect of high energy radiation on
polyethylene has been published by Chapiro (5). A comparable dis-

## Table I.    Torsional Stiffness" vs. Temperature

| Temperature, °C. | 18% Ethyl Acrylate 82% Ethylene Copolymer, p.s.i.g. | Polyethylene DYNH, p.s.i.g. |
|---|---|---|
| 25 | 4500 | 18,000 |
| 50 | 1000 | 6,500 |
| 70 | 350 | 3,000 |
| 80 | 200 | 2,000 |
| 90 | soft | 1,400 |

" ASTM-D-1043-51 test.

cussion for ethylene-alkyl acrylate copolymers was not found. The cross-linking of these copolymers with ionizing radiation was disclosed in recent patents (6, 7). The use of peroxide to crosslink ethylene–ethyl acrylate copolymers has been discussed by Bonotto (4).

*Experimental*

**Extraction Studies.** Ethylene-ethyl acrylate copolymers were used almost exclusively in the studies reported here because of their commercial availability. All radiation exposures were accomplished with a 2 million volt, 500 watt van de Graaff electron accelerator. Radiation doses are given in megareps, which is defined as $83.8 \times 10^6$ ergs per gram.

Table II shows the effect of various doses of electron irradiation on the solubility of ethylene-ethylacrylate copolymer. Extraction with boiling toluene for 64 hours revealed extensive crosslinking after absorption of a 5-megarep dose of radiation. Copolymers of ethylene with isobutyl acrylate and 2-ethylhexyl acrylate were examined briefly. A 29 wt.% isobutyl acrylate-ethylene copolymer of melt index 1.3 decigrams per minute was crosslinked to greater than 50% insolubility in boiling toluene by a radiation dose of 10 megareps. A copolymer containing 21% by weight of 2-ethylhexyl acrylate of melt index 8 decigrams per minute required a dose of 25 megareps to reach a 50% level of insolubility.

## Table II.    Extraction of 5 wt.% Ethyl Acrylate-Ethylene Copolymer with Boiling Toluene"

| Radiation Dose, megareps | % Insoluble after 64 hours Extraction |
|---|---|
| 0 | 0 |
| 5 | 24.6 |
| 8 | 42.0 |
| 12 | 55.9 |
| 16 | 65.1 |
| 20 | 70.6 |

" Initial melt index = 12 decigrams per minute.

## Results and Discussion

**Nature of Crosslinks.** Because of the presence of ethylene chain segments and alkyl acrylate chain segments in these copolymers, it is likely that they crosslink by mechanisms proposed for polyethylene cross-linking (5) and also by those proposed for poly(alkylacrylates) (8). In addition, hybrid crosslinks should also occur. Thus, these copolymers, after crosslinking, probably contain carbon-carbon crosslinks, crosslinks from ethoxy groups of one chain to ethoxy groups of another chain, and crosslinks from ethoxy groups of certain chains to the backbone of other chains. Saponification of the crosslinked copolymer should yield minute amounts of butylene glycol, pendant $-CH_2-CH_2OH$, and pendant $-COO^-M^+$ groups. These possibilities are being examined experimentally.

**Properties of Crosslinked Films.** Our purpose was to determine which commercially useful property improvements result from radiation crosslinking of ethylene-ethyl acrylate copolymers. Table III illustrates

**Table III.  Physical Properties at 25°C. of Blown Film (1.5 mils) Made from 10% Ethyl Acrylate Copolymer[a]**

| Radiation Dose, megareps | Tensile Strength, p.s.i.g. | | % Elongation to Break | | Tensile Impact Strength, ft.-lbs./sq. in. | | Shrinkage, 120°C. | |
|---|---|---|---|---|---|---|---|---|
| | MD[b] | TD[b] | MD | TD | MD | TD | MD | TD |
| 0 | 1640 | 1230 | 400 | 410 | 600 | 700 | 61 | 54 |
| 10 | 1840 | 1970 | 370 | 400 | 1144 | 1012 | 21 | 15 |
| 20 | 2460 | 2200 | 360 | 430 | 1090 | 1294 | 14 | 7 |

[a] Initial melt index = 5 decigrams per minute.
[b] MD = machine direction; TD = transverse direction.

the effect of crosslinking on the mechanical properties of hot blown film made from a 10% ethyl acrylate copolymer of initial melt index 5 decigrams per minute. These data show a significant increase in tensile strength and impact strength and a large reduction in heat shrinkage as a result of crosslinking the film. In these experiments the film was irradiated as it was unwound from the roll.

Hot blown plastic films usually do not possess sufficient orientation to be heat shrinkable at temperatures below 100°C. For certain shrink packaging applications low temperature shrinkage is essential and can be obtained by biaxial orientation below the melting point. Radiation crosslinking was found to facilitate orientation of these copolymers greatly because of the much greater bubble stability which results from crosslinking.

Table IV gives the essential parameters which were involved in successful biaxial orientation of this copolymer sample. The most im-

**Table IV.   Biaxially Oriented Copolymer Film *via* Irradiation**

| | |
|---|---|
| % Ethyl acrylate in copolymer | 10% |
| Initial melt index, decigrams per minute | 4.7 |
| Film thickness before orientation | 8 mils |
| Radiation dose, megareps | 4 |
| Thickness after orientation | 0.45 mils |
| Machine direction stretch | 3.3/1 |
| Transverse stretch | 5/1 |

portant physical properties of the resultant oriented film are listed in Table V. Tensile strengths in the machine direction (MD) and transverse direction (TD) are similar, indicating a well-balanced film. This is confirmed by the shrinkage data at 100°C. Hence, crosslinking makes it possible to obtain a high tensile strength, clear, glossy, heat-shrinkable film, suitable for flexible packaging applications.

**Environmental Stress Crack Resistance.** Ethylene-ethyl acrylate copolymers containing less than about 10% combined ethyl acrylate are subject to environmental stress cracking, as is polyethylene. A sample of copolymer containing 7 wt.% ethyl acrylate, having a melt index at 190°C. of 4.2 decigrams per minute was subjected to ASTM stress cracking test D-1693, along with similar samples which had been subjected to doses of 5, 10, and 25 megareps of electron radiation. None of the irradiated samples failed in 500 hours at 50°C. The untreated control samples (20 specimens) failed in 15 minutes.

**High Temperature Performance.** Figure 1 shows the improvement in high temperature performance which results from crosslinking a copolymer containing 85% ethylene and 15% ethyl acrylate. The secant modulus at 1% elongation was measured over the temperature range 25°–300°C. for copolymer with and without 33 parts of carbon black per 100 parts of resin. Without crosslinking, both samples melted at 85°C. and became viscous liquids. The unfilled, crosslinked polymer (25 megareps dose) became rubbery at 85°C. and remained at about the same stiffness level up to 300°C. The carbon black-filled crosslinked sample had a higher modulus over the entire temperature range, indi-

**Table V.   Properties of Crosslinked, Biaxially Oriented Copolymer Film**

| | *MD"* | *TD"* |
|---|---|---|
| Ultimate tensile strength, p.s.i.g. | 7915 | 8929 |
| Ultimate % elongation | 233 | 107 |
| 45° Gloss, % | 72 | 72 |
| Haze, % | 2.6 | 2.6 |
| Shrinkage at 100°C., % | 64 | 73 |

" MD = machine direction; TD = transverse direction.

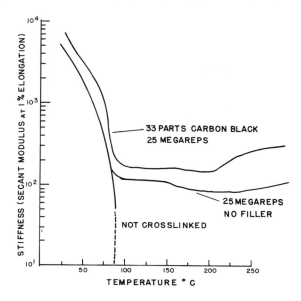

*Figure 1. Effect of radiation crosslinking on stiffness of 85/15 ethylene-ethyl acrylate copolymer over the temperature range 25°–300°C.*

cating polymer-filler interaction. In these studies fillers were incorporated into the polymers by hot fluxing in a banbury mixer.

**Low Temperature Embrittlement.** Although low density polyethylene has good low temperature embrittlement resistance, adding significant amounts of fillers such as carbon black produces low temperature embrittlement. Ethylene-ethyl acrylate copolymers are more tolerant of high loadings of fillers; the tolerance increases with increasing acrylate content. Radiation crosslinking improves the low temperature embrittlement resistance of carbon black-filled polyethylene and ethylene copolymer, as shown in Table VI. The polyethylene used was Bakelite

**Table VI. Effect of Crosslinking on Brittleness of Carbon Black-Filled Polymer**[a]

| % Ethyl Acrylate | Dose, megareps | Brittleness, Temp., °C. |
|---|---|---|
| 0 | 0 | −18 |
| | 25 | −30 |
| 7 | 0 | −38 |
| | 25 | −48 |
| 20 | 0 | −62 |
| | 25 | −72 |

[a] Samples filled with 1/3 Statex 125, 2/3 resin; aged 7 days at 70°C. in air oven.

DYNH. ASTM brittle temperature test No. D-46-44T was used in making these measurements. Statex 125 carbon black is manufactured by Columbian Carbon Co., New York, N. Y.

**Rubberlike Properties.** Figure 2 depicts the changes in the 13.7-micron infrared crystallinity band with increasing ethyl acrylate content. At 25–30% acrylate content in the copolymer, this band disappears, indicating that this polymer is essentially amorphous. This fact, plus the absence of carbon-carbon unsaturation, good filler compatibility, and

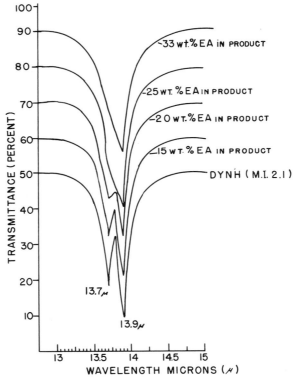

*Figure 2.    Effect of acrylate content on 13.7μ (crystallinity) band intensity*

good low temperature properties suggested that amorphous ethylene-alkyl acrylate copolymers, when crosslinked, should be useful in many rubber applications. It should be noted that Bonotto (4), in describing the properties of peroxide crosslinked ethylene-ethyl acrylate copolymer, was referring to a copolymer containing 18% ethyl acrylate, which retained a significant amount of ethylene crystallinity.

Further evidence for the rubbery properties of high acrylate copolymers is shown in Figure 3, which is a stress vs. strain plot for both

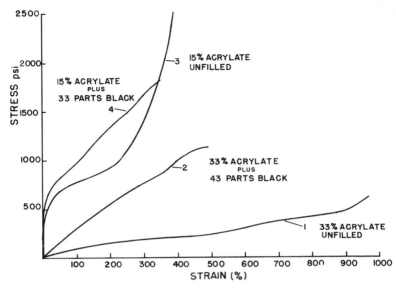

*Figure 3.   Stress–strain curves for 15 and 33% acrylate copolymers (25 megareps)*

15 and 33% acrylate copolymers after radiation crosslinking (25 megareps dose). The 15% copolymer becomes permanently deformed owing to orientation of crystallites at about 15% elongation. The 33% acrylate copolymer, which is amorphous, exhibits a large extensibility without permanent deformation. That carbon black acts as a reinforcing filler is proved by the steeper slope of the stress–strain curve for the copolymer filled with 43 parts of carbon black per 100 parts of polymer as compared with the same copolymer unfilled.

An essential characteristic of a good rubber is elastic recoverability. Table VII illustrates the high degree of elastic recovery which can be

**Table VII.   Tensile Set[a] of Filled Copolymer**

| % Ethyl Acrylate | Carbon Black | | % Tensile Set at 100% Elongation, Radiation Dose Level, megareps | | | |
|---|---|---|---|---|---|---|
| | Type | PHR[b] | 0 | 10 | 25 | 50 |
| 0 | Thermax | 33 | 100 | 100 | 100 | 100 |
| 15 | Thermax | 33 | 29 | — | 26 | — |
| 20 | Thermax | 43 | 5 | 5 | 5 | — |
| 20 | Micronex | 43 | 15 | 10 | 20 | — |
| 33 | Thermax | 100 | — | 7 | 1 | 3 |

[a] Sample elongated 100% in length at 20 inches/min; % permanent set after 1 minute is reported here.
[b] Parts per 100 parts resin.

obtained, provided crystallinity is reduced or eliminated. The 0% acrylate sample is DYNH polyethylene, which exhibits no elastic recovery regardless of crosslinking density. Thermax carbon black (R. T. Vanderbilt Co., New York, N. Y.) appears to confer slightly more resiliency to a 20% acrylate copolymer than Micronex (Binney and Smith, Inc., New York, N. Y.). The 33% acrylate copolymer exhibited excellent recovery even when loaded with an equal weight of Thermax.

### Literature Cited

(1) Bonotto, S., Walton, R., *Modern Plastics* **40**, 143 (1963).
(2) Bonotto, S., Krevsky, B. H., *Soc. Plastics Engrs. J.* **18**, 555 (1962).
(3) Bonotto, S., *Rubber Age* **98**, 79 (1966).
(4) Bonotto, S., *J. Appl. Polymer Sci.* **9**, 3819 (1965).
(5) Chapiro, A., "Radiation Chemistry of Polymeric Systems," p. 385, Interscience, New York, 1962.
(6) Potts, J. E., U.S. Patent **3,274,086** (Sept. 20, 1966).
(7) Potts, J. E., Canadian Patent **697,287** (Nov. 3, 1964).
(8) Shultz, A. R., Bovey, F. A., *J. Polymer Sci.* **22**, 485 (1956).
(9) Zutty, N. L., Burkhart, R. D., "Copolymerization," p. 639, Interscience, New York, 1964.

RECEIVED February 21, 1967.

# Transient Acceleration of Creep Rates of Polymers During High Intensity Irradiation

JAMES P. BELL,[1] ALAN S. MICHAELS,[2] ALLAN S. HOFFMAN, and EDWARD A. MASON[3]

Chemical Engineering Department, Massachusetts Institute of Technology, Cambridge, Mass.

*Creep rates of three glassy polymers are much greater during electron irradiation than before or after. Radiation heating is eliminated as a possible cause. Essentially the same concentration of unpaired electrons and ratio of crosslinking to scission were found in polystyrene samples in the presence or absence of stress. The effects of radiation intensity, stress, and temperature on creep during irradiation are examined. The accelerated creep under stress is directly related to a radiation-induced expansion in the absence of stress. This radiation expansion is decreased by increase in temperature or plasticizer content and decrease in sample thickness. It is concluded that gas accumulation within the sample during irradiation causes both the expansion under no stress and the acceleration of creep under stress.*

T he unique properties of polymers make them desirable for use in space vehicles and apparatus, as well as in nuclear reactor components and auxiliaries. In both applications intense radiation fields can be encountered routinely or occasionally. Several books have been written about the effects of radiation on polymers (1, 2, 4, 5); in general, the effects of high intensity radiation have been measured by exposing the polymer to a given amount of radiation followed by testing of properties later, outside the radiation field.

The only previous work on mechanical properties of polymers during exposure to high intensity radiation (40,000 rads per second or

[1] Present address, Chemstrand Research Center, Durham, N. C.
[2] Present address, Amicon Corp., Cambridge, Mass.
[3] Present address, Nuclear Engineering Department, Massachusetts Institute of Technology, Cambridge, Mass.

greater) was published in 1959–1960 in the Soviet Union (*10–13*). Mokul'skiĭ *et al.* (*11, 12, 13*) found significant differences in the creep rate, elastic limit, and tensile strength of many common polymers during irradiation in a nuclear reactor, as opposed to measurements before or after irradiation. Mokul'skiĭ (*10*) suggested that the different properties during irradiation were caused by a transient, high concentration of molecules possessing high energy after absorbing radiation; these "activated molecules" then led to an acceleration of the normal relaxation processes. Such a species would have a lifetime of much less than a second—*e.g.*, within the time of a few molecular collisions—as its energy is rapidly dissipated into heat (*10*). The hypothesis cannot explain why the accelerated processes can continue for minutes after irradiation is stopped or why in many cases the relative degree of acceleration increases with time of irradiation. One must postulate a species with a lifetime of minutes to explain these effects. The hypothesis was not compared with the experimental data.

The purpose of the present work was to determine if the "temporary" effect of radiation on the creep rate of polymers could be confirmed using high intensity electron radiation, and if so, to attempt to elucidate the basic cause of the effect.

### *Experimental*

**Apparatus.** The apparatus used to measure creep rates during irradiation is shown in skeleton form in Figure 1. The sample is held between two clamps as shown. The bottom clamp is held rigidly in the frame by a removable pin while the upper clamp is pinned to a square bar which is free to move vertically. The top of the square bar is connected to a braided steel cable, which passes over low-friction, aligned pulleys to a weight pan below. The core of a differential transformer is rigidly joined to the square bar, so that movement of the sample results in the same movement of the transformer core. The electrical output from the differential transformer is transmitted through a demodulator and a digital voltmeter to a printer. Curves of deflection *vs.* time are obtained from a calibration curve of sample movement *vs.* printer output and from the known rate of printing.

The sample shown in Figure 1 contains a molded-in thermocouple. Such samples were used not in creep measurements, but to study the temperature rise during irradiation.

Sample cooling was provided through the two vertical tubes shown in Figure 1. The tubes contain small holes through which water is sprayed diagonally on the sample. The water is caught in a plastic tray (not shown), which is mounted between the creep fixture and the metal table. A drain in the plastic tray permits the water to be circulated back into a heating-cooling bath, which brings the water to the desired temperature and then pumps it back to the spray tubes.

The first few tests were carried out using an 8-m.e.v. linear electron accelerator at Berkeley, Calif. In subsequent tests, a 3-m.e.v. Van de Graaff generator at MIT was used.

For runs at MIT the splashing caused by the spray tubes resulted in difficulties in measuring the beam current, owing to electrical shorting. The spray tubes were replaced by two trickle tubes, placed about 1/16 to 1/8 inch from the broad sides of the sample. Measurement of the temperature in the center of polystyrene samples showed the same temperature rise for the two cooling systems, indicating that the same sample temperature profile was obtained in each case. The heat removed by the water is in the range of 0.1 to 0.3 cal. per second.

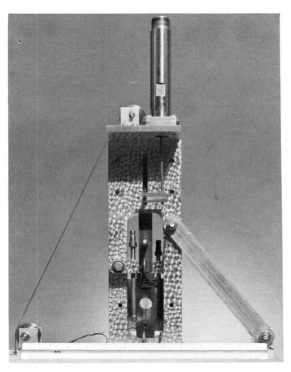

*Figure 1.   Basic creep apparatus*

To control the area of the sample which was exposed to the beam, a thick aluminum block with a ¾-inch diameter aperture in the center was constructed and placed directly in front of the sample.

The beam current to which the sample is exposed—*i.e.,* the current which passes through the ¾-inch diameter aperture in the aluminum block—is in turn captured by another block behind the sample. The amount of the current received by this second block is used as a primary measure of the radiation intensity (beam current). This second block or plate is supported behind the sample on two ceramic insulators and is easily removed to facilitate changing samples.

**Sample Geometry.** The typical sample geometry is shown in Figure 2. The sample gage length for creep studies outside of the radiation field was taken as $1\frac{1}{8}$ inches. The gage length during irradiation was taken to be approximately 1 inch, the beam diameter. The gage length after irradiation was slightly greater than before because of the creep, but in most cases the length change was so small that it could be neglected.

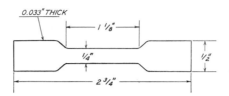

*Figure 2.   Typical sample geometry*

**Sample Materials.** Four commercial polymers were studied.

MONSANTO HI-FLOW 77 POLYSTYRENE. The viscosity-average molecular weight found in this work was 284,000. The ratio $\overline{M}_W/\overline{M}_N$ reported by the manufacturer is 2.67. The samples were prepared by injection molding in a 1-ounce Mini-Jector molding machine, followed by annealing for 24 hours at 75°C.

PLASTICIZED POLYSTYRENE. Samples of polystyrene containing 0, 5, 10, and 20% plasticizer were provided by the Koppers Co., Inc., Research Department. The plasticizer used was Union Carbide's DOP [di-(2-ethylhexyl)phthalate]. All of the samples were derived from the same base lot of polystyrene and were compounded with the plasticizer by means of a small extruder. The samples were provided as small pellets. The number-average molecular weight of the base polystyrene was measured by the Koppers Co. Research Department as 122,000. The weight-average molecular weight by several measurements was reported as approximately 260,000.

DU PONT LUCITE 130 POLY(METHYL METHACRYLATE). This material was injection-molded in the same way as the polystyrene. No molecular weight measurements were made.

BAKELIKE VSA 3310 88% POLY(VINYL CHLORIDE)–12% POLY(VINYL ACETATE) COPOLYMER. Samples were cut directly from extruded sheeting and machined to the desired thickness. The weight-average molecular weight range measured by the manufacturer was 50,000 to 70,000. The number-average molecular weight range was measured as 36,800 to 39,600.

**Sol-Gel Measurements.** Rates of crosslinking and scission during irradiation were obtained by conventional measurements of the soluble fraction, gel fraction, and weight swelling ratio of the irradiated polymers (6, 9). The soluble fraction was extracted using reagent-grade toluene as the solvent in Soxhlet extractors. Samples for the soluble fraction measurements were extracted to constant dry weight.

**Electron Spin Resonance Measurements.** The specimens used in the electron spin resonance (ESR) studies were prepared by immersing the stressed or unstressed sample in liquid nitrogen just as the radiation was stopped. The spectra were measured within a few hours after irradiation. The samples were maintained at liquid nitrogen temperature from the time of irradiation through the spectra measurements.

### Results and Discussion

**Typical Data for Creep before, during, and after Irradiation.** Curves of sample deflection *vs.* time before, during, and after irradiation for the three polymers used in this work are shown in Figure 3. The ordinate is presented as deflection after the first 2 seconds because this part of the elastic deflection could not be accurately measured. This normal elastic deflection was not of particular interest in the present work.

Data for an 88% poly(vinyl chloride)–12% poly(vinyl acetate) copolymer are shown at the top of Figure 3. In this case, the creep rate during irradiation is quite high; the normal creep before the start of

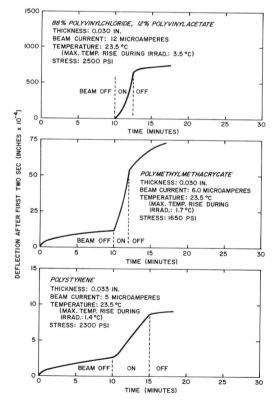

*Figure 3. Creep of three polymers before, during, and after irradiation with 3 m.e.v. electrons*

irradiation is not detectable on the ordinate scale. An increasing creep rate during irradiation is observed, and a decay period is observed when the beam is turned off.

The data for poly(methyl methacrylate) are shown at the center of Figure 3. The increase in creep rate during irradiation, as compared with before or after irradiation, is apparent. Less apparent from this figure is the fact that the creep rate gradually increases during the "beam-on" period. The deflection during the decay period is less than for poly(vinyl chloride), but the decay period lasts longer. The gradual decay can be considered indicative of a decreasing concentration of some species (whether physical or chemical) which influences the creep rate. This species and/or its effect seem to have a lifetime in the order of minutes.

Data for polystyrene are shown at the bottom of Figure 3. The deflection observed is much smaller than in the two previous cases, but the increase in creep rate during irradiation is still apparent. The relative magnitudes of creep acceleration in the three polymers bear approximately the same relation to one another as the radiation sensitivity of the polymer types (4). For polystyrene, however, the creep rate during irradiation becomes relatively constant after a short (~0.2-minute) induction period. This relative constancy of the creep rate of polystyrene during the early part of irradiation has been demonstrated many times during this work. For the longer irradiation tests the creep rate of polystyrene actually decreases somewhat with time, probably because of crosslinking. Crosslinking may also cause the slightly decreased creep rate noted after irradiation, relative to that before irradiation. There is no significant decay period after irradiation.

Since the creep rate of polystyrene samples during irradiation is relatively constant, this value minus the creep rate just before irradiation can be used as a measure of the increase in creep rate owing to the irradiation. This increase in creep rate, or "incremental creep rate," can then be related to the other experimental variables.

**Sample Temperature Rise Owing to Irradiation.** A temperature rise of 2.9°C. during irradiation was found at the center of 0.033-inch thick water-cooled polystyrene samples for a beam current of 10 $\mu a$. This temperature was measured several times, using thermocouples compression-molded into the center of the samples. The thermocouple leads entered the sample from the direction shown in Figure 1. Several different thermocouple junction sizes were used, with the same measured results.

The calculated temperature rise at the center of the samples was also 2.9°C. for the same thickness and beam current.

The calculation involved the following assumptions:

The material is isotropic.

The rate of heat generation does not vary with time of irradiation, or with position through the sample thickness.

The sample length is at least twice either of the other two dimensions (valid for samples used in this work).

The calculation was similar to that made for the problem of three-dimensional heat transmission and uniform heat generation in a rectangular parallelepiped (3) with the surfaces maintained at ambient temperature. By solving the parallelepiped equation with appropriate values, it can be shown that the temperature distribution over the sample cross section is approximately parabolic, with the maximum temperature at the center (7). (Figure 17 gives a graphical presentation of this solution.) This leads to the conclusion that the average temperature is approximately 63.5% of the maximum temperature.

The temperature rise in ⅛-inch thick samples was also measured and calculated, although no ⅛-inch samples were used for creep measurements. The measured maximum temperature rise was 41.5°C., and the calculated temperature rise was 41.7°C. The bulk of the study reported here is for 0.033-inch thick polystyrene samples, and for the typical conditions of this work the average temperature rise is 63.5% of the maximum temperature rise or 1.8°C.

The increase in polystyrene creep rate owing to a 1.8° temperature change is so small that it can be neglected relative to the increase in creep rate caused by the radiation. For example, a 1.8° temperature rise from 23.5° to 25.3°C. causes an increase of 5.6% in the creep rate in the absence of radiation (from $1.8 \times 10^{-5}$ to $1.9 \times 10^{-5}$ inches/inch-minute for a 2060 p.s.i.g. stress). This compares with an increase of 790% (from $1.8 \times 10^{-5}$ to $16 \times 10^{-5}$ inches/inch-minute) when the measurement is carried out during irradiation at 10 $\mu$a. beam current.

The calculated temperature rise for the other two polymers used is less than for polystyrene. Their normal creep rates show a dependence on temperature similar to polystyrene in this temperature range, so that again the effect of the temperature rise on creep rate is negligible relative to the change caused by the radiation.

**Effects of Independent Variables on Creep Rate of Polymers during Irradiation.** EFFECT OF APPLIED STRESS. Figure 4 shows the effect of applied stress on the creep rate of polystyrene both during irradiation and just before the beam is turned on (10 minutes after applying stress). The ordinate for the latter curve is the absolute rather than the incremental creep rate.

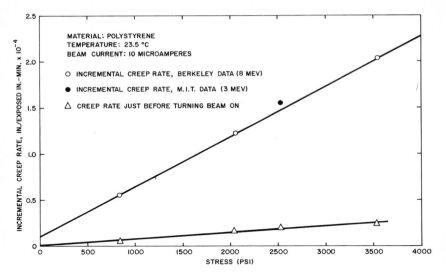

*Figure 4.    Effect of stress on incremental creep rate observed during irradiation.  Sample thickness is 0.033 inch*

The MIT 3-m.e.v. electron datum point for practical purposes coincides with the Berkeley 8-m.e.v. electron data, showing no difference in incremental creep rate caused by the difference in beam energy.

For creep in the absence of radiation the rate of deflection at a given time increases linearly with the applied stress. This relationship is also observed during irradiation. One can infer that the basic mechanism of creep in the two instances is likely to be the same.

EFFECT OF BEAM CURRENT. The relationship between beam current and the incremental creep rate owing to the radiation is shown in Figure 5. The incremental creep rate is the increase in creep rate which can be attributed to the radiation exposure. The data on Figure 5 are plotted with applied stress as a parameter. No distinction is made between the 3-m.e.v. and the 8-m.e.v. electron tests, although the points are coded so that the legend on the graph indicates the beam energy.

The radiation effect must disappear as the beam current goes to zero, as shown in Figure 5. The minimum beam current at which the effect could be observed was not determined in this study. The Soviet workers (*11*) found accelerated creep effects at absorbed dose rates as low as 16,000 rads per second.

DELAYED STRESS APPLICATION. Three experiments were carried out on polystyrene samples to determine the effect of stress application after an initial period of irradiation without stress.

Experiment I. The sample was irradiated for 5.5 minutes without significant stress ( < 10 p.s.i.g.), at which time the stress (2300 p.s.i.g.) was applied by remote control, and the beam was simultaneously turned off. Deflection measurements were continued for 10 additional minutes (Figure 6, I).

Experiment II. The sample was irradiated for 6 minutes in the absence of significant stress ( < 10 p.s.i.g.), at which time the stress (2300 p.s.i.g.) was applied by remote control without changing the irradiation conditions. Deflection measurements were continued for another 5.5 minutes, at which time the beam was turned off (Figure 6, II).

Experiment III. The sample was stressed (2300 p.s.i.g.) and allowed to creep for 10 minutes, at which time the beam was turned on for 5.5 minutes. The beam was then turned off while the stress remained on. Deflection measurements continued for 2 minutes after the beam was turned off. This run was a typical creep measurement before, during, and after irradiation (Figure 6, III).

Referring to the data for Experiment I in Figure 6, one immediately notices a high creep rate when the load is applied, despite the fact that the beam was turned off. The initial creep rate at the point of stress application is much greater than the creep rate normally noted for an unirradiated sample when the same stress is applied. Again referring to Figure 6, I, the creep rate decreases to a normal level—*i.e.*, that noted in the absence of radiation—over a period of several minutes, presumably because of a decrease in concentration of "active species" which had built up in the sample during irradiation.

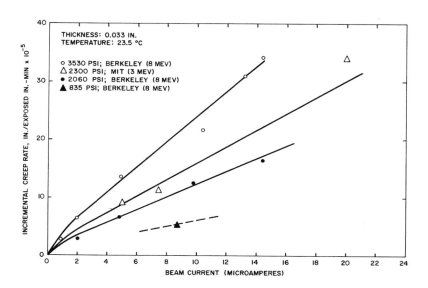

*Figure 5.   Effect of electron beam current on incremental creep rate of polystyrene during irradiation*

The results of Experiment II show that when the sample is first irradiated under no stress and then the stress is applied, the creep rate has an initially high value but decays to a steady rate after a few minutes. In contrast to this behavior, the same steady creep rate is achieved in a much shorter time—*e.g.*, less than 30 seconds in Experiment III for the same stress and radiation conditions; in this latter case, the beam

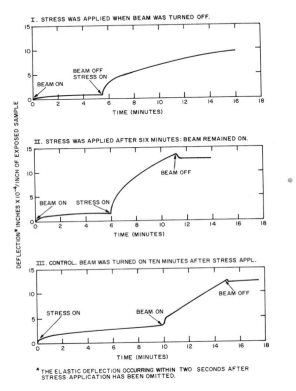

* THE ELASTIC DEFLECTION OCCURRING WITHIN TWO SECONDS AFTER STRESS APPLICATION HAS BEEN OMITTED.

*Figure 6.    Effect of delayed stress application compared with delayed irradiation*

| | |
|---|---|
| *Material: polystyrene* | *Beam energy: 3 m.e.v.* |
| *Thickness: 0.033 inch* | *Stress: 2300 p.s.i.g.* |
| *Beam current: 10 μa.* | *Temperature: 23.5°C.* |

was turned on while stress was applied rather than several minutes before applications of stress. This can be taken as an indication that the concentration of "active species," which was initially high because the sample was irradiated while not under stress, has now reached a lower equilibrium concentration consistent with the stressed state.

The sudden increase in length in Experiment III when the radiation was turned on is caused by radiation heating. In the final part of this experiment the same conditions prevail as in Experiment I—*i.e.*, the stress is on, and the beam has just been turned off. In this third case, however, the creep rate returns to a low level shortly after the beam is turned off. (The sharp drop is caused by cooling of the sample.) This difference must be attributed to the fact that the stress was applied for the entire time during the third experiment whereas no stress was present during irradiation in the first experiment. Thus, one can infer that the concentration of "active species" which accumulates during irradiation must be smaller in the cases of samples which were stressed than where the sample was unstressed during irradiation.

To summarize the results of these three tests, there is evidence of an increase in concentration of a chemical or physical species during irradiation which strongly affects the creep rate. In stressed samples it appears that an equilibrium concentration of the "species" is reached which is lower than the concentration present after a few minutes of irradiation in the unstressed state. The "species" seems to disappear more rapidly in stressed samples, and the concentration when the beam is turned off may be lower.

INTERMITTENT STRESS APPLICATION DURING IRRADIATION. An experiment was carried out in which the beam remained on continuously, but the stress was applied remotely for only 12 seconds at the beginning of each minute. The data from the experiment are shown in Figure 7.

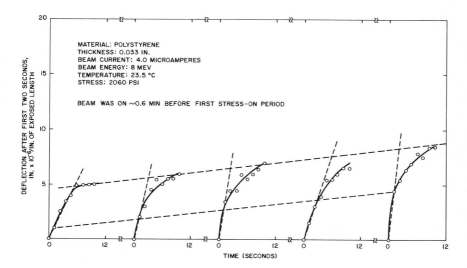

*Figure 7.    Intermittent stress application during irradiation. Stress was applied for first 12 seconds of each minute during irradiation*

The sample deflection for each of the stress-on periods does not include the elastic deflection occurring during the first 2 seconds after stress application. The periods (48 seconds each) between the stress-on periods have been omitted from the figure to make clearer the differences that appear during the stress-on periods.

The first obvious feature is that the amount of deflection at a given time after stress is applied increases with increasing time from the start of the test. This agrees with the picture developed above, indicating that the concentration of the "active species" is increasing with the total time of irradiation. The fourth beam-on period after the start of the test has a lower deflection than expected from the other periods; presumably this is caused by experimental error since it is the only inconsistency in this series of runs.

Another interesting feature of the data is that the principal difference between the deflections that occur during the stress-on periods is within the first 3.5 seconds after the stress is applied. It appears that the deflection rates for all of the stress-on periods are approximately the same—i.e., superimposable—after the first 3.5 seconds.

The creep rate during the period up to 3.5 seconds after the stress is applied is much greater than the creep rate observed when the load and beam are applied simultaneously, without prior irradiation. This again substantiates the earlier observation that the "active species" appears to disappear from stressed samples faster than from unstressed samples.

The Russian workers (12) also noted a significant effect of time of exposure to the radiation field before stress application on the resultant creep rate of poly(vinyl chloride) samples (Figure 8).

EFFECT OF TEMPERATURE. The effect of sample temperature on the creep rate of polystyrene in the absence and presence of radiation is shown in Figure 9. The actual creep rate 10 to 12 minutes after application of stress is plotted as a function of the reciprocal of the absolute temperature.

The data for the samples outside of the radiation field were obtained from the same experimental creep apparatus used to measure creep rates during irradiation. The water-cooling system was operated in the same manner as during radiation tests.

The activation energy for polystyrene creep as given by Figure 9 is approximately 8 kcal. This relatively low activation energy probably indicates that the flow units—e.g., chain segments—whose mobility causes the creep are relatively short.

The data points in the upper part of Figure 9 represent the creep rate during irradiation. Although there is some scatter in these data, a definite trend is evident, and the activation energy appears to be of the same general order as for the unirradiated samples. Points from both 8- and 3-m.e.v. electron runs are included. No difference in creep rate between the radiation sources is apparent.

**Chemical Changes.** ELECTRON SPIN RESONANCE MEASUREMENTS. Electron spin resonance (ESR) measurements were carried out to de-

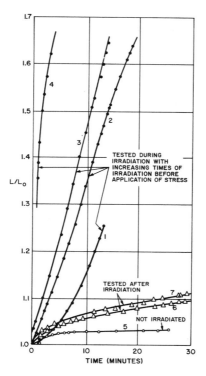

*Figure 8. Creep in poly (vinyl chloride) under a stress of 1442 p.s.i.g. at 57°–60°C. Stress applied after different times of pre-irradiation: 1–2, 10, 15, and 50 minutes for Curves 1, 2, 3, and 4, respectively. Total dose to Curve 7 exceeds all doses delivered in Curves 1–4 (11)*

termine the effect of stress on the number and type of free radicals in irradiated samples. No differences were found between stressed and unstressed samples under several irradiation conditions (Table I), and the results agreed with data reported in the literature for γ-irradiation of unstressed samples (14). Figure 10 shows a typical ESR spectrum of irradiated polystyrene.

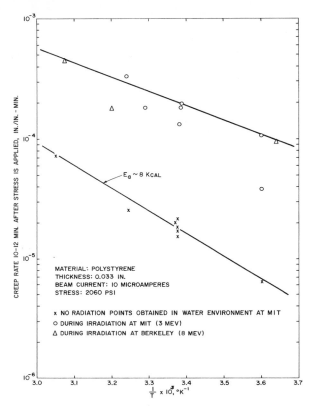

*Figure 9. Effect of sample temperature on creep rate in the presence or absence of irradiation*

**Table I. Electron Spin Resonance Study of Irradiated Polystyrene**

| Sample Irradiation Conditions | | Spectrum Height, A., Arbitrary Units | Average Spectrum Height/Mrad |
|---|---|---|---|
| 6 Mrads, 2000 p.s.i.g.[a] | | 2.5 | 0.42 |
| 20 | 2000[a] | 9.8, 9.8, 8.7 | 0.47 |
| 20 | No stress[a] | 8.9, 8.5 | 0.43 |
| 20 | 2000[b] | 8.8 | 0.44 |

[a] Quenched in liquid nitrogen immediately after irradiation.
[b] Waited 1 minute before quenching in liquid nitrogen.

SOL-GEL MEASUREMENTS. The relative rates of crosslinking and scission may be estimated from soluble-fraction measurements. For an initial random molecular weight distribution and random chain scission, extrapolating a curve of $S + \sqrt{S}$ vs. $1/D$, where $S$ = sol fraction and $D$ =

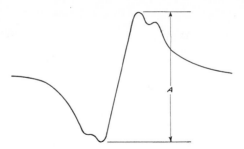

*Figure 10. Typical ESR spectrum*

dose, to $1/D = 0$ yields as the intercept the ratio of scissions to cross-links (*1*). The ratio of scission to crosslinking in the presence of stress is ∼0.0 and in the absence of stress ∼0.26 (Table II). These data agree reasonably well with the results (0.14) reported by Parkinson *et al.* (*14*), who investigated crosslinking and scission in unstressed polystyrene using low intensity γ-radiation (Table II). No significant effect on the amount of soluble fraction of irradiated polystyrene was found in this study for a 20°F. change in sample temperature or a 100% change in beam intensity, at constant dose and in the presence or absence of stress.

**Table II. Chemical Reactions Occurring during Irradiation Crosslinking and Scission (Soluble Fraction-Gel Fraction Study)**

|  | *Present Work* | | *Parkinson* et al. (14) |
|---|---|---|---|
|  | *Stressed Samples* | *Unstressed Samples* | *Unstressed Samples* |
| *Number of Scissions* ─────────────── *Number of Crosslinks* | 0.00 | 0.26 ± 0.08 | 0.14 |
| Crosslinks/100 e.v. absorbed | 0.039 | 0.050 | 0.034 |
| Scissions/100 e.v. absorbed | 0.000 | 0.013 | 0.005 |

The *G* value for crosslinking may also be estimated from the sol-gel data. In the present study the crosslinking rate of stressed samples was essentially the same as for unstressed samples, but the rate of scission in stressed samples was zero compared with 0.013 in the absence of stress. (If one were to envisage the stress plus radiation-biased creep as being caused by radiation scission followed by stress-induced flow of the scissioned chain segments, one could expect a higher rate of permanent scission in the presence than in the absence of stress. These data do not support such a picture of the creep mechanism.)

To summarize the sol-gel and ESR data, the accelerated creep during irradiation is not caused by reactions which would significantly change the rate of crosslinking, scission, concentration, or type of free radicals.

THE EFFECT OF AIR. Although the sample surfaces are covered with a layer of water during irradiation, the creep rate during irradiation of polystyrene was measured with nitrogen outside the water layer, rather than the usual air environment. Fifteen minutes were allowed for equilibration of the 0.033-inch thick samples before starting irradiation. The curve of deflection vs. time before, during, and after irradiation in the nitrogen environment was in excellent agreement with the curve for the same type of sample and the same irradiation conditions with air outside the water layer. We concluded that the presence of oxygen outside the water layer has a negligible effect on the experimental results.

The water was also circulated through a bath containing an ion-exchange resin; it is not believed that there was significant buildup of ionic species in the water during irradiation.

EFFECT OF HYDROGEN vs. AIR ENVIRONMENT DURING IRRADIATION. The presence of hydrogen gas evolved within the polystyrene matrix during irradiation could cause a plasticizing effect owing to "dissolution" and interaction with the polymer molecules. One would expect, then, that the creep rate of polystyrene in a hydrogen atmosphere in the absence of radiation would be higher than in air under the same conditions. To investigate this, a sample was equilibrated for 50 minutes in hydrogen. After the equilibration period the curve of deflection vs. time was measured for an additional 15 minutes, with the sample still in hydrogen. No significant difference between the creep curve in hydrogen and the normal creep curve was observed.

The concentration of hydrogen in the polymer during irradiation is low, on the order of $10^{-6}$ mole per cc. This is far lower than the concentrations of plasticizers required to cause any significant changes in polymer creep behavior.

## Mechanism

**Radiation Expansion of Polymer Microstructure.** While preparing the samples for the sol-gel and ESR studies, we unexpectedly discovered that they lengthened when exposed to radiation, even in the absence of a significant applied stress ($<$ 10 p.s.i.g., hereafter referred to as the "unstressed" state). Typical data showing this "radiation expansion" effect for the three polymers studied are given in Figures 11 and 12.

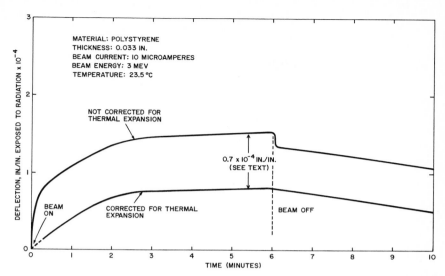

*Figure 11.   Polystyrene expansion during irradiation in the absence of signifi-cant stress (<10 p.s.i.g.)*

The expansion shown in Figure 11 for polystyrene is much less than that observed while irradiating the 88% poly(vinyl chloride)–12% poly(vinyl acetate) copolymer or of poly(methyl methacrylate) (Figure 11). In addition, 0.033-inch thick polystyrene samples expand to an equilibrium length, corresponding to a deflection of about $0.8 \times 10^{-4}$ inch per inch whereas the other two polymers at the same sample thickness expand at an increasing rate throughout the irradiation period. When the beam is turned off, polystyrene slowly decreases in length, but the other two polymers continue to expand for a short time and then appear to assume a constant level.

Since the expansion in the case of polystyrene is small, it is important to be sure that it is not a thermal effect caused by radiation heating. The data shown in Figures 11 and 12 have been corrected by subtracting the expansion owing to the small temperature rise in each of the polymers. The effect of radiative expansion in the absence of stress is real and distinct from the thermal expansion also occurring during irradiation. The data on the upper curve of Figure 11, not corrected for radiation heating, show a smaller thermal contraction when the beam was turned off than when the beam was turned on. This is perhaps caused by crosslinking which occurs during irradiation. Since the crosslinks were formed while the polymer was in the expanded condition, they may tend to keep the polymer in the expanded condition when irradiation stops.

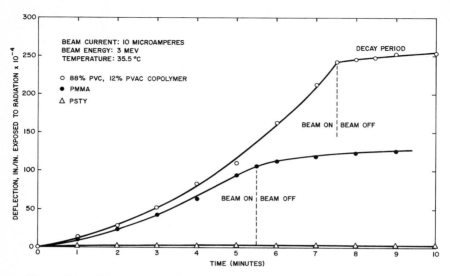

*Figure 12.    Expansion of plastics during irradiation in the absence of signifi-
cant stress (<10 p.s.i.g.).   Thickness of samples are 0.030 to 0.033 inch*

**Relation of Polymer Expansion during Irradiation in Absence of
Stress to Creep of Stressed Samples during Irradiation.**   The linear expansion of unstressed samples of plasticized polystyrene under irradiation
decreases as the plasticizer concentration increases.   The data (Figure
13) illustrate that as this expansion (curve *C*) goes to zero, the creep
rate of the stressed, unirradiated samples (curve *B*) approaches the
creep rate of the stressed samples (curve *A*) during irradiation.   Assuming that curves *A, B,* and *C* can be extrapolated as shown in Figure 4,
the acceleration of the creep rate owing to the radiation (curve *A*—
curve *B*) apparently disappears at the same plasticizer content as the
expansion owing to the radiation disappears.   Thus, the expansion observed in the unstressed samples during irradiation appears to be directly
associated with the creep rate increase for stressed samples during irradiation.

The above experiment on the effect of plasticizer content was repeated at 35.5° instead of 23.5°C.   The accelerating effect of radiation
on the creep rate of stressed samples again appears to disappear at about
the same plasticizer content where the expansion of the unstressed samples disappears; however, both vanish at a lower plasticizer concentration
(approximately 20% ) at 35.5° than at 23.5°C.   Hence, we can conclude
that an increase in temperature also diminishes the acceleration of creep
rate caused by the radiation.

**Mechanism of Radiation-Accelerated Creep.** Apparently the radiation-accelerated creep under stress and the radiation expansion under no stress are interrelated and may, in fact, result from the same cause. Thus, the mechanism of accelerated creep may be elucidated by better understanding the radiation expansion under no stress. Any hypothesis advanced to explain the mechanism of increasing creep rate during irradiation must also explain the reversible nature of the phenomenon— *i.e.*, the creep rate returns to a low value when the beam is turned off. If the mechanism is based on chemical changes, a chemical species must exist during irradiation which does not exist before or long afterward. The only reasonable species of this type with adequate lifetimes are the free radicals, ions, or electrons, and gases formed when polymers are irradiated.

One can estimate the maximum free radical concentration and, more important, calculate the number of crosslinks formed and chain scissions occurring for any particular time period of irradiation. These estimates are based on known or estimated G values for radical formation, crosslinks, or scissions. The G value is the magnitude of a particular reaction occurring per 100 e.v. of energy absorbed—*e.g.*, G(scission) is the number of scissions that take place per 100 e.v. absorbed. G(crosslink) may be obtained from the sol-gel data presented earlier, while values of G(scission) and G(radicals) may be estimated from values in the literature—*e.g.*, *see* (*4*). The former value may also be compared with established literature values—(*e.g.*, *see* Ref. *14*). For a 5.5-

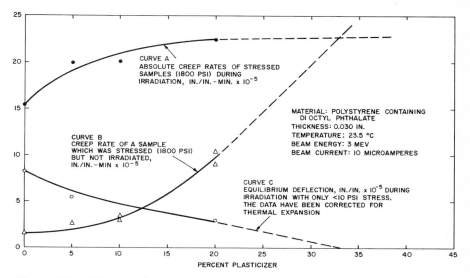

*Figure 13.  Effect of plasticizer content on creep rate or unstressed expansion of polystyrene during irradiation at 23.5°C.*

minute irradiation period at a 10-$\mu$a. beam current, the total dose delivered is approximately 155 Mrads. Table III presents the results of calculations or estimations of radical concentrations and relative numbers of chain scissions and crosslinks in a 33-mil polystyrene sample for this particular radiation history.

### Table III.   Calculations of Radical, Scission, and Crosslink Concentrations in Irradiated Polystyrene

*Radiation:* 5.5 minutes at 10 $\mu$a. current, 3-m.e.v. Van de Graaff
*Dose:* 155 Mrads = 965 $\times$ 10$^{19}$ e.v./gram
*G values*

| Radicals | $\sim$ 0.03 | Radicals formed/100 e.v. absorbed |
| Scissions | $\sim$ 0.01 | Scissions occurring/100 e.v. absorbed (assumed value based on Ref. *14*) |
| Crosslinks | $\sim$ 0.04 | Crosslinks occurring/100 e.v. absorbed |

*Concentration of bonds*

Molecular weight of polystyrene (av.) = 235,000 grams/gram mole

$$\text{Wt. per chain} = \frac{235,000}{6 \times 10^{23}} = 3.9 \times 10^{-19} \text{ grams/chain}$$

*Total radicals, scissions, crosslinks*

3.9 $\times$ 10$^{-19}$ g./chain $\times$ (G value) $\times$ (dose) = free radicals, scissions or crosslinks/chain

(3.9 $\times$ 10$^{-19}$) (0.03) (965 $\times$ 10$^{17}$)   1.1 radicals/chain
(3.9 $\times$ 10$^{-19}$) (0.01) (965 $\times$ 10$^{17}$)   0.4 scission/chain (or one scission per 2.6 chains)
(3.9 $\times$ 10$^{-19}$) (0.04) (965 $\times$ 10$^{17}$)   1.5 crosslinks/chain

The free radical concentration is quite small relative to the number of chains present. Also, the number of crosslinks formed are sufficient to gel the network, which could lead only to a decrease in creep rate. Finally, the crosslinks exceed the scissions, and the latter could not reduce the molecular weight sufficiently—even temporarily—to yield the significant increases in creep noted in the glassy polystyrene. Recombination of chain scission radicals has also been neglected.

Selective bond rupture at entanglement points, or other such sites of stress concentration, could magnify the "effect" of a chain scission in the presence of an external stress, but it seems unlikely that this is occurring since the sol-gel data actually indicated a (slightly) lower ratio of scissions to crosslinks with an imposed stress. It also is difficult to visualize how the formation of free radicals, scissions, and crosslinks could directly cause the radiation expansion noted under no stress. Therefore, the mechanism of accelerated creep is probably not caused by the formation and reaction of macromolecular free radicals in the polymer specimens.

An irradiation-induced expansion could conceivably be caused by the ions, formed as precursors of the radicals, or by thermalized electrons trapped within the polymer. Irradiation induces electrical conductivity in polymers, and this conductivity decays after irradiation is ceased (*4, 5*). The decay process is accelerated by increased temperature or plasticity of the specimen, presumably by facilitating leakage of the trapped electrons or ions to ground. One might speculate that the sample expands upon irradiation because of the local mutual electrical repulsions of like charges which are trapped in the polymer matrix, and that both increased temperature and plasticizer content diminish this expansion because of charge leakage out of the specimen. It is difficult to prove or disprove this hypothesis.

A physical process has been advanced by Mokul'skiĭ (*10*), in which a concentration of "highly energetic molecules" accumulates during irradiation as a result of the primary step in absorbing radiation energy. The problem with this hypothesis is that in addition to its vagueness, such highly energetic species should be able to convert their energy to thermal energy in fractions of a second. When the energy is converted to heat and this heat is removed, the effectiveness of this particular species for increasing the creep rate is destroyed. These processes should reach equilibrium within a fraction of a second after the beam is turned on, and stop within a fraction of a second after the beam is turned off (*10*). This rapid appearance and disappearance does not occur in the present data, nor indeed in Mokul'skiĭ's data (*11, 12, 13*).

Gas evolution from irradiated polymers is a commonly observed phenomenon. The gases evolved during irradiation could affect the creep rate by expanding the internal free volume. Gases would be generated internally and would accumulate in the sample at a rate which depends

### Table IV.  G Values for Gas Evolution

| Polymer | Primary Gases Evolved | Approximate G Value for Gas Evolution molecules/ 100 e.v. | Ratio of G values | Ratio of Creep Rates from Figure 2[a] |
|---|---|---|---|---|
| Polystyrene | $H_2$ | 0.022 | 1 | 1 |
| Poly (methyl methacrylate) | $CO$, $CO_2$, $H_2$, $CH_4$ | 1.7 | 77 | 10 to 43 |
| Poly (vinyl chloride) | $HCl$, $H_2$ | 7.0 | 328 | 100 to 400 (PVC/PV Ac copolymer) |

[a] Range of initial to final rates from start to finish of irradiation period.

on the relative rates of generation within and diffusion out of the specimen. The relative magnitudes and compositions of radiation-generated
gases are well known for the common polymers. The average $G$ values
for gas evolution for the polymers used in this study are represented in
Table IV (estimated from Ref. 4).

There is about a 300-fold difference in quantities or rates of gas
evolved as one goes from polystyrene to poly(methyl methacrylate) to
the poly(vinyl chloride–vinyl acetate) copolymer and, indeed, the relative
creep rates observed in Figure 3 are of the same order of magnitude as
the relative $G$ values for total gas formation on irradiation.

If the gases which accumulate within the specimen cause the free
volume to expand, thus leading to both radiation expansion under no
stress and radiation acceleration of creep under stress, one would expect
these effects to be diminished by conditions which enhanced gas diffusion out of the sample. Such conditions would include lower sample
thicknesses and higher temperature or plasticizer content.

**Effect of Sample Thickness.** Sample thickness significantly affects
the radiation-induced expansion of unstressed samples (Figure 14). The
equilibrium asymptotic deflection values vary approximately as the
square of the sample thickness for the 20- and 30-mil samples. The deflection values for all thicknesses above 0.010 follow the same curve at
short times ($\sim$0.2 minute), where diffusion out of the sample has probably not yet become significant.

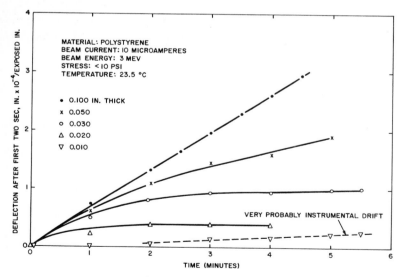

*Figure 14. Effect of sample thickness on expansion of polystyrene
during irradiation in the absence of significant stress*

Most of the deflection shown for the 0.010-inch thick sample can be attributed to either electrical drift in the instrumentation or a slight cooling water temperature change. A detectable change in deflection reading does not occur until after the first minute of irradiation, and the drift is approximately linear with time. Such drift in this low deflection range (1 to 2 $\times$ 10$^{-5}$ inches) was not uncommon.

One would also expect an increase in creep rate with sample thickness for these same samples. Creep data as a function of sample thickness for polystyrene are shown in Table V.

**Table V. Effect of Sample Thickness on Creep Rate of Polystyrene during Irradiation** [a]

| Sample Thickness, inch | Creep Rate during Irradiation,[b] inches/inch-minute |
|---|---|
| 0.100 | 1.3 $\times$ 10$^{-4}$ |
| 0.050 | 1.5–1.7 $\times$ 10$^{-4}$ |
| 0.033 | 1.5 $\times$ 10$^{-4}$ |
| 0.017 | 1.4–1.6 $\times$ 10$^{-4}$ |
| 0.017 | 1.5–1.8 $\times$ 10$^{-4}$ |

[a] Irradiation conditions:
  Beam current. 10 $\mu$a.
  Beam energy. 3 m.e.v.
  Applied stress. 1650 p.s.i.g.
[b] Corrected for temperature rise owing to radiation heating.

Surprisingly, there appear to be no significant differences in creep rate values with increasing sample thickness for polystyrene, although the scatter of this set of data is large. No completely satisfactory explanation can be offered at this time.

In the cases of poly(methyl methacrylate) (PMMA) and poly(vinyl chloride–vinyl acetate) (PVC/PV Ac), these polymers generate much more gas during irradiation than polystyrene. Thus, even if the gases accumulated in microvoids, where their enhancement of creep rate might be lessened, the local gas concentration between the polymer chains should still be much higher than in the case of polystyrene. One would thus expect to see an effect of film thickness on creep rate for these polymers.

Curves of deflection *vs.* time for two different thicknesses of the PVC/PV Ac copolymer are shown in Figure 15. The upper curve represents two experimental tests on 0.030-inch thick samples. The lower curve represents three tests on the thinner 0.010-inch samples. The difference between the deflection *vs.* time curves for the two thicknesses is in the direction one would expect if gas accumulation were causing the increased creep rates during irradiation. The two samples show

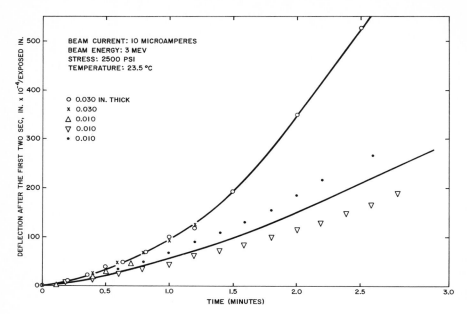

*Figure 15. Effect of sample thickness on creep during irradiation; 88% PVC–12% PV Ac copolymer*

approximately the same rate of deflection at the start of irradiation, but the rates of deflection diverge with time.

Increasing the temperature or plasticizer content should increase gas diffusivities in the polymer specimens. The diffusivities of $H_2$ in two polystyrene samples, one containing 20% plasticizer, were measured as a function of temperature (Figure 16). Diffusivities increase with temperature and plasticizer content. One would expect that as the gases are generated inside the polymers, the internal pressure would increase until the rate of diffusion of gas out of the polymer equals the rate of gas generation. Knowing the diffusion constant and $G$ value for gas generation of a given polymer, it is possible to calculate the gas concentration and pressure in the polymer as a function of time. It is clear that, at any time, this concentration will be greater at any point in the sample, the greater the sample thickness.

**Calculated *vs*. Measured Expansion in Absence of Significant Stress.** An expansion during irradiation without stress can be calculated for comparison with the measured expansion by the following procedure.

The gas concentration in the center of the polymer is calculated. This calculation is perfectly analogous to the temperature calculation in the center of the polymer described above. The problem is one of uniform generation of gas or heat in the sample with transmission of the gas or heat to outer surfaces which are maintained at an arbitrary zero temperature or zero gas concentration. Since the solution to the temperature case can be given in terms of dimensionless coordinates, the same solution applies to the mass transfer case if dimensionless coordinates are used (16). Figure 17 presents a graphical solution of the temperature distribution. In the case of gas diffusion, the ordinate becomes $[4\,DC_{max}/Rr_o^2]$, and the abscissa becomes $[Dt/r_o^2]$, where $D$ is the gas diffusivity in the polymer, $C$ is the gas concentration, $R$ is the rate of gas generation, $r_o$ is the radius of the equivalent cylinder, and $t$ is time. Using Figure 17 with these coordinates permits one to calculate the gas concentration at the center of the sample as a function of time. The average gas concentration is approximately 63.5% of the maximum, analogous to the temperature case.

The same assumptions apply for gas generation as for heat generation—that the sample is isotropic, that the gas generation rate does not vary with time or location in the radiation area, and that the sample length is more than twice either of the other dimensions.

The gas pressure is next calculated from the concentration. The additional assumption is that the incremental gas pressure inside the sample is the same as the external gas pressure required to yield the same amount of dissolved gas within the polymer at equilibrium (from a solubility–external pressure isotherm). This procedure gives approxi-

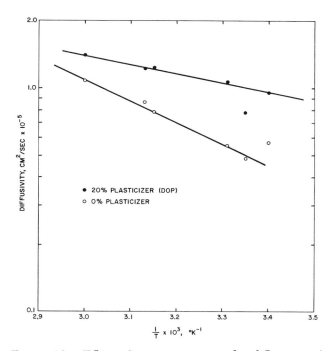

*Figure 16. Effect of temperature on the diffusivity of hydrogen in plasticized and unplasticized polystyrene*

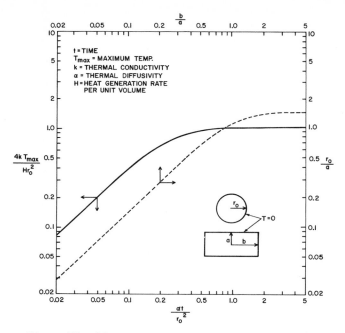

*Figure 17.  Maximum temperature vs. time for rods
of circular and rectangular cross section with uniform
heat generation, zero initial and surface temperature,
and negligible axial heat conduction.  Dotted curve
gives value of $r_o$ to use in dimensionless temperature
and time scale for rectangular cross sections (3)*

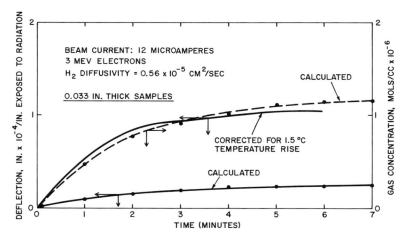

*Figure 18.  Calculated gas buildup and sample expansion compared
with measured sample expansion.  Sample thickness is 0.033 inch*

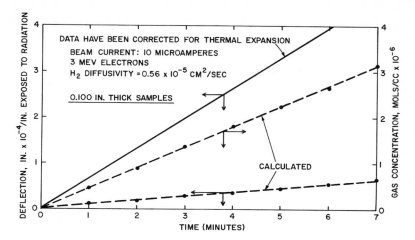

*Figure 19. Calculated gas buildup and sample expansion compared with measured sample expansion. Sample thickness is 0.100 inch*

mately the same result as the assumption that the gas occupies a polymer-free volume of 0.025 cc. per cc. The pressure corresponding to the 5 to 7 minute region of Figure 18 is calculated to be *ca.* 2 atm.

A deflection is next calculated from the internal pressure. It is assumed that the polymer compressibility may be applied for this calculation—*i.e.*, it is assumed that the deflection caused by the gas in the inside of the polymer is the same, but with opposite sign, as would occur if the gas were on the outside and were compressing the sample.

It is apparent that the assumptions used in calculating the gas concentration probably approximate the actual conditions more closely than the assumptions used to calculate the sample deflection from the gas concentration. The calculated deflections should be within the same order of magnitude, however.

The calculations depend upon knowing the diffusivity of the gas in the polymer and the rate of gas generation per unit volume. The diffusivity of hydrogen in polystyrene at room temperature was found to be $0.56 \times 10^{-5}$ sq. cm./sec. by measuring the flow rate of hydrogen through a 0.014-inch thick polystyrene membrane (Figure 16). The rate of gas generation is obtained from the $G$ values noted in Table IV, multiplied by the rate of energy absorption in the sample (in units of 100 e.v./second).

Calculated gas concentration and deflection curves are shown with measured deflection curves for two polystyrene samples of different thickness in Figures 18 and 19.

The agreement between the shape of the calculated curves and the measured expansion curves is evident, even when the shape of the measured curve changes radically because of a change in sample thickness, as shown by comparing Figures 18 and 19.

The quantitative agreement between the measured and calculated curves for sample deflection is within a factor of 5, and this is good when one considers the assumptions used to calculate the deflection from the gas concentration—e.g., the equilibrium solubility was used to obtain the Henry's law constant, whereas on this scale of a few minutes a smaller value might be more appropriate. Using a smaller value would result in a higher gas pressure and therefore a higher deflection, but the same curve shape. Using the compressibility to calculate the amount of an internal expansion is also subject to some error since the potential distance function for dispersion interactions is not symmetrical about the potential energy minimum. In fact, the dilatability of a polymer should be greater than its compressibility so that the predicted deflections are probably underestimated.

The equilibrium gas concentration, and thus the equilibrium sample deflection of plasticized polystyrene samples, should be inversely proportional to the diffusivity of the gas in a plasticized polymer. The measured diffusivities for hydrogen in unplasticized polystyrene and polystyrene containing 20% plasticizer differ by a factor of about 2 (Figure 16). From the 0 and 20% plasticizer points in Figure 13, curve $C$, we see that the equilibrium deflections also differ by a factor of about 2 to 3.

In Figure 14 the deflection of the 20- and 30-mil unstressed samples during irradiation reaches an asymptotic value which varies approximately as the square of sample thickness. The calculated gas concentration for polystyrene reaches a constant value. When the calculated gas concentration becomes constant with time, the ordinate of Figure 17, $4 DC_{max}/R(r_o)^2$, also becomes constant. For given irradiation conditions, $D$ and $R$ are constant, so that one would predict that $C_{max}$, the gas concentration in the center of the sample, should vary directly as $(r_o)^2$. The length, $r_o$, is linearly related to the sample thickness (for the type of sample geometry used in this study), so that the $C_{max}$ level is assumed to be a direct measure of the asymptotic level of expansion during irradiation in the absence of stress. Thus, there appears to be good agreement between theory and observation for the relationship of sample expansion and sample thickness for the two different thicknesses noted. This agreement between the predicted and observed thickness dependence gives added support to gas concentration as being the cause of polystyrene expansion during irradiation in the absence of significant stress.

All of the above comparisons of measured and calculated results have been for polystyrene.

The gas molecules produced in the 88% poly(vinyl chloride) copolymer (probably primarily HCl) have much higher molecular weight and would be expected to show much lower diffusion rates than hydrogen. The gas molecules liberated in poly(methyl methacrylate) are similarly large. Diffusivities in both cases would be expected to be of the order of $10^{-6}$ sq. cm. per second or less (*15*). Furthermore, the rates of gas generation in these two polymers are much higher than the rate of hydrogen generation in polystyrene.

When gas concentrations are calculated for these polymers, the combined effects of low diffusivity and higher gas generation rate result in the conclusion that gas diffusion out of the polymer has a small effect on the gas concentration in the polymer for samples in the 0.033 to 0.100-inch thickness range. As a further result, the calculated gas concentration for these samples increases linearly with time in the manner observed for the thicker polystyrene samples (Figure 19). The calculated gas concentration will start to approach an equilibrium concentration at some greater time, when the rate of gas diffusion out equals the rate of gas generation, but this point is evidently not reached within the time scale of the present experiments.

The measured curves for expansion of the PVC/PV Ac and PMMA samples during irradiation in the absence of stress are given in Figure 12. Rather than showing a linear increase with time as predicted from the above calculation, the rate of expansion accelerates with time. This may be caused by an acceleration in gas evolution from the polymers with time. It is known, for example, that HCl evolution in PVC homopolymers may proceed via an "unzipping" reaction owing to allylic-group activation of the H atom on the succeeding vinyl chloride polymer unit. Furthermore, it has been shown in Figure 18 that when the calculated internal gas concentration reaches an equilibrium level (within 3 minutes) for the thinner polystyrene samples, the expansion under no stress also levels out. Consequently, the accelerated creep rate would be expected to be constant, as observed in Figure 3. When the gas concentration continues to increase, as it must for poly(methyl methacrylate) and the poly(vinyl chloride) copolymer during the time scale of the experiments here, the creep rate would also be expected to continue to increase with time, again as seen in Figure 3. This does not take acceleration of the gas generation rate into account; when increasing gas evolution with time is included, the creep rate should increase at an even faster rate. Finally, it is possible that monomer fragments in PMMA or HCl in PVC/PV Ac could plasticize the polymer and cause the acceleration in creep rate during irradiation.

The data obtained here for intermittent stress application (Figure 8) on a polystyrene sample and the data of Mokul'skiǐ *et al.* (Figure 9) for creep of a PVC sample after various times of exposure to the nuclear radiation field can now be interpreted in terms of continued gas buildup within the samples during radiation exposure. This leads to the higher initial creep rates when stress is applied after the radiation beam has been on for a while (as observed in the polystyrene sample where the diffusion of $H_2$ is rapid) and to the over-all higher creep rates observed in the PVC sample, where the HCl diffusion is much slower.

The results of the delayed stress on radiation studies presented above (Figure 7) are also consistent with the mechanism of gas buildup within the polymer specimens as the cause of the accelerated creep. An additional interesting conclusion is that applied stress should increase the rate at which gases diffuse out of a polymer specimen. This is not unreasonable in view of the fact that this conclusion is reached for stress application during irradiation, when expansion of the polymer matrix by the internally generated gas would be expected to facilitate gas diffusion. (Actually, one would expect increased gas diffusion in stressed glassy polymers, even in the absence of radiation, owing to the low Poisson ratio in such materials.)

When the expansion of unstressed samples is plotted on log-log coordinates against the elongation of stressed samples at the same times after the samples are exposed to radiation, a definite correlation is obtained between these two types of deflection for the PMMA and PVC/PV Ac materials. Figure 20 shows this correlation, which may be expressed by the equation:

$$D_1 = KD_2{}^2 + C$$

where

$D_1$ = deflection of the stressed sample at a given time during irradiation

$D_2$ = deflection of the unstressed sample at the same time during irradiation

$K, C$ = constants

This relationship holds for both polymers, only the constants being different. One quantity of particular interest is the rate of deflection at a given time, which is the same as the creep rate at that time for the stressed sample. By differentiating the above equation with respect to time:

$$\frac{dD_1}{dt} = 2kD_2 \left[ \frac{dD_2}{dt} \right] = \text{creep rate of stressed sample during irradiation}$$

This differential equation states that the creep rate during irradiation is directly related not only to the deflection of the unstressed sample which has occurred up to that time ($D_2$, which may be related to the increase in polymer free volume) but also to the rate of increase of $D_2$ with time. The reason for the dependence of the creep rate on $dD_2/dt$ is not apparent but may be related to the fact that gas is being generated at an increasing rate as time progresses (as in the case of PVC). This relationship emphasizes the strong dependence of the accelerated creep rate in these two polymers during irradiation on the sharply rising expansion of the unstressed samples in the radiation field.

**Equivalence of Temperature and Radiation in Increasing the Creep Rate.** It is possible to calculate a temperature rise which would give the same free volume increase as that calculated for a given gas concentration. When this is done, the free volume increase caused by the gas in the 0.033-inch polystyrene sample is equivalent to a temperature rise of

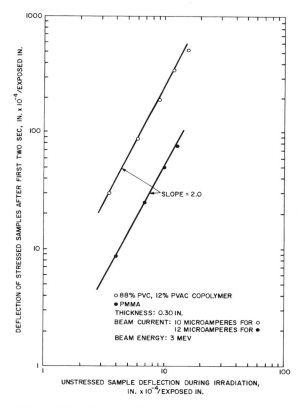

*Figure 20.  Relation between creep during irradiation and expansion during irradiation in the absence of significant stress*

less than 5°C. This magnitude of temperature rise does not result in a large increase in creep rate, such as is observed during irradiation (*see* Figure 10). One therefore wonders why the radiation process is more effective in increasing the creep rate than an increase in temperature for the same change in free volume.

In another study (8) it has recently been found that poly(methyl methacrylate) samples which were heated to 150°C. and then quenched in ice water exhibited creep rates (between room temperature and 60°C.) 10 times greater than control samples which had not been heated. No measurable difference in density between the two samples was found. The temperature required to achieve the same creep rate as that noted for the quenched sample would have caused a distinct measurable expansion of the sample.

One possible explanation is that creep in glassy materials probably occurs *via* molecular segmental motions in the neighborhood of submicroscopic defects where stresses become concentrated. As gas is generated locally along and between the chain molecules, local "free volume" is also generated, permitting increased segmental motions. These local segmental motions may then be translated through the entangled chain network and appear as increased stresses at nearby points of stress concentration. Thus, the combination of gas-induced and externally imposed stresses could act together synergistically to accelerate creep. In contrast, an increase in temperature causes isotropic and homogeneous expansion, without preference for localized defects, and without introducing stresses *per se;* hence, the creep rate change owing to thermal expansion should be lower than that caused by equivalent expansion created by internal dilatory stresses.

### Conclusions

The creep rates of polystyrene, poly(methyl methacrylate), and an 88% poly(vinyl chloride)–12% poly(vinyl acetate) copolymer are higher during irradiation than before or after. The magnitude of the increased creep rate varies from a factor of about 5 for polystyrene to more than 1000 for the poly(vinyl chloride) copolymer. These were the only three polymers tested, but it is expected that most if not all other organic polymers will show an increase in creep rate during irradiation. Typical radiation intensities used in this work resulted in an energy absorption rate in the samples of 40,000 to 500,000 rads per second. A 3-m.e.v. Van de Graaff generator and an 8-m.e.v. linear accelerator were used as the radiation sources.

The increased creep rate cannot be attributed to radiation heating of the sample. The average temperature rise in the present work was typically 1.8°C. or less, as determined both by thermocouples molded into polystyrene samples and by calculation.

The amounts of crosslinking, scission, and number and type of free radicals produced in unstressed polystyrene samples by the radiation agreed well with literature values. Stressed samples gave the same results as unstressed samples, with the possible exception of a slightly lower amount of chain scission for stressed samples. This is opposite from the result one would predict if a high rate of scission in samples contributed to the accelerated creep rate.

The increase in polystyrene creep rate owing to the radiation is directly proportional to the applied stress for a constant radiation intensity. The activation energy at constant radiation intensity for creep of polystyrene during irradiation at different temperatures is similar to the activation energy for creep without radiation.

The polymers expand during irradiation even in the absence of significant stress. This expansion can be accounted for by the generation of gas pressure within the sample. The shape of the curves of deflection *vs.* time, the magnitude of the deflection, and the differences between materials can be explained by the relative rates of gas generation within and gas diffusion out of the samples.

The equilibrium deflection of unstressed polystyrene samples varies as the square of the sample thickness as does the calculated gas concentration, establishing a strong tie between the gas concentration and the equilibrium deflection. No other species besides the evolved gas should depend on the sample thickness.

The creep rate of the poly(vinyl chloride) copolymer during irradiation depends on sample thickness, probably because of the dependence of the gas pressure in the polymers on sample thickness. An equilibrium gas pressure is not obtained in this polymer because of the high gas (HCl) generation rates and low gas diffusivity. The creep rate increases with time because of the accumulation of gas within the sample as well as the possibility that gases are generated at an increasing rate with time. The creep rate of stressed polystyrene during irradiation does not appear to show a significant dependence on sample thickness. This unexpected result is not explained at present.

### Acknowledgment

The support of the research project by the University of California Lawrence Radiation Laboratory is gratefully acknowledged, as is the assistance in the area of dosimetry and Van de Graaff generator operation provided by Ken Wright and Jerome Fouan of the MIT High Voltage Research Laboratory.

The plasticized polystyrene materials provided by the Koppers Co. Research Department are also appreciated.

### Literature Cited

(1) Battelle Memorial Institute, "The Effect of Nuclear Radiation on Elastomeric and Plastic Materials," **REIC 21** (1963).
(2) Bolt, R. C., Carroll, J. G., "Radiation Effects in Organic Materials," Academic Press, New York, 1963.

(3) Carslaw, J. S., Jaeger, J. C., "Conduction of Heat in Solids," 2nd ed., pp. 8–10, Clarendon Press, Oxford, 1959.
(4) Chapiro, A., "Radiation Chemistry of Polymeric Systems," Interscience, New York, 1962.
(5) Charlesby, A., "Atomic Radiation and Polymers," Pergamon Press, London, 1960.
(6) Ibid., pp. 284–287 and Chap. II.
(7) Edwards, A. C., Holzman, R. L., "Temperatures Induced in Plastic Samples by Irradiation in an Electron Beam," Internal Report of Chemical Engineering Section, Lawrence Radiation Laboratory, Livermore, Calif.
(8) Ender, D. H., M.I.T. Mechanical Engineering Department, private communication, December 1965.
(9) Flory, P. J., "Principles of Polymer Science," Cornell University Press, Ithaca, N. Y., pp. 308–314, 1953.
(10) Mokul'skiĭ, M. A., Vysokomol. Soedin. 2, 119 (1960).
(11) Mokul'skiĭ, M. A., Lazurkin, Iu. S., Fiviskiĭ, M. B., Vysolkomol. Soedin. 2, 110 (1960).
(12) Mokul'skiĭ, M. A., Lazurkin, Iu. S., Fiviskiĭ, M. B., Kozin, V. I., Dokl. Akad. Nauk SSSR 125, 1007 (1959).
(13) Mokul'skiĭ, M. A., Lazurkin, Iu. S., Fiviskiĭ, M. B., Kozin, V. I., Vysokomol. Soedin. 2, 103 (1960).
(14) Parkinson, W. W., Bopp, C. D., Binder, D., White, J. E., J. Phys. Chem. 69, 828 (1965).
(15) Vieth, W. R., Tam, P. M., Michaels, A. S., "Dual Sorption Mechanisms in Glassy Polystyrene," J. Coll. Interfacial Sci. 22, 360 (1966).
(16) Vivian, J. E., Chemical Engineering Department, Massachusetts Institute of Technology, personal communication, July 1965.

RECEIVED May 16, 1966. Work done as part of Sc.D. thesis of J. P. Bell, MIT Chemical Engineering Department.

# 8

# Radiation Modification of Poly(ethylene oxide)

P. A. KING

Nuclear Research Center, Union Carbide Corp., Tuxedo, N. Y.

*The electron or gamma irradiation of high molecular weight poly(ethylene oxide) (Polyox) causes marked changes in solution properties, molecular-weight distribution, and molecular weight. Crosslinking and degradation both occur, but their relative importance is determined by experimental conditions such as dose rate, oxygen concentration, and particle size. At low dose rates and in the presence of air, the G (scission) value is about 200. Changes in molecular weight and molecular-weight distribution have been measured and related to the gross improvements observed in solution properties: lower viscosity, increased shear stability, and longer shelf life.*

The polymerization of ethylene oxide with heavy metal catalysts yields a polyether ranging in molecular weight from about $10^5$ to $10^7$. The trade name Polyox has been given to this class of water-soluble resins (9). Alternative polymerization methods produce low molecular weight ($<10^5$) materials called Carbowaxes. Although the two polymers are chemically identical, there are large differences in molecular weight and molecular-weight distribution and important differences in physical properties.

Solutions of Polyox resins are less stable than the lower molecular weight Carbowax series. McGary studied the chemical degradation of Polyox (10) and found that aqueous or organic solutions of Polyox degrade upon long term aging—*i.e.*, the solution viscosity decreases. This degradation is "accelerated by strong acids, certain oxidizing agents, ultraviolet light, and certain heavy metal ions." He concluded that Polyox degrades primarily by a chain oxidation process.

Mechanical agitation is also an important degradation method in the higher molecular weight series. In fact, care must be taken in preparing solutions of high molecular weight samples since rapid agitation often decreases the bulk viscosity greatly.

113

Little has been published on irradiating the Carbowax series of polyethylene oxides and even less on the Polyox class. Most workers have studied the crosslinking reaction; in fact, degradation was minimized in most investigations by excluding oxygen. In one of the earliest papers (14), Pearson concluded that the cobalt-60 irradiation of poly(ethylene oxide) (M.W. = 9000) in air causes crosslinking at low doses (1 megarad), after which chain degradation predominates. He also stated that irradiation in vacuum leads to a crosslinked but unstable product that undergoes degradation upon exposure to air. He measured changes in intrinsic viscosity as a function of dose and related these to the number-average molecular weights. Since the relationship between viscosity and molecular weight would be altered in an unknown manner by branching, crosslinking, degradation, and distributional changes (4), his conclusions as to the amounts of crosslinking and degradation are probably incorrect. Salovey and Dammont (15) recently studied the crosslinking of a series of Carbowaxes and the lowest molecular weight Polyox, WSR-35. They observed that the electron irradiation of poly(ethylene oxide) in vacuum produced both degradation and crosslinking, with the ratio of main chain scission to the density of crosslinked units being equal to 0.6. They emphasized that the intrinsic viscosity is not a simple indication of molecular weight changes in crosslinking polymers. Nitta and his associates (12, 13) reported that poly(ethylene oxide) of about 4000 molecular weight is crosslinked when exposed to cobalt-60 gamma or electron irradiation. Their evaluation of the ESR spectra led them to conclude that both main chain scission and hydrogen removal occurred. However, since all radicals disappeared by second-order processes, they suggested that the final result was a combination of end linking, branching, and crosslinking, with no degradation.

Crouzet and Marchal (6) studied the cobalt-60 radiation-induced crosslinking and degradation of poly(ethylene oxide) solutions. They postulated two opposing mechanisms, one leading to crosslinking and ultimate gelation, and the other to oxidative degradation with molecular weight decreases. More recently, Spragg and Mangun (17) investigated the high molecular weight poly(ethylene oxides) and the Carbowax series. They irradiated air-saturated solutions of Polyox and observed "spectacular viscosity decreases and ultimate gelation."

Despite discrepancies among the various investigators, it appears that radiation causes both crosslinking and main chain scission in poly(ethylene oxides). In the work reported here degradation of Polyox has been emphasized by controlling the reaction conditions carefully. Both crosslinking and degradation do occur, but their relative importance is determined by experimental conditions such as dose rate, oxygen concentration, particle size, and moisture content.

8. KING   *Poly(ethylene oxide)*                                   **115**

*Experimental Methods*

**Materials.** The polyethylene oxides were the commercial grades of Polyox produced by the Union Carbide Corp. Distilled water was used in all solutions.

**Solution Preparation.** The polymer solutions were prepared by one of two methods.

METHOD 1. The required amount of dry resin was added to a screw-capped jar containing a measured amount of distilled water. The polymer–water mixture was shaken vigorously for a few moments to disperse the polymer, and the jar was rolled on a ball mill until the polymer dissolved. The rolling period ranged from a few hours to overnight.

METHOD 2. The resin was dispersed quickly with a high speed, multi-bladed stirrer, then agitated slowly until the polymer dissolved. The time necessary ranged from a few minutes to 8 hours. This method is preferred since it produces higher viscosity solutions.

**Viscosity Measurements.** The bulk-viscosity measurements were made with a Model LVT Brookfield viscometer at 25°C. The largest spindles and the lowest speeds that gave reproducible readings were used in all cases.

**Shear Degradation.** Aqueous solutions of Polyox were agitated vigorously with a 10-blade stirrer turning at 1080 r.p.m. The solution viscosities were measured at various times during the stirring period.

**Measurement of Pituitousness Value** (2). The pituitousness (stringiness) values were obtained with a conventional duNouy tensiometer. The wire ring was lowered into the solution and then raised above the surface. The time required for the solution to break all contact with the ring was recorded as the pituitousness value, thus giving an empirical measure of the stringiness of the solutions.

**Cobalt-60 Irradiations.** The cobalt-60 source used in these irradiations was located inside a conventional hot cell equipped with viewing window, access ports, master-slave manipulators, and a sample-transfer conveyor. The 4000-curie source consisted of 12 pencils of 6-inch active length arranged in holders in a 6-inch diameter circle. The holders were attached to an aluminum plate containing a series of tapped holes in concentric circles. The large samples were placed on these circles at the desired distance from the source. This right-cylinder source design is the best compromise between dose rate and homogeneity, but the dose varies along the center line of the right cylinder about 30% from mid-point to top. The large samples were rotated during irradiation and blended afterward to increase homogeneity, thus producing representative samples with a reasonably accurate dose. For smaller samples (approximately 5 grams), a holder positioned the material at the midpoint of the cylinder formed by the cobalt-60 pencils. Samples irradiated in air were in loosely capped jars; those irradiated in vacuum were degassed at less than 1 micron for at least 20 hours and sealed under vacuum. The cobalt-60 source was calibrated using the Fricke dosimeter solution —aqueous sulfuric acid containing ferrous ammonium sulfate plus sodium chloride. The ferric ion produced was measured spectrophotometrically at 25°C. A $G$ value of 15.5 for ferric ion production was used to calculate the absorbed dose. The doses in small samples are believed to be accurate within 5 to 10%.

**Van de Graaff Irradiations.** The vertically mounted Van de Graaff accelerator (High Voltage Engineering Co.), used for the electron irradiations, was operated at 2 m.e.v. at all times.

The beam-scan length was continuously variable from 3 to 15 inches, and the beam was about ½ inch wide. Electron current was adjustable to a maximum of 250 $\mu$a. The material was carried under the beam on a variable-speed, continuous belt, the dry powder being exposed to air at all times. Dosage was controlled by varying scan width, electron beam current, or belt speed. To ensure complete penetration, the polymer bed depth was kept at 0.5 inch or less.

TYPICAL EXPERIMENT. Polyox resin, Grade WSR-5M5, was transferred to a stainless steel hopper positioned over a vibrating feeder. The belt speed was set at 90 inches per minute, and the accelerator was adjusted (with the shutter closed) to deliver a current of 250 $\mu$a. at 2 m.e.v. The shutter was opened, and the feeder was activated. The calculated dose was 0.75 megarad. After irradiation, the viscosity of each sample was measured. The average 5% aqueous solution viscosity for 27 samples of one particular blend was 78 ± 7 cp., and the average for 16 samples of another was 80 ± 5 cp.

Absolute dosimetry with the electron accelerator is less accurate than with the cobalt-60 source since penetration of the electron is a variable—directly proportional to the energy of the beam and inversely proportional to the density of the material. The absorbed dose varies with depth (18) and is about 60% of maximum at the surface with a steady increase to a maximum at about one-third of the total penetration depth. At about two-thirds of the total penetration, the dose is equivalent to that absorbed at the surface. Therefore, if all parts of the sample are to receive the same minimum dose, the useful penetration is approximately two-thirds of the total, or about 0.33 gram per square centimeter per m.e.v.

The reported doses are for the surface of the polymer and were calculated from the electron energy and current.

### Results

The striking changes in solution viscosity produced by the cobalt-60 $\gamma$-ray irradiation of dry Polyox are shown in Table I.

It is appropriate to note the large changes produced by relatively small doses. This effect is especially pronounced in the higher molecular weight series, WSR-301, where a decrease of at least a factor of $10^4$ occurs after a 0.5-megarad dose. The magnitude of the viscosity reduction decreases as the molecular weight of the starting polymer decreases. Viscosity reductions occur in the air-free series but are much smaller than the corresponding air-saturated experiments. Continued irradiation in the absence of air produces insoluble, crosslinked material. The initial drop in viscosity in the absence of air is probably caused by a combination of crosslinking, branching, and degradation.

Although electron and gamma irradiations are usually considered equivalent in effect, differences in dose rate can be important. The decrease in solution viscosity caused by 2-m.e.v. electron and cobalt-60 γ-ray irradiations can be compared in Figure 1. The gross effect (viscosity reduction) occurs with either type of radiation. However, the low dose-rate gamma irradiation (0.1 megarad per hour) is about three times more effective than the higher dose-rate electron irradiations (200 to 4000 megarads per hour). The increased availability of oxygen during

**Table I.   Effect on Bulk Viscosity: Irradiation of Dry Polyox**

| Sample | Initial $\overline{M}_v$ | In Air | | In Vacuum | |
|---|---|---|---|---|---|
| | | Dose, megarads | Viscosity, cp. | Dose, megarad | Viscosity, cp. |
| WSR-35 | $2 \times 10^5$ | 0 | 680 | 0 | 680 |
| | | 0.05 | 70 | 0.05 | 550 |
| | | 0.1 | 40 | 0.15 | 250 |
| | | 0.5 | 12 | 0.3 | 125 |
| | | 4.6 | 8 | — | — |
| WSR-205 | $6 \times 10^5$ | 0 | 1620 | 0 | 1620 |
| | | 0.05 | 405 | 0.05 | 1160 |
| | | 0.1 | 182 | 0.1 | 1020 |
| | | 0.5 | 23 | 0.3 | 125 |
| | | 4.0 | 11 | — | — |
| WSR-301 | $3 \times 10^6$ | 0 | $>3 \times 10^6$ | 0 | 1740 (1%) |
| | | 0.05 | 48000 | 0.03 | 864 (1%) |
| | | 0.1 | 13000 | 0.08 | 390 (1%) |
| | | 0.5 | 144 | 0.12 | 120 (1%) |
| | | 4.0 | 45 | — | — |

Bulk viscosities were of 5% aqueous solutions except where otherwise noted.
Dose rate 0.1 megarad/hr. or $6.24 \times 10^{18}$ e.v./gram/hr.

the low dose-rate irradiation is believed responsible for the increased efficiency. The three points for the double-pass electron irradiations were obtained by irradiating the dry powders in two equal increments. Since local oxygen replenishment can occur between irradiations, an increase in degradation would be expected.

The initial molecular weight is an important factor in Polyox irradiations. The viscosities of 5% aqueous solutions are plotted as a function of total dose in Figure 2. The Polyox powder was irradiated in air with 2-m.e.v. electrons at rates of 200 to 4000 megarads per hour. The samples in decreasing molecular weight were as follows: WSR-701, WSR-301, WSR-5M5, and WSR-35. The range is from about $10^7$ to $2 \times 10^5$. This

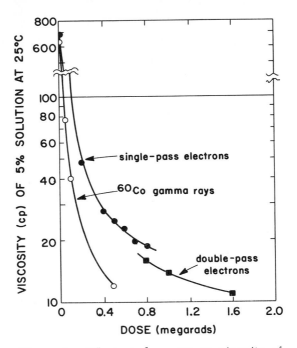

*Figure 1. Effect of dose rate on viscosity of
5% aqueous solutions. Dry WSR-35 Polyox
irradiated in air*

family of curves demonstrates the behavior of the various molecular-
weight grades and, in particular, illustrates the importance of low dose
irradiations. The initial viscosity of the WSR-701 sample was $>> 3 \times 10^6$ centipoises; a dose of 0.5 megarad caused the viscosity to decrease
by at least a factor of $10^4$. Further irradiation has relatively little effect;
tripling the dose decreases the viscosity by only one-tenth.

The effect of irradiation on the shear stability of Polyox solutions is
shown in Figure 3. The viscosities before agitation were comparable,
and it is apparent that after doses of approximately 0.4 megarad the
solutions are much more stable than the unirradiated control.

Polyox resins are almost unique in one property. The solutions are
stringy, or more correctly, pituitous. The empirical measure of this
pituitousness is plotted against the radiation dose in Figure 4. The
changes in the pituitousness value are marked: WSR-301 polymer before
irradiation had a pituitous value greater than 10 whereas a dose of
approximately 0.5 megarad produced a solution that was not stringy
and could be handled with ease. The same effect was observed with
the lower molecular weight WSR-35 polymer, but the initial stringiness
was less marked.

## Discussion

Radiation effects on polymers are more subtle than normal radiation chemistry, in that small chemical changes may have pronounced effects on the physical properties. Because of the sensitivity of these physical properties, the radiation chemistry of Polyox is best discussed in two parts—the chemical reactions occurring and the effects of these reactions on the physical properties.

The doses used in this work cause so little chemical conversion that conventional chemical analyses of the products are not possible; consequently, a model system must be used. Fortunately, a detailed study of the radiolysis of diethyl ether was recently published by Ng and Freeman (*11*). They measured the various products, and by analyzing the product ratios they concluded that the relative probabilities (per bond) for cleavage of the various types were as follows: C—H, $G = 0.34$; C—O, $G = 1.6$; C—C, $G = 0.28$. Cleavage of the carbon-hydrogen bond occurs predominantly at the alpha carbon and leads to 2,3-diethoxybutane. The

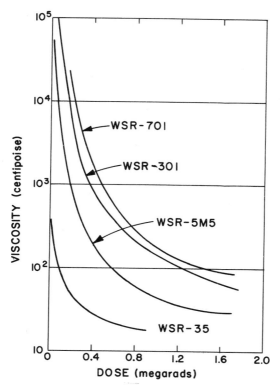

*Figure 2.    Effect of initial molecular weight on radiation degradation of Polyox*

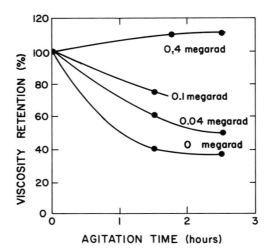

*Figure 3. Effect of 2-m.e.v. electron radiation on shear stability of Polyox solution. 5% aqueous solutions prepared from dry irradiated polymer*

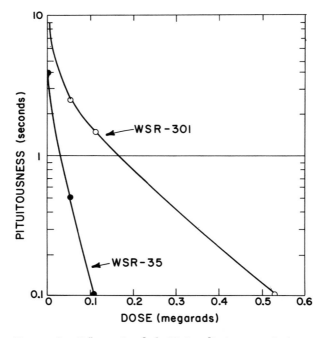

*Figure 4. Effect of cobalt-60 irradiation on pituitousness of 5% aqueous solutions of dry irradiated Polyox*

precursor to this dimer ($CH_3$—$\overset{\bullet}{CH}$—O—$CH_2$—$CH_3$) was approximately 40 times as abundant as the radical produced by the loss of a beta hydrogen. Cleavage of the carbon-oxygen bond produces alkoxy and alkyl radicals, which can undergo several reactions. The alkoxy radical can abstract or disproportionate. The abstraction reaction apparently predominates since the ratio of ethanol to acetaldehyde is 8.

Although the radiation chemistry of Polyox would not be expected to be exactly the same (because of the influence of crystal structure on radical migration, deactivation of excited species, etc.), it is still reasonable to use their ratios to estimate the initial radical production in our system. The corresponding values for total bond cleavage in Polyox are as follows (calculated for a molecule containing 8 C—H bonds, 4 C—O bonds, and 2 C—C bonds):

$$
\begin{array}{ll}
\text{—CH}_2\text{—CH—O—} & G = 2.7 \\
\text{—CH}_2\text{—CH}_2\text{—}\text{\textsmall{\textbackslash}}\text{—O—} & G = 6.4 \\
\text{—CH}_2\text{—}\text{\textsmall{\textbackslash}}\text{—CH}_2\text{—O—} & G = 0.6
\end{array}
$$

The situation becomes considerably less predictable after the primary bonds are broken. However, the expected products and some of their reactions are shown in the following equations:

$$\text{—CH}_2\text{—CH—O—} \longrightarrow \text{—CH}_2\text{—CH—O—}$$
$$+ \text{—CH}{=}\text{CH—O—} + H\cdot + H_2 \tag{1}$$

$$\text{—CH}_2\text{—CH}_2\text{—}\text{\textbackslash}\text{—O—} \longrightarrow \text{—CH}_2\text{—CH}_2\cdot + \cdot\text{O—CH}_2\text{—CH}_2\text{—} \tag{2}$$

$$\text{—CH}_2\text{—}\text{\textbackslash}\text{—CH}_2\text{—O—} \longrightarrow \text{—CH}_2\cdot + \text{CH}_2\text{—O—} \tag{3}$$

The number of backbone radicals produced in Equation 1 is not simply the C—H cleavage value since an appreciable amount of hydrogen removal can proceed by a molecular process to give an unsaturated group. Ng and Freeman's work indicates that approximately half of the hydrogen atoms are scavengeable. If these atoms react by abstraction (Reaction 4), more polymer backbone radicals would be formed:

$$\text{—CH}_2\text{—CH}_2\text{—O—} + H\cdot \longrightarrow \text{—CH}_2\text{—CH—O—} + H_2 \tag{4}$$

Nitta *et al.* (*12, 13*) observed a persistent doublet in the ESR spectrum above 0°C. and ascribed it to this backbone polymer radical. Our corresponding measurements on Polyox at room temperature are qualitatively identical (*20*). These backbone radicals are the ones presumed to enter into the crosslinking reaction, especially in the absence of oxygen.

The fates of the radicals produced in the second and third equations are matters for conjecture. Since the ESR signals attributed to them decay by second-order processes (*12, 13*), disproportionation reactions such as

$$—O—CH_2—CH_2 \cdot + \cdot O—CH_2—CH_2—O—$$
$$\longrightarrow —O—CH_2—CH_3 + OHC—CH_2—O— \qquad (5a)$$

$$—O—CH_2—CH_2 \cdot + \cdot O—CH_2—CH_2—O—$$
$$\longrightarrow —O—CH=CH_2 + HO—CH_2—CH_2—O— \qquad (5b)$$

or an abstraction reaction followed by disproportionation,

$$—O—CH_2—CH_2—O \cdot + —CH_2—CH_2—O—$$
$$\longrightarrow —O—CH_2—CH_2—OH + —CH_2—\overset{\cdot}{C}H—O— \qquad (6)$$

$$—CH_2—\overset{\cdot}{C}H—O— + \cdot CH_2—CH_2—O—$$
$$\longrightarrow —O—CH=CH—O— + CH_3—CH_2—O— \qquad (7)$$

would be consistent with the kinetic decay scheme. The alkoxy radical would be expected to abstract the weakly bound hydrogen atoms from another polymer molecule as does the corresponding radical from diethyl ether ($CH_3—CH_2—O \cdot$). However, since the radicals produced by C—O cleavage are in a crystal, restrictions in movement may alter the reactions greatly. In the absence of easily abstractable hydrogen atoms, an alkoxy and an alkyl radical lead to a carbonyl compound and a hydrocarbon (*16*), as shown in Reaction 5a. This occurs even though the association reaction has zero activation energy (*8*). The propinquity of these two radicals should favor disproportionation over abstraction from the neighboring polymer chain. The alkyl radical can participate in several reactions, similar to Reaction 7, to give a mixture of combination and disproportionation products.

The —O—CH_2 · radicals formed by C—C breakage apparently recombine or abstract since no formaldehyde is detected in the absence of air. In any case, the yield is low in comparison to Reactions 1 and 2.

Maximum and minimum values for chain scission and backbone radical formation can be estimated by assuming complete abstraction or combination of the radicals from Reactions 2 and 3.

Total abstraction would lead to a $G$ value for ($-CH_2-\overset{\cdot}{C}H-O-$) of 16.7 and a value for chain scission of 7.0. $G(CH_2-\overset{\cdot}{C}H-O-)$ = ½ $G(C-H$ cleavage) + $G(H$ scavengeable) + $2G(C-O$ cleavage) + $2G(C-C$ cleavage); $G$(scission) = $G(C-O$ cleavage) + $G(C-C$ cleavage)

The minimum values, assuming complete recombination of the radicals from Steps 2 and 3, would be $G(CH_2-\overset{\cdot}{C}H-O-)$ = 2.7 and $G$(scission) = 0. Salovey and Dammont (*15*) showed, by an analysis of the solubility *vs.* dose measurements, that degradation occurs even in the absence of air. They reported a value of 0.6 for the ratio of scission to crosslinking; our measurements, by the Charlesby (*5*) method, ranged from 0.7 to 0.95. These measurements mean that crosslinking and degradation occur with almost equal probability. Therefore, the initial values for chain scission and backbone radical formation should lie between the extremes estimated above.

The only radical observable at room temperature by ESR spectrometry is thought to be the polymer backbone radical. Therefore, it is logical to assume that radicals formed by carbon-oxygen and carbon-carbon bond cleavages decompose quickly under our conditions. The foregoing arguments lead to the conclusion that abstraction and disproportionation reactions, rather than recombinations, are the modes of decay. In any case, it is reasonable to assume that these radicals do not persist long enough for oxygen to diffuse to their site; thus, the important species in the oxidative degradation is the backbone radical. Some expected reactions of this polymer (*3, 19*) radical are shown below:

$$2-CH_2-\overset{\cdot}{C}H-O- \longrightarrow \quad \begin{array}{c} -CH_2-CH-O- \\ | \\ -CH_2-CH-O- \end{array} \qquad (8)$$

$$-CH_2-\overset{\cdot}{C}H-O- \longrightarrow -CH_2-CHO + \cdot CH_2-CH_2-O- \qquad (9)$$

$$-CH_2-\overset{\cdot}{C}H-O- + O_2 \longrightarrow \begin{array}{c} -CH_2-CH-O- \\ | \\ O-O\cdot \end{array} \xrightarrow[\text{steps}]{\text{several}} \text{chain scission} \qquad (10)$$

$$\begin{array}{c} -CH_2-CH-O- \\ | \\ O-O\cdot \end{array} + -CH_2-CH_2-O- \longrightarrow \qquad (11)$$

$$\begin{array}{c} CH_2-CH-O- \\ | \\ O-OH \end{array} + -CH_2-\overset{\cdot}{C}H-O-$$

$$\begin{array}{c} -CH_2-CH-O- \\ | \\ O-OH \end{array} \xrightarrow[\text{steps}]{\text{several}} \text{chain scission} \qquad (12)$$

The combination of two backbone radicals leads to crosslink forma-tion, Reaction 8, or the radical can rearrange with chain scission to an aldehyde and an alkyl radical, Reaction 9. In the presence of oxygen, Reaction 10 competes with crosslink formation. The relative proportions of each reaction will depend on the steady-state concentration of radicals (a function of dose rate) and the local accessibility of oxygen at the radical sites. Because of the relatively rapid diffusion of oxygen, Reaction 10 would be favored at low dose rates. This leads to the peroxy radical which can decompose with chain scission. One of the reactions of the peroxy radical is the abstraction of a hydrogen atom, Reaction 11, to form the hydroperoxide and an additional backbone radical. The hydro-peroxide can also decompose, causing chain scission (Reaction 12). The presence of unstable peroxides or hydroperoxides is consistent with the observed rapid drop and subsequent leveling off in the viscosity of Polyox solutions prepared at various times during the first 24 hours after irradia-tion of the dry polymer. Such a reaction scheme satisfies the requirements for the chain oxidation of ethers, described by Walling and Bell *et al.* (*3*, *19*) and is consistent with the chemical degradation reported by McGary (*10*).

No precise G values can be calculated in this system since no inde-pendent determinations of number-average molecular weights are avail-able for the high molecular weight irradiated polymers. However, the viscosity-average molecular weights were determined for a series of irradiated Polyox samples. Bailey, Kucera, and Imhoff (*1*) developed the relationship between viscosity-average molecular weight and weight-average molecular weight (determined by light scattering) for unirra-diated Polyox. Elias (*7*) measured the weight-to-number-average ratio for a WSR-301 grade Polyox sample, and his value of 22 points out the broad molecular weight distribution of this type of polymer. The number-average molecular weights for the series of irradiated Polyox samples were determined from the viscosities using the molecular weight rela-tions described above. G values for chain scission have been calculated from these number-average molecular weights:

| Dose, Megarad | $\overline{M}n$ | $G_{scission}$ |
|---|---|---|
| 0.0 | 123,000 | — |
| 0.1 | 33,000 | 210 |
| 0.2 | 20,500 | 185 |
| 0.4 | 9,600 | 250 |

The G values should be considered as estimates since the molecular weight relations are continuously altered because of the degradation, crosslinking, and branching that occur during irradiation. For example, if the radiation-induced oxidation quickly produces a random (or near-random) distribution, the above G values approach a value of about 10. The value of about 200 chain breaks per 100 e.v. does not prove but is consistent with the chain oxidation process postulated above. These G values were calculated from the low dose-rate cobalt-60 irradiations and would be lower for electron irradiations at the high dose rates if a chain process were involved.

The unusual solution properties of Polyox reflect the broad molecular weight distribution; it is likely that a small portion of extremely large molecules control the solution properties. The high viscosity and shear susceptibility of dilute solutions are logically ascribed to the high molecular weight fraction. The marked pituitousness of the solutions is also related to the broad molecular weight distribution (2). In a polymer such as Polyox, these extremely large molecules are the most likely to be affected in a random process such as irradiation. This would lead to a narrowing of the molecular weight distribution and an ultimate approach to a random polymer that would be less sensitive to a small number of breaks in the polymer molecules. The rapid decrease in viscosity (especially pronounced in the high molecular weight series), decreases in pituitousness, and increases in shear stability are all consistent with the hypothesis that radiation-induced chain oxidation converts a polymer of broad molecular weight distribution to one approaching random distribution.

### Conclusions

The radiation-induced degradation of Polyox in air is a chain reaction (with a G value of approximately 200) that leads to greatly decreased viscosity, increased shear stability, and decreased stringiness. These changes are presumed to be caused by a lowering of the molecular weight and—more important—to a narrowing of the molecular weight distribution.

### Acknowledgment

Many people contributed significantly to this work. I thank especially F. E. Bailey, R. D. Lundberg, F. W. Stone, D. B. Kelley, J. A. Faucher, J. J. Stratta, and E. B. Whipple of the Union Carbide Corp. for important measurements and helpful suggestions and interpretations.

### Literature Cited

(1) Bailey, F. E., Kucera, J. L., Imhof, L. G., *J. Polymer Sci.* **32**, 517 (1958).
(2) Bailey, F. E., Lundberg, R. D., Callard, R. W., private communication.
(3) Bell, E. R., Raley, J. H., Rust, F. F., Seubold, F. H., Vaughan, W. E., *Discussion Faraday Soc.* **10**, 242 (1951).

(4) Chapiro, A., "Radiation Chemistry of Polymeric Systems," p. 367, Interscience, New York, 1962.
(5) Charlesby, A., "Atomic Radiation and Polymers," p. 172, Pergamon Press, New York, 1960.
(6) Crouzet, C., Marchal, J., *J. Polymer Sci.* **59**, 317 (1962).
(7) Elias, H. G., *Angew. Chem.* **73**, 209 (1961).
(8) Gray, P., Williams, A., *Chem. Revs.* **59**, 239 (1959).
(9) Hill, F. N., Bailey, F. E., Fitzpatrick, J. T., *Ind. Eng. Chem.* **50**, 5 (1958).
(10) McGary, C. W., Jr., *J. Polymer Sci.* **467**, 51 (1960).
(11) Ng, M. K. M., Freeman, G. R., *J. Am. Chem. Soc.* **87**, 1935 (1965).
(12) Nitta, I., Onishi, Fujimoto, E., Annual Report of Japanese Association for Radiation Research on Polymers, Vol. 1, p. 320 (1958-59), AEC-tr-6231.
(13) Nitta, I., Onishi, S., Nakajima, Y., Annual Report of Japanese Association for Radiation Research on Polymers, Vol. 3, p. 437 (1961), AEC-tr-6372.
(14) Pearson, R. W., "Radioisotopes in Scientific Research," Proceedings of First UNESCO International Conference, Paris, 1957, Vol. 1, p. 151, Pergamon Press, New York, 1958.
(15) Salovey, R., Dammont, F. R., *J. Polymer Sci.* Pt. **A1**, 2155 (1963).
(16) Spinks, J. W. T., Woods, R. J., "Introduction to Radiation Chemistry," p. 184, Wiley, New York, 1964.
(17) Spragg, H. R., Mangun, G., "Process Radiation Development Program Summaries," Brookhaven Natl. Lab., **BNL-949 (C-47)**, 43 (1965).
(18) Trump, J. G., Van de Graaff, R. J., *J. Appl. Phys.* **19**, 599 (1948).
(19) Walling, C., "Free Radicals in Solution," Chap. 9 and 10, Wiley, New York, 1957.
(20) Whipple, E. E., private communication.

RECEIVED June 9, 1966.

# Radiation Chemistry of Polyethylene Terephthalate

D. T. TURNER

Camille Dreyfus Laboratory, Research Triangle Institute, Durham, N. C.

*Initial G values for polyethylene terephthalate exposed in vacuo to $\gamma$-rays at a dose rate of $10^{-2}$ Mrad per minute are $-COOH = 0.8$, $CO_2 = 0.17$, $CO = 0.11$, $H_2 = 0.015$, and $CH_4 = 0.003$. These values decrease with increased dose except for $CO_2$, which is roughly sustained up to 5000 Mrad. With an increase of dose rate $G(-COOH)$ decreases, and the fall in the limiting viscosity number of the polymer is less. This dependence on dose rate is explained by a chain reaction involving the free radical (I) which was identified by ESR spectroscopy: $C_6H_4$—CO—O—CH—$CH_2$—O—CO —$C_6H_4$— $\longrightarrow$ $C_6H_4$—CO—O—CH=$CH_2$ + O—CO—$C_6H_4$ —$C_6H_4$—CO—O· + —$C_6H_4$—CO—O—$CH_2$—$CH_2$—O— CO—$C_6H_4$— $\longrightarrow$ —$C_6H_4$—COOH + $C_6H_4$—CO—O—ĊH —$CH_2$—O—CO—$C_6H_4$—*

Two aspects of the radiation chemistry of polyethylene terephthalate (PET) are reviewed here: the dependence of product yields on radiation dose and on dose rate. The review is limited to work with thin films from which air and water were pumped prior to irradiation. Moreover, it is judged that in the experiments described postirradiation effects were negligible.

### Structure of PET

The PET studied was Mylar C film (DuPont) of 12 to 25 micron thickness. Such films are biaxially oriented and are about 50% crystalline. The glass transition and melting temperatures are about 70° and 250°C., respectively. The polymer contains several parts per thousand of inorganic materials, moisture, and 1 to 2% cyclic oligomers (mostly trimer) (8). The number-average molecular weight of the polymer molecules is in the range 15,000 to 20,000, and their distribution of sizes is not far from random. The main repeat unit in the molecule has structure I, but there are also units of structure II (2 to 8% by weight). The predominant end group is III. There are also carboxyl end groups ($0.3 \times 10^{-4}$ mole per gram; IV) and, presumably, an equivalent number of other unidentified end groups of, or derived from, structure V (7).

$$-\!\!\left\langle\!\!\bigcirc\!\!\right\rangle\!\!-CO-O-CH_2-CH_2-O-CO- \qquad\qquad I$$

$$-\!\!\left\langle\!\!\bigcirc\!\!\right\rangle\!\!-CO-O-CH_2-CH_2-O-CH_2-CH_2-O-CO- \qquad II$$

$$-\!\!\left\langle\!\!\bigcirc\!\!\right\rangle\!\!-CH_2-CH_2-OH \qquad\qquad\qquad III$$

$$-\!\!\left\langle\!\!\bigcirc\!\!\right\rangle\!\!-COOH \qquad\qquad\qquad\qquad IV$$

$$-\!\!\left\langle\!\!\bigcirc\!\!\right\rangle\!\!-CO-O-CH=CH_2 \qquad\qquad\qquad V$$

### Predominant Free Radical Trapped in PET (1, 3)

Stacks of Mylar films were gamma-irradiated at $-196°C$. The electron spin resonance signal at $-196°$, a singlet, was attributed to unspecified ionic species. On warming to room temperature the number of spins was reduced by about one order of magnitude. A relatively stable population of free radicals remained: $G$(trapped radicals) $= 0.02$. Spectra were recorded after brief access of air to destroy unoriented free radicals in the amorphous regions. A spectrum of eight approximately equivalent lines, obtained at a particular orientation of the stack with respect to the magnetic field, was assigned to interaction of an unpaired electron with three nonequivalent protons (Figure 1, $a$). At an orientation perpendicular to this, two of these protons become equivalent, and only six lines are observed (Figure 1, $b$). These spectra were assigned to the free radical $-O-\overset{\cdot}{C}H-CH_2-O-$, which accounted for more than 90% of all the trapped radicals.

### Dependence of Product Yields on Dose (2)

Exposure of PET to gamma-radiation at a dose rate of $2 \times 10^{-2}$ Mrad per minute results in the following changes.

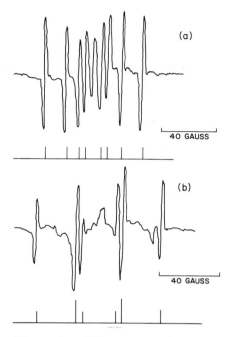

Figure 1. *ESR spectra of gamma-irradiated Mylar film after postirradiation exposure to air (3). Dose rate: $3 \times 10^{-3}$ Mrad/min. Dose: 10 Mrad. Spectra in a and b obtained at mutually perpendicular orientations of sample in magnetic field*

The polymer becomes yellow-brown and brittle.

The concentration of —OH end groups decreases, confirming the work of Sobue and Kajiura (*17*), but the concentration of —COOH end groups increases (*12*) (Figure 2, *a*).

Absorption maxima develop near 12.9 and 13.3 microns (Figure 2, *b*). This may be caused by the formation of groups of the kind —O—CO— $C_6H_4$—R—, in which R is not a —CO—O— group (*4*).

$CO_2$, CO, $H_2$, and $CH_4$ are evolved (confirming Ref. *17*).

$G(—COOH)$, $G(CO)$, and $G(H_2)$ decrease with increase of dose up to 5000 Mrad, but $G(CO_2)$ appears to pick up again after an initial decrease (Figure 3). The latter effect might be attributed to second radiation hits on carboxyl end groups, on the grounds that $CO_2$ is known to be the predominant gaseous product on gamma-irradiation of solid benzoic acid (*19*).

A quantitative test made with assumptions which included that Reactions 1 are first-order and that a rate constant calculated for

$$\text{--}\langle\!\!\!\bigcirc\!\!\!\rangle\text{--CO--O--CH}_2\text{--CH}_2\text{--O--CO--} \qquad \qquad (1)$$

with decarboxylation producing —COOH \~→ CO₂ at the top and CO₂ at the bottom.

the formation of $CO_2$ from benzoic acid, under similar conditions, could be used for the decarboxylation of end groups in PET proved to be inadequate.

A further question considered with respect to Reactions 1 is whether the decrease in concentration of repeat units (I) follows first-order kinetics with respect to dose—*i.e.*, whether $\log_e (C/C_o) = kR$, in which $C$ and $C_o$ are the concentrations of repeat units at doses $R$ and 0, respectively, and $k$ is a constant. According to Reaction 1, $C = C_o - [\text{—COOH}] - [CO_2]$ which, using data in Figure 3, gives a better fit to a straight line over the range 100 to 5000 Mrad than does the choice of $C = C_o - [\text{—COOH}]$ (Figure 4).

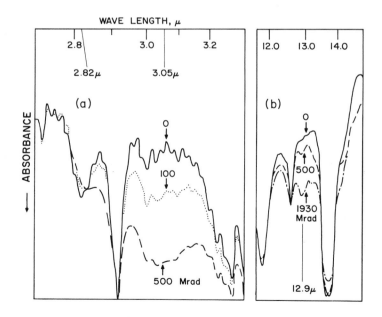

*Figure 2. Changes in infrared absorption following gamma-irradiation of Mylar film (4, 12). Absorption maxima of —OH and —COOH near 2.82 and 3.05 microns, respectively*

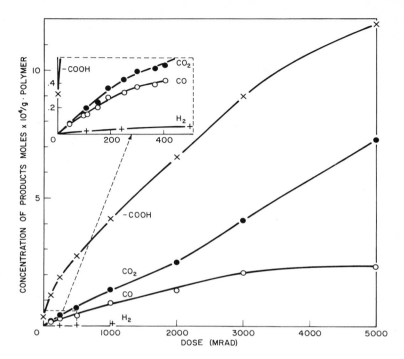

*Figure 3.    Dependence of product yields from Mylar on dose (2).
Carboxyl groups estimated by titration (Pohl's method) (13)*

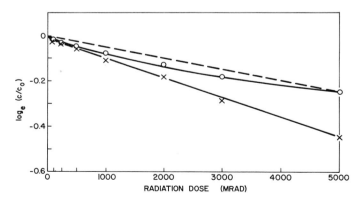

*Figure 4.    Plot of $log_e(C/C_o)$ vs. dose (3)*

$\bigcirc$:  $C = C_o - [-COOH]$
$\times$:  $C = C_o - [-COOH] - [CO_2]$

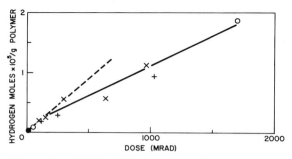

*Figure 5.   Yields of hydrogen vs. dose over range
of dose rates*

×: $6 \times 10^{-3}$ Mrad/min. [γ(17)]
+: $2 \times 10^{-2}$ Mrad/min. [γ(5)]
●: 8.7 Mrad/min. [e(16)]
○: 67 Mrad/min. [e(16)]

The high value of $G(-COOH + CO_2)$ at doses < 100 Mrad, suggested by the plot in Figure 4, might be attributed to "weak links" in the polymer molecules. Previously, weak links were invoked as a possible explanation for higher G(fracture) values at low doses in a number of polymers (10). In the case of PET it is possible that II units would be specially sensitive to radiation damage. Consistent with this idea is the report that more complex gaseous products have been detected after the low dose of 0.43 Mrad, the major component being tentatively identified as diethyl ether (17). On the other hand, an indication that the weak link explanation is not the whole story is provided by an observation that $G(-COOH)$ also drops sharply with increasing dose in the case of ethylene glycol dibenzoate crystals (20); in this case there can be no question of weak links!

### Influence of Dose Rate

Dose rate has little or no influence on the evolution of hydrogen from PET (Figure 5) nor, apparently, on the evolution of other gases (Table I). An indication that the yield of a product might depend on

**Table I.   G Values for Gaseous Products at Low Doses**

| Dose, Mrad | Dose Rate, Mrad/min. | $CO_2$ | $CO$ | $H_2$ | $CH_4$ |
|---|---|---|---|---|---|
| | | \multicolumn{4}{c}{G Values} | | | |
| 114 (2) | $2 \times 10^{-2}$ (γ) | 0.17 | 0.11 | 0.017 | 0.003 |
| 93 (17) | $6 \times 10^{-3}$ (γ) | 0.09 | 0.13 | 0.020 | 0.007 |
| 0.43 (16) | $8.7 \times 10^6$ (e) | 0.08 | — | 0.016 | — |

dose rate may be discerned in the report that an increase in absorption at 3250 A., following irradiation of Mylar in air with γ-rays or electrons, is smaller the higher the dose rate in the range $10^{-2}$ to 10 Mrad per minute (*14*). Decisive evidence of such an influence was found in the case of carboxyl groups, $G(—COOH)$ increasing with decrease in dose rate over the range investigated of 1.4 to 0.025 Mrad per minute (Figure 6, *a*). Consistently, the limiting viscosity number of the irradiated polymer was found to depend on dose rate in the opposite sense (Figure 6, *b*) (*11*). The latter observation would explain why gelation of PET, after doses in the range 200 to 1000 Mrad, has been observed only in

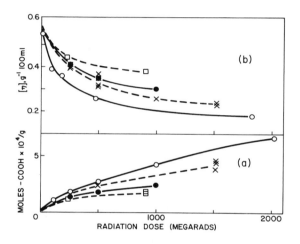

Figure 6.   *Influence of dose rate on values.  Plot (a),  COOH  groups  (Pohl's  method);  (b),  [η]. Dose rates, Mrad/min.*

☐:  *1.4 (e)*
●:  *0.17 (e)*
✕:  *0.15 (γ)*
○:  *0.025 (γ)*

experiments conducted at high dose rates of the order 10 Mrad per minute. At a low dose rate of $10^{-2}$ Mrad per minute no gel was formed even after a dose as high as 5000 Mrad.

In principle, detailed information about the radiation chemistry of a polymer may be obtained using sol-gel analysis as a function of dose to provide estimates of both crosslinks ($x$) and fractures ($F$) (*5*). Such estimates have been made in only one case for PET (*18*) but are supplemented by estimates made from other data obtained at high dose rates in Table II. The data used are scanty, generally only three points, and more detailed work is desirable. In addition, further work is required to check whether $G($—$COOH)$ values continue to follow the trend shown in Figure 6, *a*, to high dose rates.

**Table II.   Estimates of $G(x)$ and $G(F)$ from Sol-Gel Analysis**

| Reference | (18) | | (15) | | (q)[a] |
|---|---|---|---|---|---|
| Polymer | Amorphous pellets | | 25-$\mu$ film (?) | | 100-$\mu$ film (Mylar) |
| Radiation | 1.5 m.e.v. electrons | | 0.2 m.e.v. electrons | | 1-m.e.v. electrons |
| Dose rate, Mrad/min. | 9 | | ? | | 13 |
| Temp., °C. | −20 to −40 | 80 | Hot (?) | | Water-cooled |
| Number-av. molecular weight at R = O | | | Assumed extremes | | |
| | 11,900 | | 10,000 | 20,000 | 17,500 [b] |
| $G(x)$ | 0.08[c] | 0.14 | 0.14 | 0.07 | 0.035 |
| $G(F)$ | 0.16[c] | 0.17 | 0.14 | 0.07 | 0.09 |

[a] Postirradiation changes in gel content observed.
[b] Calculated here from value of $[\eta]$ given in Ref. 9 using relationship of Ref. 6.
[c] Values reported in Ref. 18.

### Discussion

In a rigid medium such as PET it is conceivable that the chemical products are formed in small isolated volumes, which include a limited number of reactive intermediates generated along the track of a single electron. A consequence which agrees with experimental data in the range 100 to 5000 Mrad is that the concentration of repeat units should decrease exponentially with dose. However, compelling evidence that there is a correlation among events generated by more than one electron is provided by the observed dependence of yields of some reaction products on dose rate.

The reactive intermediates mentioned above are initially ions and excited molecules and subsequently may be free radicals. Many ions are probably formed on irradiating PET, as judged by the large concentration of spins detected at −196°C. by electron spin resonance (ESR), but nothing is known directly about their chemical structure or reactivity. Any chemical role of excited molecules is equally a matter of conjecture. In these circumstances, the influence of dose rate will be discussed by reference to free radicals. Eventually, when more quantitative experimental data are obtained, the adequacy of free radical reactions may be better assessed, and the role of ions and excited molecules brought into perspective.

Two modes of free radical formation seem likely on irradiating PET. First, hydrogen atoms are probably formed and, being little restricted by the "cage" effect, tend to escape recombination (Reaction 2). Since cyclohexadienyl type radicals have been carefully sought but not detected in gamma-irradiated PET (*1, 3*), it may be supposed that a hydrogen atom forms a molecule of hydrogen by abstraction (Reaction 3) and perhaps also by combination with a second atom. Hydrogen atoms which travel more than a few atomic diameters before they react ("thermal" hydrogen atoms) might be intercepted by a low concentration of a scavenger. Studies with deliberately added scavengers have not been attempted, but if the decrease in $G(H_2)$ with increasing dose shown in Figure 5 is attributed to the action of a scavenger formed by radiation damage of PET, then it may be estimated that 40% of the hydrogen has thermal hydrogen atom precursors. This agrees well with much better established estimates of the proportion of hydrogen formed from thermal hydrogen atoms in the radiolysis of hydrocarbons. It may be supposed that associated with the reactions of thermal hydrogen atoms there will be formed a population of isolated free radicals of the type $—O—\dot{C}H—CH_2—O—$, as detected by ESR, to the extent $G(\text{radicals}) = 0.006$ to $0.008$ [calculated from the range of $G(H_2)$ values in Table 1]. In addition, by analogy with the radiation chemistry of saturated hydrocarbons, there may also be close-spaced pairs of radicals associated with hydrogen formation.

A second probable mode of free radical formation stems from the formation of $CO_2$ and CO—*e.g.*, by Reaction 4. Even though $G$ values for $CO_2$ and CO are relatively high (Table I), it is known from ESR studies that radicals such as those shown in Reaction 4 do not remain trapped in the polymer at room temperature. Presumably such radicals, being formed at a separation of only one or two atomic diameters, react readily in pairs. For example, the absorption band at 12.9 microns might be caused by the group formed by combination of the radicals formed by Reaction 4 (*4*). Possibly, a proportion of such radicals abstract hydrogen atoms from neighboring repeat units to form $—O—\dot{C}H—CH_2—O—$, some of which become isolated and contribute to the experimentally observed result of $G(\text{trapped radicals}) = 0.02$.

To account for the influence of dose rate, it is postulated that carboxyl end groups are formed by a chain reaction (Reactions 5 and 6). The free radical $—O—\dot{C}H—CH_2—O—$ is supposed to undergo $\beta$-bond scission to form a carboxyl radical and a vinyl end group (Reaction 5). The carboxyl radical then abstracts a hydrogen atom from another repeat unit to yield a $—COOH$ end group and another $—O—\dot{C}H—CH_2—O—$ radical (Reaction 6). This chain sequence (Reactions 5 and 6) continues until the $-O-\overset{\cdot}{C}H-CH_2-O-$ combines or disproportionates with a second unspecified free radical, designated in Reaction 7 as $R\cdot$. It would be expected that the lower the dose rate the less Reaction 7 would be favored. This would result in long chains and hence high values of $G(-COOH)$ and low ratios of crosslinks to fractures. However, it is not known to what extent crosslinking can be attributed to Reaction 7

$$-\overset{\overset{\displaystyle O}{\|}}{C}-O-CH_2-CH_2-O-\overset{\overset{\displaystyle O}{\|}}{C}- \longrightarrow -\overset{\overset{\displaystyle O}{\|}}{C}-O-CH_2-\overset{\cdot}{C}H-O-\overset{\overset{\displaystyle O}{\|}}{C}- + H\cdot$$

$$(2)$$

$$-\overset{\overset{\displaystyle O}{\|}}{C}-O-CH_2-CH_2-O-\overset{\overset{\displaystyle O}{\|}}{C}- + H\cdot$$

$$\longrightarrow -\overset{\overset{\displaystyle O}{\|}}{C}-O-CH_2-\overset{\cdot}{C}H-O-\overset{\overset{\displaystyle O}{\|}}{C}- + H_2$$

$$(3)$$

$$-\overset{\overset{\displaystyle O}{\|}}{C}-C_6H_4-\overset{\overset{\displaystyle O}{\|}}{C}-O-CH_2-CH_2-$$

$$\rightsquigarrow -\overset{\overset{\displaystyle O}{\|}}{C}-C_6H_4\cdot + CO_2 + \cdot CH_2-CH_2-$$

$$(4)$$

$$-\overset{\overset{\displaystyle O}{\|}}{C}-O-CH_2-\overset{\cdot}{C}H-O-\overset{\overset{\displaystyle O}{\|}}{C}- \longrightarrow -\overset{\overset{\displaystyle O}{\|}}{C}-O\cdot + CH_2{=}CH-O-\overset{\overset{\displaystyle O}{\|}}{C}-$$

$$(5)$$

$$-\overset{\overset{\displaystyle O}{\|}}{C}-O-CH_2-CH_2-O-\overset{\overset{\displaystyle O}{\|}}{C}- + -\overset{\overset{\displaystyle O}{\|}}{C}-O\cdot$$

$$\longrightarrow -\overset{\overset{\displaystyle O}{\|}}{C}-O-CH_2-\overset{\cdot}{C}H-O-\overset{\overset{\displaystyle O}{\|}}{C}- + -\overset{\overset{\displaystyle O}{\|}}{C}-OH$$

$$(6)$$

$$-\overset{\overset{\displaystyle O}{\|}}{C}-O-CH_2-\overset{\cdot}{C}H-O-\overset{\overset{\displaystyle O}{\|}}{C}- + R\cdot$$

$$\longrightarrow \text{combination or disproportionation}$$

$$(7)$$

as there may be other unidentified reactions. The dependence on dose rate of the yield of the group which absorbs at 3250 A. could, in principle, be explained along similar lines—for example, by postulating that it is caused by some subsequent reaction of the vinyl end group formed in Reaction 5.

One of the referees has pointed out that as the $G$ values change with dose it is important to state at what dosage they were calculated. The initial values were, in fact, estimated from initial slopes defined by data obtained at doses of less than 100 Mrad (2). A second point made is that the ESR spectrum in Figure 1, *a*, includes nine lines whereas the text refers to only eight, which were assigned to the radical —O—CH— CH₂—O—. The central line is not assigned but probably has a component owing to a phenyl type radical, which remains after decay of the eight-line spectrum when the irradiated polymer is heated *in vacuo* for 20 minutes at 160°C. This latter radical (3) is tentatively identified as:

### Acknowledgment

The author is grateful to his colleagues, G. F. Pezdirtz and G. D. Sands of Langley Research Center, for their cooperation in the program of work on which this article is based. He is especially indebted to D. Campbell, not only for his cooperation with the work but also for a daily exchange of ideas.

### Literature Cited

(1) Araki, K., Campbell, D., Turner, D. T., *Polymer Letters* 3, 993 (1965).
(2) Burow, S. D., Pezdirtz, G. F., Sands, G. D., Turner, D. T., *J. Polymer Sci.* 4, 613 (1966).
(3) Campbell, D., Araki, K., Turner, D. T., *J. Polymer Sci.* 4, 2597 (1966).
(4) Campbell, D., Marcotte, F. B., Turner, D. T., *J. Polymer Sci.*, in press.
(5) Charlesby, A., Pinner, S. H., *Proc. Roy. Soc.* A249, 367 (1959).
(6) Conix, A., *Makromol. Chem.* 26, 226 (1958).
(7) Goodings, E. P., "Thermal Degradation of Polymers," p. 211, Society of Chemical Industry, London, 1961.
(8) Goodman, I., Nesbitt, B. F., *Polymer* 1, 384 (1960).
(9) Hellwege, K. H., Johnsen, U., Seufert, W., *Kolloid-Z.* 188, 11 (1963).
(10) Keyser, R. W., Clegg, B., Dole, M., *J. Phys. Chem.* 67, 300 (1963).
(11) Pezdirtz, G. F., Sands, G. D., Turner, D. T., *J. Polymer Sci.* 4, 252 (1966).
(12) Pezdirtz, G. F., Sands, G. D., Turner, D. T., unpublished work.
(13) Pohl, H. A., *Anal. Chem.* 26, 1614 (1954).
(14) Ritz, V. H., *Radiation Res.* 15, 460 (1961).

(15) Slovokhotova, N. A., Sadovskaya, G. K., Kargin, V. A., *J. Polymer Sci.*
     **58**, 1293 (1962).
(16) Sobue, H., Kajiura, A., *Kogyo Kagaku Zasshi* **62**, 1766 (1959).
(17) *Ibid.*, p. 1771.
(18) Sobue, H., Tabata, Y., Hiraoka, M., *Kogyo Kagaku Zasshi* **64**, 372 (1961).
(19) Tolbert, B. M., Noller, R., *Radiation Res.* **3**, 52 (1955).
(20) Turner, D. T., unpublished work.

RECEIVED February 16, 1966. Most of the work sponsored by the Langley
Research Center, National Aeronautics and Space Administration, under NASA
Contract NASI-3183.

# Radiation Crosslinked Ionomers and Polyethylenes

B. J. LYONS and C. R. VAUGHN

Research and Development Division, Raychem Corp., Redwood City, Calif.

*The effects of ionizing radiation on a low and a high density polyethylene and an ionomer indicate that similar networks are formed in the ionomer and in the low density polyethylene. The former crosslinks about 1.5 times as readily as the latter. In the high density resin, the network characteristics, and hence, presumably, the type and distribution of links, differ considerably from those in the other two resins. As a result, crosslinking rates in the high and low density polyethylenes cannot be directly compared.*

The influence of crystallinity on the radiolytic crosslinking of polyethylenes has been studied by several authors. Epstein (*18*) and Schumacher (*27*) (from the equilibrium stress-strain behavior) and Charlesby (*9*), and Waddington (*30*) (both used swelling and elastic modulus measurements) concluded that crosslinking rates were identical within experimental error in low and high density polyethylenes. Lawton *et al.* (*22*) concluded from gel formation measurements that crosslinking occurred mainly in the amorphous phase of the polymer. Chapiro has pointed out (*6*) that Lawton *et al.* allowed the trapped radicals (which are formed much more copiously in high density polyethylene) to decay in air at room temperature before measuring the soluble fraction. However, these authors quote a value for G(crosslinks) from stress-strain measurements on Marlex 50 irradiated at room temperature, then annealed at 150°C., similar to that given by Waddington and Charlesby.

Various authors—for example, Dole, Milner, and Williams (*15*) and Lyons (*25*)—have suggested that the decay of vinyl groups initially present in some types of high density polyethylene involves an end-linking process, these authors disagreeing only about the mechanism involved. If such were the case, some difference in solubility or elastic behavior above 140°C. would be expected between low and high density polyethylenes. Dole, Milner, and Williams (15) calculated $G$(crosslinks) for Marlex 50 (Phillips designation Marlex 6009) to be 0.5 (after allowing for a contribution from end linking) which differs appreciably from their value (0.8) for a low density polyethylene, using values of the gelling dose obtained by extrapolating solubility measurements. Quite apart from the accuracy of the extrapolation method, as Chapiro (7) has pointed out, measurements which involve estimating a low threshold dose are particularly sensitive to traces of oxygen which may remain in the polymer even after exhaustive degassing. It would be preferable to seek evidence of end linking and of differences in crosslinking yields from results obtained over a range of doses where most of the oxygen has already been consumed. Furthermore, most, if not all, commercial polyethylenes contain small traces (0.01 to 0.05%) of antioxidants. Removing these by solvent extraction exposes the sample to possible oxidation during extraction or during removal of absorbed solvent. Many of these additives decay rapidly on irradiation, and their effect on measurements carried out at doses much over 5 megarads becomes negligible (1).

Three common methods of measuring crosslinking (swelling, elastic modulus, and gel point measurements) have recently been critically appraised by Dole (14). A fourth method using a plot of sol $+ \sqrt{\text{sol}}$ against the reciprocal dose has also been used extensively. However, Lyons (23) has pointed out that this relation, even for polyethylenes of closely random distribution, does not have the rectilinear form required by the statistical theory of crosslinking. Flory (19) pointed out many years ago that the extensibility of a crosslinked elastomer should vary as the square root of the distance between crosslinks. More recently Case (4, 5) has calculated that the extensibility of an elastomer is given by:

$$\sqrt{\frac{3}{2\ln[1 + \rho(F - 2)]}}$$

where $\rho$ is the concentration of branch points, and $F$ is the functionality of the branch point. An advantage of extensibility measurements is that this property depends not on the average distance between crosslinks, as do the other methods above, but on the minimum distance. Thus, it is sensitive to variations in the distribution of crosslinks, but if a network has been formed, it should be relatively insensitive to molecular weight or molecular weight distribution. DiGuillio et al. (11) have verified experimentally the dependence of extensibility upon crosslink density. They show that in peroxide-cured ethylene-propylene rubbers the elongation at rupture is directly related to the reciprocal square root of the molar concentration of peroxide and is not affected by the type of peroxide used or by the initial Mooney viscosity of the polymer over a wide range (10 to 60). [Unfortunately, the utility of their work is weakened by the absence of a given relation between Mooney viscosity and molecular weight although they state that a polymer with a Mooney viscosity of 50 has a $\overline{M}_v$ of $2 \times 10^5$. At the high shear rates used in the Mooney viscometer the measured viscosity probably varies as the weight-average molecular weight to between the first and second power (20). Thus we may conclude that the molecular weight range encompassed by DiGuillio's work lies between 2 to 1 and 4 to 1, and is probably close to that of most commercial polyethylenes.]

The radiolytic behavior of Surlyn A has not been described in detail, although a preliminary announcement of the effect of ionizing radiation on the tensile strength and elongation at rupture at room temperature was made recently (29). This polymer, one of the so-called "ionomers," has some formal similarities to the carboxylated elastomers (2), which have been known for some time. Radiolytic studies have been made on elastomeric carboxylic butadiene-styrene copolymers (12, 13) and liquid carboxylic nitrile copolymers (3). It has been suggested in both cases that the presence of carboxylic groups results in somewhat greater crosslinking yields, the carboxylic groups participating through decarboxylation to polymer radicals. Irradiated metal oxide compositions of carboxylic elastomers are described as having improved heat stability and strength (12).

## Experimental

**Materials and Irradiation Procedure.** The materials examined are shown in Table I.

### Table I.   Materials Examined

| Commercial Name | Description | Supplier |
|---|---|---|
| Surlyn A (ER-1552) | Ethylene–methacrylic acid random copolymer neutralized with sodium ion | E. I. du Pont de Nemours & Co., Inc. |
| DFD 6040 | Low density polyethylene | Union Carbide Co. |
| DPD 6169 | Ethylene–ethyl acrylate random copolymer | Union Carbide Co. |
| DQDA 1868 | Ethylene–vinyl acetate random copolymer | Union Carbide Co. |
| Tenite 3310 | High density polyethylene | Eastman Chemical Products, Inc. |
| Copolymer 45,578 | Experimental ethylene-butadiene random copolymer | Phillips Petroleum, Inc. |
| QX 2375.0 | Ethylene–acrylic acid random copolymer | Dow Chemical Co. |

The Surlyn A ionomers (E. I. du Pont de Nemours & Co.) are believed to be derived from copolymers of ethylene with minor amounts of methacrylic acid which are treated subsequently, so that substantial amounts of the carboxylic acid are converted to the sodium or other metal carboxylate. Resins similar to the one studied in this work contain about 10 weight % methacrylic acid. The ash (sodium carbonate) indicates about 40% neutralization. This resin, which contains 0.05% Santowhite Powder (Monsanto Chemical Co.), a phenolic antioxidant, is of medium molecular weight—*i.e.*, probably corresponding to an ethylene homopolymer with a melt flow index around 20 (17). The molecular weight distribution is broad (17).

Rees and Vaughn (26) state that this type of ionomer is prepared by high pressure polymerization using free radical initiators. They are presumably random copolymers. The crystallinity as determined by x-ray diffraction is about 10% (26).

Tenite 3310 and DFD 6040 (formerly DYNK) have been described (23). Both contain 0.05% Santonox (Monsanto Chemical Co.), a thiobisphenolic antioxidant.

Irradiation conditions and procedures have been described (23), except that the irradiation cell in these experiments was flushed continuously with nitrogen. Samples, where noted, were annealed at 100°C. for 30 minutes immediately after irradiation.

In several instances 0.5-mm. thick sheets of Surlyn A were hung over concentrated aqueous hydrochloric acid in a desiccator for about one week, then dried in vacuum and irradiated. Infrared examination of thin films conditioned in this way for 3 days indicated little or no increase in crystallinity; x-ray examination indicated the presence of small amounts of crystalline sodium chloride.

**Gel Fraction.** As in previous work (23), a modified Charlesby-Pinner technique was used. However, reproducible gel fractions from Surlyn A samples were only obtained if a slow stream of gaseous hydrogen chloride was passed through the extracting solvent for several hours during the third extraction.

**Physical Properties.** Tensile test pieces were cut with an ASTM T50 die, modified by putting a radius as specified in Bell Telephone Laboratories, Inc., drawing B604844, on the junction between the tongues and the reduced section. Dumbbells of this small size were used to facilitate simultaneous irradiation in the water-cooled cell under nitrogen. These dumbbells were pulled at 2 inches a minute for both tensile strength and elongation at rupture measurements at ambient temperature.

Elastic modulus was measured by a dynamic method at 160°C. on samples with 2-inch bench marks elongated at a constant rate of 100% per minute. The stress at strains of 25, 50, 75, and 100% was used to calculate Young's modulus. Elongation at rupture at 160°C. was measured at the same relative rate of elongation, the mean of four measurenents being used for each sample. Each irradiation series was repeated between three and four times for measuring physical properties or gel raction.

**Unsaturation Changes.** Unsaturation changes were followed by monitoring the appropriate infrared absorbance bands using a Model 221 Perkin-Elmer spectrophotometer.

Our initial measurements of *trans*-vinylene growth in Surlyn A during radiolysis gave low absorbance values at 10.35 microns. This prompted us to attempt to measure relative "extinction coefficients" at 10.35 microns for a number of ethylene homo- and copolymers. The relative absorbance heights per mm. at 10.35 microns of polyethylenes and ethylene copolymers containing 5 weight % of an experimental Phillips ethylene-butadiene copolymer (containing 23 *trans*-vinylene groups per 1,000 carbon atoms) and using a differential base line measurement technique are given in Table II. Assuming an extinction coefficient of 139 for *trans*-vinylene groups in a high density polyethylene, this table also gives derived coefficients in other polyolefins.

**Table II.  Extinction Coefficients for *trans*-Vinylene Unsaturation in Various Ethylene Homo- and Copolymers**

| Resin | Comonomer | Density | Absorbance per Mm. at 10.35$\mu$ | "Extinction Coefficient" at 10.35$\mu$ |
|---|---|---|---|---|
| Tenite 3310 | None | 0.960 | 0.534 | 139[a] |
| DFDA 6040 | None | 0.920 | 0.503 | 131 |
| DFD 6169 | Ethyl acrylate | 0.931 | 0.491 | 128 |
| DQD 1868 | Vinyl acetate | 0.943 | 0.297 | 77 |
| QX 2375.0 | Acrylic acid | 0.934 | 0.393 | 102 |
| Surlyn A (acid-treated) | Methacrylic acid | ≈0.94 | 0.331 | 86 |

[a] Value given by Hampton (*21*).

We did not measure a mixture of the Phillips experimental polymer with Surlyn A itself since phase contrast microscopy indicated that the former had segregated as a separate crystalline phase. However, the differential absorbance at 10.35 microns of a Surlyn A sample irradiated to a 50-megarad dose decreased only 6.0% after sample and reference were exposed to HCl for 2 weeks. Furthermore, the rate of *trans*-vinylene growth with dose in Surlyn A was sensibly unaffected by prior exposure to HCl.

## Results

**Physical Properties.** Figure 1 shows the variation of tensile strength at room temperature with radiation dose for Surlyn A, untreated and treated with hydrochloric acid, and a low (DFD 6040) and high density

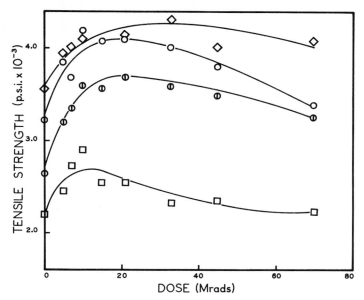

*Figure 1.   Variation of tensile strength with ionizing radiation dose*

○: *Surlyn A*
⊕: *Surlyn A treated with HCl*
□: *DFD 6040*
◇ : *Tenite 3310*

(Tenite 3310) polyethylene. The tensile behavior of Surlyn A on irradiation follows closely that of the high density polyethylene. Displacing sodium ion from the polymeric environment with HCl reduces the tensile strength of Surlyn A by about 20% at lower doses. All four resins show an increase of tensile strength on irradiation to a maximum at 15 to 30 megarads. The percentage maximum increase for Surlyn A ( ≈ 30% ) is about what would be expected for a low density polyolefin. High density polyethylenes, in general, show proportionately smaller increases.

Figure 2 shows the variation of elongation at rupture at room temperature with dose for these samples. The catastrophic drop in elongation of the high density polyethylene is notable. However, all these samples were tested without prior annealing at, say, 140°C. Such treatment, by reducing crystallinity and crystallite size (16) in Tenite 3310, would greatly affect its tensile and elongation behavior, but the other samples would be affected to an almost negligible extent.

Figure 3 shows the variation of elastic modulus at 160°C. with dose for these samples. In the case of Surlyn A, untreated or treated with HCl, and DFD 6040, heating for 30 minutes at 100°C. after irradiation had no significant effect on the modulus. The figure, therefore, shows only results for both annealed and unannealed samples in the case of Tenite 3310, where there was a considerable difference between modulus values obtained from samples left at room temperature for several weeks and those annealed immediately after irradiation. The marked differences in slope between these various resins will be noted. Work in this laboratory (*24*) has demonstrated that marked differences in rate of increase of modulus with dose between the many polyethylenes and polyolefin co-polymers occur, especially with annealed samples.

Figure 4 shows the elongation at rupture at 160°C. of the irradiated and annealed polymers plotted against the reciprocal square root of the dose. If crosslinking in these polymers is directly proportional to the dose, a linear relation should be obtained. Figure 4 shows that, within experimental error, linear relations can be fitted to the results. Deviations from linearity occur at doses much below 5 megarads, as would be

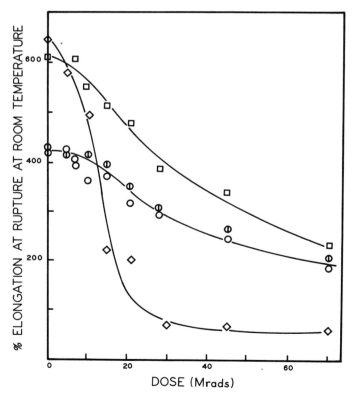

*Figure 2.   Variation of room temperature elongation at rupture with ionizing radiation dose. Symbol designations as for Figure 1*

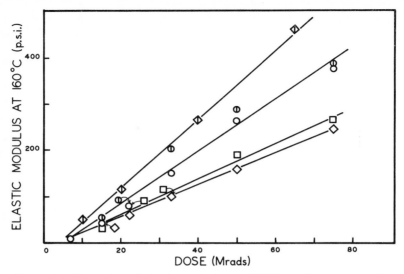

*Figure 3. Variation of elastic modulus at 160°C. with ionizing radiation dose*

◊ : *Tenite 3310 annealed after irradiation. Other symbol designations as for Figure 1.*

expected, and similar deviations apparently occur at doses greatly exceeding 150 megarads.

**Solubility Behavior.** The variation of sol + square root of sol with dose is shown on a logarithmic plot in Figure 5. Annealing has little effect on the results for Surlyn A and DFD 6040; more pronounced but still small effects are seen with Tenite 3310. The slopes of the relations are, for Surlyn A, 0.54; for DFD 6040, 0.44 [0.43 in a previously reported measurement (23)]; and for Tenite 3310, 0.43 [0.44 previously (23)]. Estimated gelling doses are, for Surlyn A (ER 1552), 1.7 megarads; for DFD 6040, 1.2 megarads; and for Tenite 3310, 3 to 4 megarads. However, since these resins contain small quantities of antioxidants, the gelation dose values are without absolute significance.

**Unsaturation Changes.** The spectra between 10 and 12 microns of a number of polyethylenes and related copolymers in the form of films 0.3 mm. thick are shown in Figure 6, the machine settings being unaltered during all the scans. *trans*-Vinylene growth in these materials during radiolysis is compared in Figure 7. The results, up to 4-megarad dose, show no evidence outside experimental error of any difference in the *trans*-vinylene formation reaction. However, it appears that the decay reaction can differ considerably in efficiency. Even so, Figure 8 shows that the *trans*-vinylene concentration at infinite dose is very similar in all these polymers, implying, as would be expected, that the radiolytic *trans*-vinylene decay reactions are much more similar at high doses. Because of marked changes in the base line during radiolysis, the initial absorbance values for the ethylene–vinyl acetate copolymer may be considerably in error.

The rapid decay of vinyl unsaturation in Surlyn A with dose is shown in Figure 9. Assuming an extinction coefficient of 153 for the band at 11.03 microns (we have not been able to test the validity of this assumption), the initial vinyl concentration is about $1.2 \times 10^{-5}$ mole per gram—*i.e.*, about one-fifth of that initially present in Tenite 3310. A band at 11.25 microns which also decayed during radiolysis is attributed to vinylidene groups initially present in concentration of about $4 \times 10^{-6}$ mole per gram. The vinyl decay does not show the marked deviations from a first-order relation noted in previous work on high density polyethylenes (*15, 25*). It has been suggested (*25*) that vinyl decay in an amorphous polyethylene will follow a first-order relation to much lower concentrations than is observed with highly crystalline polyethylenes. Vinyl unsaturation in Tenite 3310 is present to about the same degree

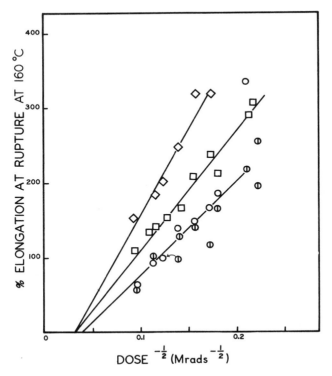

*Figure 4.  Variation of elongation at rupture at 160°C. with ionizing radiation dose. Designations as for Figure 1*

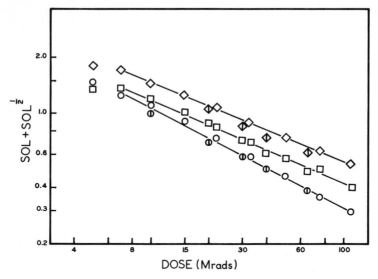

*Figure 5.   Variation of sol plus square root of sol with ionizing radiation dose.  Designations as for Figures 1 and 3*

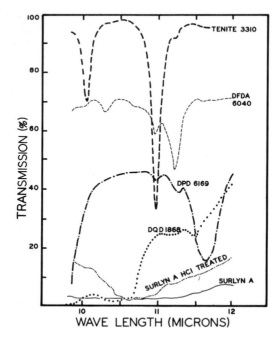

*Figure 6.    Infrared absorption curves between 10 and 12 microns for various ethylene homo- and copolymers*

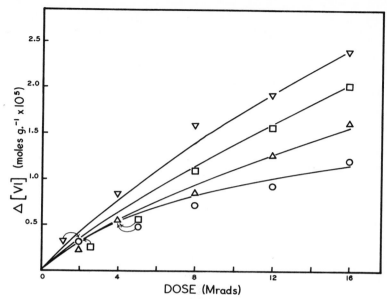

*Figure 7.   Growth of* trans-vinylene *unsaturation at low doses of ionizing radiation*

○: *Surlyn A*
□: *DFD 6040*
△: *DPD 6169*
▽: *DQD 1868*

as in Marlex 50 and follows an essentially identical decay pattern on exposure to ionizing radiation (*25*).

## Discussion

Ionomers are completely crosslinked three-dimensional polymers at ambient and moderately higher temperatures (*26*). The crosslinks are electrostatic: a mono- or dipositive metal ion is surrounded by up to six carboxyl groups, collectively bearing one or two negative charges and deficient one or two protons. Thus, ionic crosslinks may possess a functionality (up to duodecimal) much greater than that known in covalent crosslinks. Moreover, ionic crosslinks, being electrostatic, are "elastic" and may be sundered or may reform reversibly as a result of thermal motion or mechanical stress (*3, 26*). We find that ionomers form thixotropic gels in some solvents such as toluene or xylene. These are probably not true solutions but tenuous ionically crosslinked gels whose swollen volume is that of the extracting solvent. When sufficient covalent crosslinks are introduced to reduce the swelling ratio to manageable proportions, the gel fraction obtained approaches unity. The extent to which

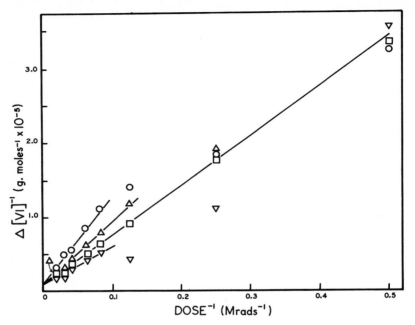

*Figure 8.    Variation of* trans-vinylene *unsaturation with dose up to high dose levels.  Designations as for Figure 7*

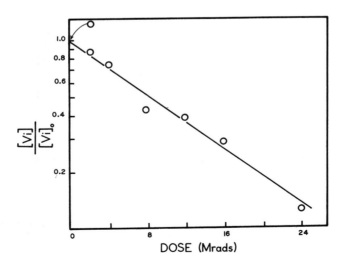

*Figure 9.    Decay of vinyl unsaturation in Surlyn A exposed to ionizing radiation*

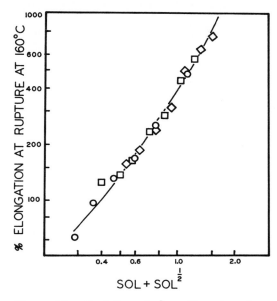

*Figure 10.   Variation of elongation at rupture at 160°C. with sol plus square root of sol. Designations as for Figure 1*

decomposition of the ionic bonds and dissolution occur depends not only on the solvent and temperature but also on the ionic charge. The stronger ionic bonds from divalent ions resist mechanical or thermal stress or swelling to a greater degree than do monovalent ions (*26*). The nature of the acid moiety will also influence the thermal behavior (*26*). A true measure of the covalently crosslinked gel fraction after irradiation can be obtained conveniently by removing metal ion from the polymeric environment with, for example, gaseous hydrogen chloride.

The results indicate that segregation of sodium ion as sodium chloride from a Surlyn A resin, without appreciably disturbing the resin's morphology, has no observable effect on the radiolytic reactions which it undergoes. The comparison of Surlyn A with a high and a low density polyethylene shows that modulus and gel increases and elongation diminishes on irradiation more rapidly in Surlyn A than in the low density polyethylene of higher molecular weight. The annealed high density resin which has a molecular weight between the other two resins develops modulus more rapidly but gels more slowly and gives a much greater elongation at rupture at 160°C. for a given dose. Figure 10 shows that the elongation at rupture for a given sol plus square root of sol value is the same for all three resins. It follows that gel formation and elongation at rupture measure the same fundamental changes in each of these polymers.

Figure 11 shows the variation of modulus with elongation at rupture for these three resins. The results, though scattered, clearly indicate that the ionomer and low density resin follow the same relation. However, a completely different relation is followed by the annealed high

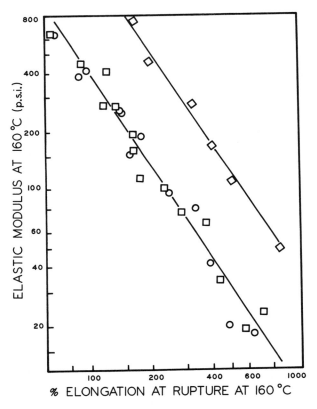

*Figure 11. Variation of elastic modulus at 160°C.*
*with elongation at rupture at this temperature.*
*Designations as for Figure 1*

density resin, indicating that its elastic modulus does not necessarily respond to the same type of change as do the others.

In view of the similarity in behavior of the networks in the ionomer and low density resin, we are able to deduce from modulus and elongation at rupture measurements the relative crosslinking rates. It appears that Surlyn A crosslinks 50 to 60% more rapidly than DFD 6040. The increased crosslinking in the ionomer may be associated with the radiolytic sensitivity of the carboxyl groups, as has been suggested to occur in other carboxylated (*12, 13*) resins. However, in view of the relatively small amount of carboxyl present, we prefer to postulate it also results from the increased *trans*-vinylene decay. There is, presumably, also a slight contribution from vinyl decay.

The differences in physical behavior between Tenite 3310 and the other two resins are quite marked. At a given dose the annealed high density resin has an almost 50% greater elongation at rupture and 100% greater modulus and about a 30% larger sol + square root of sol value than the low density resin. Unusually high modulus values for a given degree of crosslinking in, for example, natural rubber, have been associated with entanglements. However, such a contribution would also reduce the elongation at rupture for a given crosslinking density (*11*) while gel formation would be unaffected.

We suggest that the differences seen in this present work indicate a fundamental difference in the type of network that is formed when irradiating these low and high density resins. The marked effect of annealing on the elastic modulus of the high density resin and the known effect of such treatment in increasing vinyl decay suggest that these may be connected. Even so, the further decrease in elongation at rupture resulting from this annealing indicates an increase in end links far too small ($<10\%$) to account for the increase in modulus. However, this end linking increases $M_n$ and $M_w$ considerably, as has been suggested (*16, 23*), probably to the point where the relaxation time of the molten polymer becomes appreciable. Tobolsky and McLoughlin (*28*) have shown that, for polyisobutylenes of a viscosity-average molecular weight around $10^6$, the contribution of relaxation processes to dynamic elasticity is of an order ($10^7$ dynes per sq. cm.) similar to the modulus differences being considered in the present work. In the more flexible (and hence more easily entangled) polyethylene molecules such relaxation effects should become apparent at even lower molecular weights.

If elongation at rupture measurements at 160°C. in high and low density polyethylenes are related in the same way to crosslinking density, it follows that the crosslinking G values in the high density resin are only one half that of the low density resin, or that end linking rather than crosslinking occurs in the former. Case (5) calculates that uniform crosslinking could lead to increases in extensibility of up to 30% over the equivalently but randomly crosslinked polymer. However, while crystallinity may have some effect in narrowing the distribution of inter-crosslink distances, the degree of uniformity required to explain the differences observed here is beyond reason. Differing crosslink yields would require a considerable difference in the yields of crosslinking precursors—*i.e.*, polymer radicals. Such a difference has not yet been reported despite the considerable published literature on the formation and decay of alkyl radicals in polyethylene—for example, Charlesby *et al.* (*10*).

The remaining hypothesis, end linking, should have an important effect on extensibility only while appreciable amounts of vinyl unsaturation remain unreacted—*i.e.*, during the first 15 megarads. [We here exclude possibilities such as Charlesby's mechanism of end linking preceded by chain scission (*8*) on the grounds that this would demand a fundamentally different radiolytic mechanism for high and low density polyethylenes.] In high density polyethylenes such as Tenite 3310 the chain ends probably reside in the amorphous phase. If the suggestion of Lawton *et al.* (*22*) that radicals formed in the crystalline phase migrate to and crosslink in the amorphous phase is adopted [one of us has already pointed out that certain features of the decay of unsaturated groups in polyethylene may be explained by assuming such a transfer (*25*)], then the chances that crosslinking will occur near the ends of the chains must be appreciably greater than statistical, though presumably still small. In these circumstances, the crosslink process would slightly resemble a chain extension process, and one would expect a somewhat higher elastic modulus with increased elongation at rupture and increased sol plus square root of sol values at a given dose. It follows from this postulate that high density polyethylenes which do not contain appreciable amounts of vinyl unsaturation should also show differences in network behavior when compared with low density polyethylenes. Work at this laboratory (*24*) has shown that high density resins in general do show increased modulus and elongation at rupture at a given dose when compared with low density polyethylenes, the differences, however, being more marked in the case of resins containing terminal unsaturation.

### Acknowledgment

The authors express their thanks to the Raychem Corp. for permission to publish.

### Literature Cited

(1) Althouse, V. E., Am. Chem. Soc., Division of Polymer Chemistry, Preprints, Vol. II 4(1), 256 (1963).
(2) Atwood, F. C., U.S. Patent **2,400,477** (May 21, 1946).
(3) Brown, H. P., *Rubber Chem. Technol.* **36**, 931 (1963).
(4) Case, L. C., *Macromol. Chem.* **31**, 243 (1960).
(5) *Ibid.*, **39**, 119 (1960).
(6) Chapiro, A., "Radiation Chemistry of Polymeric Systems," p. 417, Interscience, New York, 1962.
(7) *Ibid.*, p. 432.
(8) Charlesby, A., *Radiation Res.* **2**(1), 96 (1955).

(9)  Charlesby, A., Von Arnim, E., Callaghan, L., *Intern. J. Appl. Radiation Isotopes* **3**, 226 (1958).
(10) Charlesby, A., Libby, D., Ormerod, M. G., *Proc. Roy. Soc. (London)* **A262**, 207 (1961).
(11) DiGuillio, E., Bellini, G., Giandanoto, G. V., *Chim. Ind.* **47**, 156 (1965); *Rubber Chem. Technol.* **39**, 726 (1966) (English trans.).
(12) Dogadkin, B. A., Tarasova, Z. N., Petrova, S. B., *Kolloid Zhur.* **22**, 253 (1960); *C. A.* **54**, 25944b (1960).
(13) Dogadkin, B. A., Tarasova, Z. N., Petrova, S. B., *J. Polymer Sci.* **61**, 235 (1962).
(14) Dole, M., "Crystalline Olefin Polymers," Part I, Chap. 16. R. A. V. Raff and K. W. Doak, eds., Interscience, New York, 1965.
(15) Dole, M., Milner, D. C., Williams, T. F., *J. Am. Chem. Soc.* **80**, 1580 (1958).
(16) Dole, M., Williams, T. F., *J. Am. Chem. Soc.* **81**, 2919 (1959).
(17) Du Pont de Nemours & Co., E. I., Plastics Research Division, private communication.
(18) Epstein, L. M., *J. Polymer Sci.* **26**, 399 (1957).
(19) Flory, P., "Principles of Polymer Chemistry," p. 487, Cornell University Press, Ithaca, N. Y., 1953.
(20) Fox, T. G., Gratch, S., Loshaek, S., "Rheology," F. R. Eirich, ed., Vol. I, pp. 444, 490-491, Academic Press, New York, 1956.
(21) Hampton, R. R., *Anal. Chem.* **21**, 923 (1949).
(22) Lawton, E. J., Balwit, J. S., Powell, R. S., *J. Polymer Sci.* **32**, 257 (1958).
(23) Lyons, B. J., *J. Polymer Sci.* **A3**, 777 (1965).
(24) Lyons, B. J., unpublished data.
(25) Lyons, B. J., Crook, M., *Trans. Faraday Soc.* **59**, 2334 (1963).
(26) Rees, R. W., Vaughn, D. F., Am. Chem. Soc., Division of Polymer Chemistry, Preprints, **6**(1), 296 (1965).
(27) Schumacher, K., *Kolloid-Z.* **157**, 161 (1958).
(28) Tobalsky, A. V., McLoughlin, J. R., *J. Polymer Sci.* **8**, 543 (1952).
(29) Vermes, R. N., Brenner, W., Maniscalo, P., *Plastics Technol.* **2**(7), 43 (1965).
(30) Waddington, F. B., *J. Polymer Sci.* **31**, 221 (1958).

RECEIVED May 4, 1966.

# 11

# Radiation Crosslinking of Some New Ethylene Copolymers

RUDOLPH VERMES

Central Research Laboratory, Allied Chemical Corp., Morristown, N. J.

WALTER BRENNER

Research Division, New York University, Bronx, N. Y.

*Electron beam–initiated crosslinking at ambient temperatures in the presence of air is a convenient way to upgrade the thermal stability of new polymeric materials and improve their physical and chemical properties. Response of irradiation-crosslinked ionomers, ethylene–vinyl acetate and ethylene-butadiene copolymers, to ionizing radiation dosages is different from that of low density polyethylene. In general, mechanical properties reach a maximum at a given total ionizing radiation dosage and begin to decline upon further exposure. Thermal stability and chemical resistance improve significantly after exposure to dosages on the order of 5 to 10 megarads or more.*

The commercial availability of an increasingly large variety of ethylene copolymers has stimulated interest in developing processing technology to broaden their possible industrial market applications. In the work reported here the electron beam–initiated irradiation crosslinking of the following ethylene copolymers was experimentally investigated in terms of resulting mechanical strength properties, thermal stability, chemical resistance, etc.: duPont ethylene methacrylic acid ionomer resins (Table I); ethylene–vinyl acetate copolymers (U.S. Industrial Chemical Co. NE 630X-1; U.C.C. DQD 1868); ethylene–ethyl acrylate copolymer (U.C.C. DQDB 6169), and ethylene–butadiene copolymer (Phillips Chemical Co.).

156

Table I.    duPont Ethylene–Methacrylic Acid Ionomer Resins

| Sample Designation | Wt. % Methacrylic Acid | Neutralizing Ion | Percent Neutralized | Approx. Melt Index | Antioxidant[a] Used |
|---|---|---|---|---|---|
| 2 | 10.0 | Zinc | Partial | 1.8 | No |
| 2A | 10.0 | Zinc | Partial | 1.8 | Yes |
| 3 | 12.0 | Zinc | Partial | 1.7 | No |
| 3A | 12.0 | Zinc | Partial | 1.7 | Yes |
| 4 | 15.0 | Zinc | Partial | 2.2 | No |
| 4A | 15.0 | Zinc | Partial | 3.4 | Yes |
| 5 | 10.0 | Sodium | Partial | 1.0 | No |

[a] Antioxidant Agerite resin D, 1000 p.p.m.

## Experimental

Samples for irradiation crosslinking were prepared by milling in the antioxidant, followed by compression molding. Sample dimensions were $6 \times 7 \times 0.083$ inch. Details of the milling and compression molding procedures are given in Table II.

The compression-molded test samples were exposed to various dosages and dosage rates of electron-beam irradiation in air at ambient temperatures. Sample sheets of the copolymers were mounted on wire racks and passed across the electron beam source by a conveyor system. A 1.5-m.e.v. Dynamitron (Radiation Dynamics, Inc., Westbury, L. I., N. Y.) electron-beam accelerator was used to supply the ionizing radiation. Sample residence time under the beam was of the order of 1.5 seconds per pass. The samples were exposed at dosage rates of 1.0 and 2.6 megarads per second to total dosages ranging from 3 to 54 megarads. The irradiation conditions to which the various duPont ionomer samples were exposed are shown in Table III.

The following polymer characteristics were obtained on the variously irradiated test specimens: melt index (ASTM 1238-62T), Vicat softening temperature (modified ASTM 1525-58T); heat distortion (ASTM D 1220-63T); physical strength; yield strength; ultimate tensile strength; percent elongation at break (ASTM D 412-64T); chemical resistance to boiling toluene.

For the sake of brevity detailed tables of all tests performed are shown for duPont ionomer resins only (Tables II, III, IV, VI to X). The other ethylene copolymers were similarly treated and evaluated. The effects of increasing radiation dosages on certain physical properties of selected duPont ionomers are shown graphically in Figures 1, 2, and 3.

## Discussion

**duPont Ethylene–Methacrylic Acid Ionomer Resins.** Possibly the most useful advantage of irradiation-crosslinked ionomer resins is their improvement in thermal stability. The melt index of suitably irradiated

**Table II.   Milling and Compression Molding Procedures
for duPont Ionomer Samples**

Milling (Samples 2, 2A, 3, and 3A only)
    Mill type. 6-inch D × 13-inch Farrell
    Roll surface temperature. 140°C.
    Charge. 450 grams
    Total time. 7 minutes
    Antioxidant. Sprinkled on resin as soon as resin became molten

Compression molding (all standard samples)
    Press type. Pasadena Hydraulics, Inc., Model P-210
    Mold cavity. 6 × 7 × 0.083 inch
    Press temperature. 180°C.
    Timing
        1.   Touch pressure for 5 minutes
        2.   Force up to 40,000 pounds in 1 minute
        3.   Force of 40,000 pounds for 2 minutes, then cooling water on
        platens

**Table III.   Irradiation Conditions for duPont Ionomer Samples**
(Sample Designation Vs. Radiation Dosage Conditions)

| Sample Designation | Radiation Rate, Mrads/sec. | Total Radiation Dosage, Mrads |
|---|---|---|
| 2HD-1, 2AHD-1, 3HD-1, 3AHD-1 | 2.6 | 4 |
| 2-2, 2A-2,3-2, 3A-2, 4-2, 4A-2, 5-2 | 1.0 | 3 |
| 2-5, 2A-5, 3-5, 3A-5, 4-5, 4A-5, 5-5 | 1.0 | 7.5 |
| 2-10, 2A-10, 3-10, 3A-10, 4-10, 4A-10, 5-10 | 1.0 | 15 |
| 2-13, 2A-13, 3-13, 3A-13 | 1.0 | 19.5 |
| 2-15, 2A-15, 3-15, 3A-15 | 1.0 | 22.5 |
| 2-18, 2A-18, 3-18, 3A-18 | 1.0 | 27 |
| 2-20, 2A-20, 3-20, 3A-20 | 1.0 | 30 |
| 2-25, 2A-25, 3-25, 3A-25 | 1.0 | 37.5 |
| 2-29, 2A-29, 3-29, 3A-29 | 1.0 | 43.5 |
| 2-33, 2A-33, 3-33, 3A-33 | 1.0 | 49.5 |
| 2-36, 2A-36, 3-36, 3A-36 | 1.0 | 54 |

samples decreases drastically even after exposures to dosages of only 3 to 4 megarads. The Vicat softening temperatures also increase with exposure to larger irradiation dosages. The 121°C. heat distortion test data are in general accord with the melt index and Vicat softening temperature test results. The dosages necessary to obtain a degree of thermal stability which may be proposed as suitable for extending the service temperature of ionomer resins to above 100°C. depend on both the acid content and the dose rate, with crosslinking appearing to be more effective at both higher acid contents and greater dose rates. The heat distortion data suggest that antioxidant may inhibit the efficacy of irradiation crosslinking.

### Table IV.   Melt Index *vs.* Irradiation Dosage for duPont Ionomer Samples

| Sample Designation | Radiation Rate, Mrads/sec. | Total Radiation Dosage, Mrads | Melt Index, Decigrams/Min. |
|---|---|---|---|
| 2 Control | — | 0 | 0.6 |
| 2 HD-1 | 2.6 | 4 | No flow |
| 2-2 | 1.0 | 3 | No flow |
| 2A Control | — | 0 | 1.2 |
| 2AHD-1 | 2.6 | 4 | No flow |
| 2A-2 | 1.0 | 3 | No flow |
| 3 Control | — | 0 | 0.9 |
| 3 HD-1 | 2.6 | 4 | No flow |
| 3-2 | 1.0 | 3 | No flow |
| 3A Control | — | 0 | 1.2 |
| 3AHD-1 | 2.6 | 4 | No flow |
| 3A-2 | 1.0 | 3 | No flow |
| 4 Control | — | 0 | 2.2 |
| 4-2 | 1.0 | 3 | No flow |
| 4A Control | — | 0 | 3.4 |
| 4A-2 | 1.0 | 3 | No flow |
| 5 Control | — | 0 | 1.0 |
| 5-2 | 1.0 | 3 | No flow |

### Table V.   Vicat Softening Temperatures for duPont Ionomer Samples
(Modified ASTM D 1525-58T)

| Procedure | ASTM D 1525-58T | Du Pont |
|---|---|---|
| Specimen | | |
| Thickness, mils | 125 + 40 or –10 | 75 ± 10 |
| Min. diam., in. | — | 0.5 |
| Min. width, in. | 0.75 | — |
| Needle | | |
| Area, sq. mm. | 1 ± 0.015 circ. or square | 1 ± 0.015 circ. |
| Load, kg. | 1 | 1 |
| Penetration, mm. | 1 | 1 |
| Bath | | |
| Fluid | — | DC-550 Silicone fluid |
| Temp. rise, °C./hr. | 50 ± 1 | 50 ± 10 |

Results—Average of 2

| Sample Designation | Total Radiation Dosage, Mrads | Vicat, °C. | Sample Designation | Total Radiation Dosage, Mrads | Vicat, °C. |
|---|---|---|---|---|---|
| 2 Control | — | 75 | 2A | — | 76 |
| 2HD-1 | 4 | 78 | 2AHD-1 | 4 | 75 |
| 2-2 | 3 | 80 | 2A-2 | 3 | 74 |
| 2-5 | 7.5 | 79 | 2A-5 | 7.5 | 80 |
| 2-10 | 15.0 | 79 | 2A-10 | 15 | 79 |

**Table V.  Continued**

| Sample Designation | Total Radiation Dosage, Mrads | Vicat, °C. | Sample Designation | Total Radiation Dosage, Mrads | Vicat, °C. |
|---|---|---|---|---|---|
| 2-13 | 19.5 | 79 | 2A-13 | 19.5 | 82 |
| 2-15 | 22.5 | 79 | 2A-15 | 22.5 | 81 |
| 2-18 | 27.0 | 81 | 2A-18 | 17.0 | 79 |
| 2-20 | 30.0 | 79 | 2A-20 | 30.0 | 82 |
| 2-25 | 37.5 | 79 | 2A-25 | 37.5 | 82 |
| 2-29 | 43.5 | 80 | 2A-29 | 43.5 | 84 |
| 2-23 | 49.5 | 81 | 2A-33 | 49.5 | 82 |
| 2-36 | 54.0 | 83 | 2A-36 | 54.0 | 84 |
| 3 Control | — | 80 | 3A Control | — | 82 |
| 3HD-1 | 4 | 79 | 3AHD-1 | 4 | 84 |
| 3-2 | 3 | 80 | 3A-2 | 3 | 83 |
| 3-5 | 7.5 | 81 | 3A-5 | 7.5 | 81 |
| 3-10 | 15.0 | 83 | 3A-10 | 15.0 | 82 |
| 3-13 | 19.5 | 82 | 3A-13 | 19.5 | 84 |
| 3-15 | 22.5 | 82 | 3A-15 | 22.5 | 84 |
| 3-18 | 27.0 | 87 | 3A-18 | 27.0 | 85 |
| 3-20 | 30.0 | 85 | 3A-20 | 30.0 | 83 |
| 3-25 | 37.5 | 85 | 3A-25 | 37.5 | 85 |
| 3-29 | 43.5 | 86 | 3A-29 | 43.5 | 86 |
| 3-33 | 49.5 | 85 | 3A-33 | 49.5 | 88 |
| 3-36 | 54.0 | 87 | 3A-36 | 54.0 | 87 |
| 4 Control | — | 78 | 4A Control | — | 79 |
| 4-2 | 3.0 | 80 | 4A-2 | 3.0 | 80 |
| 4-5 | 7.5 | 81 | 4A-5 | 7.5 | 79 |
| 4-10 | 15.0 | 81 | 4A-10 | 15.0 | 81 |
| 5 Control | — | 78 | | | |
| 5-2 | 3.0 | 81 | | | |
| 5-5 | 3.0 | 81 | | | |
| 5-10 | 15.0 | 81 | | | |

Irradiation of ionomers leads to a rather moderate increase in physical properties (average ultimate tensile strength) at fairly low dosages comparable with that found for low density polyethylene (Tables VIII and IX). Similarly, the percent elongation decreases with increasing dosage, as expected. At high dosages the ultimate tensile strength is equal to or below that of the starting material. These data suggest that irradiating ionomers to moderate levels can lead to increase in creep resistance and other associated physical properties. Experimental verification is needed.

Preliminary results indicate a marked increase in chemical resistance, such as shown by boiling samples subjected to even moderate levels of irradiation in toluene. Other chemical tests (alkali and acid resistance are currently being conducted) emphasize the improved chemical resistance to many organic and selected inorganic substances.

Certain ionomer samples (75 mils thick) containing both zinc and sodium metal ions exhibited the so-called Lichtenberg discharge effect. This phenomenon involves the buildup of charges in the polymer during irradiation and its subsequent internal discharge, giving rise to a "tree" pattern within the plastic. The zinc-containing samples showed a greater number of these patterns than the sodium samples, suggesting qualitatively at least the importance of the size and valence charge of the metal ion incorporated in the polymer. Theoretical calculations are currently being done to ascertain the effects of different metal ions on the path of the electrons which enter these specimens.

**Ethylene–Vinyl Acetate.** Two ethylene–vinyl acetate copolymers were evaluated (U.S. Industrial Chemicals NE 630X-1 and U.C.C. DQD 1868). Similar behavior was shown by both samples—*i.e.*, upon exposure to increasing dosages the tensile strength showed a maximum between 10 and 20 megarads with little effect upon elongation. Heat and chemical resistance appeared to be below that of irradiated polyethylene.

**Table VI.    Heat Distortion at 121°C. for duPont Ionomer Samples**

| Sample Designation | Heat Distortion, % (Av. of 2) | Sample Designation | Heat Distortion, % (Av. of 2) |
|---|---|---|---|
| 2 Control | 80 | 4 Control | 89 |
| 2HD-1 | 28 | 4-2 | 42 |
| 2-2 | 44 | 4-5 | 16 |
| 2-5 | 16 | 4-10 | 6 |
| 2-10 | 11 | | |
| | | 4A Control | 93 |
| 2A Control | 100 | 4A-2 | 65 |
| 2AHD-1 | 41 | 4A-5 | 14 |
| 2A-2 | 58 | 4A-10 | 5 |
| 2A-5 | 15 | | |
| 2A-10 | 8 | 5 Control | 95 |
| | | 5-2 | 53 |
| 3 Control | 78 | 5-5 | 20 |
| 3HD-1 | 12 | 5-10 | 18 |
| 3-2 | 25 | | |
| 3-5 | 9 | | |
| 3-10 | 9 | | |
| 3A Control | 94 | | |
| 3AHD-1 | 19 | | |
| 3A-2 | 34 | | |
| 3A-5 | 6 | | |
| 3A-10 | 4 | | |

Table VII.   Average Yield Strength *vs.* Irradiation Dosage
for duPont Ionomer Samples

| Sample Designation | Testing Rate, in./min. | Av. Yield Strength, p.s.i.g. | Sample Designation | Testing Rate, in./min. | Av. Yield Strength, p.s.i.g. |
|---|---|---|---|---|---|
| 2 Control | 20 | 1928 | 2A Control | 20 | 1929 |
| 2HD-1 | 2 | 1915 | 2AHD-1 | 20 | 2075 |
|  |  |  |  | 2 | 1776 |
| 2-2 | 2 | 1892 | 2A-2 | 20 | 2166 |
| 2-5 | 2 | 1967 | 2A-5 | 20 | 2140 |
| 2-10 | 2 | 1979 | 2A-10 | 20 | 2086 |
| 2-13 | 2 | 1993 | 2A-13 | 20 | 2058 |
| 2-15 | 2 | 2006 | 2A-15 | 20 | 2048 |
| 2-18 | 2 | 1989 | 2A-18 | 20 | 2095 |
| 2-20 | 2 | 1988 | 2A-20 | 20 | 2068 |
| 2-25 | 2 | 1946 | 2A-25 | 20 | 2049 |
| 2-29 | 2 | 2002 | 2A-29 | 20 | 1999 |
| 2-33 | 2 | 1989 | 2A-33 | 20 | 2016 |
| 2-36 | 2 | 1922 | 2A-36 | 20 | 2016 |
| 3 Control | 20 | 1776 | 3A Control | 20 | 1758 |
| 3HD-1 | 20 | 2066 | 3AHD-1 | 20 | 1846 |
| 3-2 | 20 | 1915 | 3A-2 | 20 | 1927 |
| 3-5 | 20 | 2017 | 3A-5 | 20 | 1904 |
| 3-10 | 20 | 2096 | 3A-10 | 20 | 1905 |
| 3-13 | 20 | 2007 | 3A-13 | 20 | 2031 |
| 3-15 | 20 | 2011 | 3A-15 | 20 | 1941 |
| 3-18 | 20 | 1996 | 3A-18 | 20 | 1877 |
| 3-20 | 20 | 1993 | 3A-20 | 20 | 1874 |
| 3-25 | 20 | 1915 | 3A-25 | 20 | 1824 |
| 3-29 | 20 | 1874 | 3A-29 | 20 | 1835 |
| 3-33 | 20 | 1860 | 3A-33 | 20 | 1802 |
| 3-36 | 20 | 1830 | 3A-36 | 20 | 1796 |
| 4 Control | 20 | 1844 | 4A Control | 20 | 1766 |
| 4-2 | 20 | 1819 | 4A-2 | 20 | 1903 |
| 4-5 | 20 | 2008 | 4A-5 | 20 | 1943 |
| 4-10 | 20 | 2025 | 4A-10 | 20 | 1839 |
| 5 Control | 20 | 1976 |  |  |  |
| 5-2 | 20 | 1996 |  |  |  |
| 5-5 | 20 | 1989 |  |  |  |
| 5-10 | 20 | 1935 |  |  |  |

With dosages over 20 megarads decreases were indicated in both tensile strength and elongation; above 30 megarads values were only a small fraction of the original.

**Ethylene–Ethyl Acrylate.** Behavior of U.C.C. DQDB 6169 ethylene–ethyl acrylate copolymer was somewhat similar to that of ethylene–vinyl

### Table VIII.   Average Ultimate Tensile Strength *vs.* Dosage for duPont Ionomer Samples

| Sample Designation | Testing Rate, in./min. | Av. Ultimate Tensile Strength, p.s.i.g. | Sample Designation | Testing Rate, in./min. | Av. Ultimate Tensile Strength, p.s.i.g. |
|---|---|---|---|---|---|
| 2 Control | 20 | 3239 | 2A Control | 20 | 3250 |
| 2HD-1 | 2 | 4006 | 2AHD-1 | 20 | 3644 |
|  |  |  |  | 2 | 3934 |
| 2-2 | 2 | 3900 | 2A-2 | 20 | 3620 |
| 2-5 | 2 | 3956 | 2A-5 | 20 | 3576 |
| 2-10 | 2 | 3468 | 2A-10 | 20 | 3539 |
| 2-13 | 2 | 3704 | 2A-13 | 20 | 3508 |
| 2-15 | 2 | 3522 | 2A-15 | 20 | 3406 |
| 2-18 | 2 | 3634 | 2A-18 | 20 | 3437 |
| 2-20 | 2 | 3530 | 2A-20 | 20 | 3335 |
| 2-25 | 2 | 3315 | 2A-25 | 20 | 3245 |
| 2-29 | 2 | 3271 | 2A-29 | 20 | 3032 |
| 2-33 | 2 | 3227 | 2A-33 | 20 | 2924 |
| 2-36 | 2 | 3050 | 2A-36 | 20 | 2923 |
| 3 Control | 20 | 3658 | 3A Control | 20 | 3604 |
| 3HD-1 | 20 | 4108 | 3AHD-1 | 20 | 3854 |
| 3-2 | 20 | 4228 | 3A-2 | 20 | 4351 |
| 3-5 | 20 | 4274 | 3A-5 | 20 | 4269 |
| 3-10 | 20 | 4057 | 3A-10 | 20 | 4166 |
| 3-13 | 20 | 3841 | 3A-13 | 20 | 4149 |
| 3-15 | 20 | 3859 | 3A-15 | 20 | 3994 |
| 3-18 | 20 | 3779 | 3A-18 | 20 | 3823 |
| 3-20 | 20 | 3828 | 3A-20 | 20 | 3778 |
| 3-25 | 20 | 3839 | 3A-25 | 20 | 3804 |
| 3-29 | 20 | 3595 | 3A-29 | 20 | 3786 |
| 3-33 | 20 | 3549 | 3A-33 | 20 | 3488 |
| 3-36 | 20 | 3490 | 3A-36 | 20 | 3714 |
| 4 Control | 20 | 3415 | 4A Control | 20 | 3472 |
| 4-2 | 20 | 4036 | 4A-2 | 20 | 4084 |
| 4-5 | 20 | 4455 | 4A-5 | 20 | 4404 |
| 4-10 | 20 | 4400 | 4A-10 | 20 | 4452 |
| 5 Control | 20 | 3725 |  |  |  |
| 5-2 | 20 | 4610 |  |  |  |
| 5-5 | 20 | 4905 |  |  |  |
| 5-10 | 20 | 4690 |  |  |  |

Data of Lanza (1) for Low Density P E

| Sample, Mrads | Ultimate Tensile Strength, p.s.i.g. |
|---|---|
| Control | 1600 |
| 5 | 2300 |
| 10 | 2450 |
| 20 | 2450 |
| 30 | 2450 |

## Table IX.    Percent Elongation at Break *vs.* Dosage
## for duPont Ionomer Samples

| Sample Designation | Testing Rate, in./min. | % Elongation at Break | Sample Designation | Testing Rate, in./min. | % Elongation at Break |
|---|---|---|---|---|---|
| 2 Control | 20 | 425 | 2A Control | 20 | 445 |
| 2HD-1 | 2 | 375 | 2AHD-1 | 20 | 383 |
| 2-2 | 2 | 365 | | 2 | 338 |
| | | | 2A-2 | 20 | 400 |
| 2-5 | 2 | 347 | 2A-5 | 20 | 345 |
| 2-10 | 2 | 290 | 2A-10 | 20 | 295 |
| 2-13 | 2 | 295 | 2A-13 | 20 | 270 |
| 2-15 | 2 | 299 | 2A-15 | 20 | 265 |
| 2-18 | 2 | 272 | 2A-18 | 20 | 265 |
| 2-20 | 2 | 268 | 2A-20 | 20 | 253 |
| 2-25 | 2 | 230 | 2A-25 | 20 | 230 |
| 2-29 | 2 | 218 | 2A-29 | 20 | 197 |
| 2-33 | 2 | 200 | 2A-33 | 20 | 160 |
| 2-36 | 2 | 175 | 2A-36 | 20 | 161 |
| 3 Control | 20 | 562 | 3A Control | 20 | 553 |
| 3HD-1 | 20 | 490 | 3AHD-1 | 20 | 490 |
| 3-2 | 20 | 505 | 3A-2 | 20 | 540 |
| 3-5 | 20 | 452 | 3A-5 | 20 | 477 |
| 3-10 | 20 | 370 | 3A-10 | 20 | 397 |
| 3-13 | 20 | 331 | 3A-13 | 20 | 357 |
| 3-15 | 20 | 323 | 3A-15 | 20 | 340 |
| 3-18 | 20 | 303 | 3A-18 | 20 | 310 |
| 3-20 | 20 | 292 | 3A-20 | 20 | 300 |
| 3-25 | 20 | 280 | 3A-25 | 20 | 287 |
| 3-29 | 20 | 259 | 3A-29 | 20 | 275 |
| 3-33 | 20 | 232 | 3A-33 | 20 | 246 |
| 3-36 | 20 | 213 | 3A-36 | 20 | 225 |
| 4 Control | 20 | 530 | 4A Control | 20 | 533 |
| 4-2 | 20 | 440 | 4A-2 | 20 | 482 |
| 4-5 | 20 | 412 | 4A-5 | 20 | 414 |
| 4-10 | 20 | 350 | 4A-10 | 20 | 364 |
| 5 Control | 20 | 465 | | | |
| 5-2 | 20 | 450 | | | |
| 5-5 | 20 | 425 | | | |
| 5-10 | 20 | 380 | | | |

### Data of Lanza (1) for Low Density P E

| Sample, Mrads | % Elongation at Break |
|---|---|
| Control | 500 |
| 5 | 675 |
| 10 | 650 |
| 20 | 580 |
| 30 | 530 |

**Table X.   Chemical Resistance for duPont Ionomer Samples**[a]

| Sample Designation | Loss of Weight, % | Sample Designation | Loss of Weight, % |
|---|---|---|---|
| 3 Control | 51.0 | 3A Control | 51.0 |
| 3-1 | 6.7 | 3A-1 | 8.1 |
| 3-2 | 6.8 | 3A-2 | 6.4 |
| 3-5 | 4.7 | 3A-5 | 5.1 |
| | | | |
| 4 Control | 51.0 | 4A-1 | 7.8 |
| 4-1 | 7.7 | 4A-5 | 5.5 |
| 4-2 | 7.3 | 5-1 | 2.6 |
| 4-5 | 5.4 | | |

[a] 2 Hours' boiling toluene.

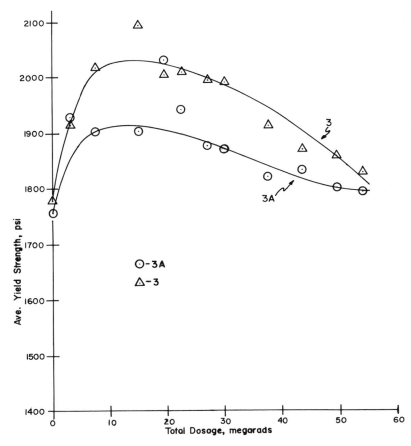

*Figure 1.   Effect of total dosage on average yield strength*

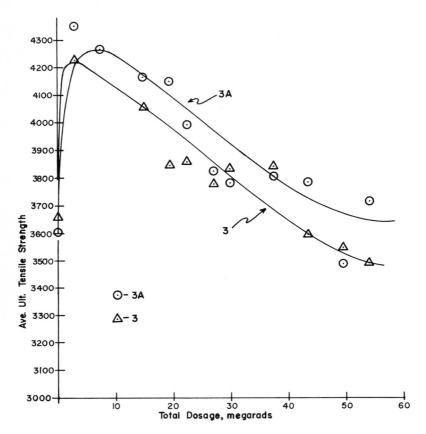

*Figure 2.   Effect of total radiation dosage on ultimate tensile strength*

acetate. A maximum tensile strength was reached at 10 to 20 megarads, with no apparent change in elongation. Thermal and chemical stability were improved, but the gain was less than that shown by crosslinked polyethylene. Above 20 megarads, significant decreases in both tensile strength and elongation were observed.

**Ethylene–Butadiene Copolymers.** Ethylene–butadiene copolymers are significantly less sensitive to ionizing radiation than any of the previously mentioned copolymers. A moderate improvement in physical strength properties is accompanied by some gains in chemical and thermal stability after exposure to dosages of about 20 to 30 megarads. Higher dosages result in marked lowering of tensile strength and increased brittleness. Thermal stability increases, however.

## Application Potential and Costs

Some consideration has been given to the possible industrial suitability of irradiation crosslinking of these new ethylene copolymers. The 1.5-m.e.v. Dynamitron accelerator used is manufactured to specifications which are based on a product rate capability equivalent to 9000 megarad-pounds per hour at 50% absorbtion efficiency operating at 1.5 m.e.v. Other pertinent equipment characteristics are: current range 1.0 to 15.0 ma.; beam scan (100 c.p.s. scan rate) 12 to 24 inches. The maximum material thickness which can be penetrated by the electron beam with this equipment is shown in Table XI for a unit density material with equal entrance and exit dosage. Since the specific gravity of these unfilled copolymers is in the 1.0 range, these data are directly applicable.

The relationship between conveyor speed with which a material can be moved under the electron beam and the obtainable radiation dosage, assuming 50% beam absorption efficiency, is shown in Table XII. These data show that a 1.0 specific gravity material could obtain a dosage of

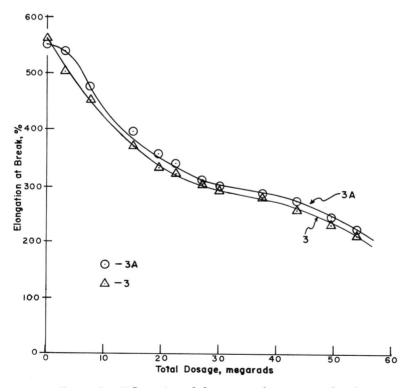

*Figure 3.   Effect of total dosage on elongation at break*

**Table XI.   Maximum Penetration in Operating Level
(for Unit Density Material)**

| M.e.v. | Mils |
|--------|------|
| 0.75 | 90 |
| 1.0 | 125 |
| 1.5 | 185 |

5 megarads while passing under the electron beam at a speed of 16 feet per minute (2-foot scan) or 8 feet per minute (4-foot scan). The figures for a 2.0-specific gravity material also receiving a 5-megarad dosage would be identical, but the maximum penetration would be half.

**Table XII.   Conveyor Speed _vs_. Dosage for a 100-C.p.s.
Scan Rate and 15-Ma. Beam Current**
(Assuming 50% Beam Utilization Efficiency)

| Absorbed Dose Density = 1 Mrads | 2-Foot Scan, Ft./Min. | 4-Foot Scan, Ft./Min. |
|--------|--------|--------|
| 1 | 80 | 40 |
| 2 | 40 | 20 |
| 5 | 16 | 8 |

Larger 3- and 4-m.e.v. Dynamitron electron beam accelerators are likewise available commercially. Service capabilities increase with the m.e.v. level of the electron beam accelerator. A 3.0-m.e.v. Dynamitron electron beam accelerator furnishes radiation capable of penetrating a maximum 370 mils of a unit density material or 185 mils of 2.0-density material; other performance capabilities are doubled as well. The overwhelming majority of polyolefin plastic products now being manufactured have section thicknesses which can be penetrated safely even by a 1.5-m.e.v. electron beam accelerator. Two possible exceptions would be printed circuit board and thick-walled pipe. A 3-m.e.v. accelerator could readily meet such requirements. The performance capabilities of the 3-m.e.v. accelerator (12-ma. power supply) are increased not only with respect to maximum depth of penetration but also processing capability, which amounts to 14,000 megarad-pounds per hour at 50% absorption efficiency.

Electron beam irradiation processing equipment is also commercially marketed by the High Voltage Engineering Co., Burlington, Mass., and the General Electric Co., Milwaukee, Wis. General Electric produces a line of resonant beam transformers for radiation processing applications. High Voltage Engineering likewise manufactures a range of particle accelerator systems, including the recently developed ICT line for industrial processing as well as scientific research and medical therapy. Detailed equipment and performance specifications can be obtained readily from both companies.

The installed price of a 1.5-m.e.v. Dynamitron electron beam accelerator is quoted at an average of $180,000, exclusive of shielding. Based upon actual recent experience, the cost of a complete radiation facility properly shielded, etc., has been estimated at around $230,000. Assuming 7-year amortization and accelerator operation for 2000 hours per year, operating costs are estimated at $34 per hour. This figure is based on amortization at $16.50 per hour, utilities including electricity and water at $1.50 per hour, an operator at $3.00 per hour with 100% overhead, maintenance $7.00 per hour, and 10% for miscellaneous expenses. For 4000 hours of operation per year, the operating cost will be of the order of $26 per hour, again assuming 7-year amortization and an operator at $3.00 per hour with 100% overhead.

Given the 1.5-m.e.v. Dynamitron electron beam accelerator operating cost of $34 per hour, 50% utilization, and a 5-megarad dosage for effecting cure, the cost of electron beam—initiated irradiation curing will be 1.89 cents per pound or 0.53 pound per cent. The total production capacity will be 1800 pounds per hour for a 5-megarad dosage. This cost of 1.89 cents per pound includes operator costs. The present cost of benzoyl peroxide paste (50% active) in large quantities is quoted at $0.95 per pound. Hence, catalyst costs for conventional curing amount to between $0.95 and $1.90 per pound, depending on the amount of catalyst employed; this does not include operator costs, heating costs, etc. Therefore, electron beam radiation curing could be essentially competitive with conventional catalysis, providing that production quantities are large enough to warrant the capital investment involved and that the product geometries are suitable for operating this process. In addition, irradiation crosslinking simplifies processing as it eliminates problems such as premature cure in the extruder, etc., common with chemical crosslinking.

Three likely candidate product lines for irradiation crosslinking of these new ethylene copolymers are pipe and tubing, packaging film and sheeting, and coatings, including wire insulation and paper coatings. Some of these products are already being commercially produced, using low density polyethylene. Extending this processing technique to these new ethylene copolymers should considerably enhance their utility for applications where the properties of irradiation-crosslinked low density polyethylene cannot meet product performance requirements.

*Literature Cited*

(1)  Lanza, V. L., *Mod. Plastics* **34** (11), 129 (1957).

RECEIVED June 15, 1966.

# 12

# Radiation–Induced Polymerization of Pure Liquid α-Methylstyrene

DONALD J. METZ

Brookhaven National Laboratory, Upton, N. Y.

*A method for preparing α-methylstyrene to investigate its radiation-induced polymerization yields samples which exhibit reproducible kinetics. The kinetic results are interpreted as indicating that free radicals, carbonium ions, and carbanions can all propagate simultaneously, the relative importance of each species depending upon the dryness of the monomer and all associated glassware. This viewpoint is further supported by data from a preliminary investigation of the transients formed in α-methylstyrene, as studied by the pulse radiolysis technique.*

S. C. Lind, the father of radiation chemistry, long advocated the view that ions produced by "ionizing" radiation were responsible for many of the processes that were observed. During the latter part of the 1940's and through most of the 1950's, nearly every study of the radiation-induced polymerization of liquid vinyl monomers was interpreted in terms of a free radical mechanism. Indeed, the kinetic behavior of those systems which remained homogeneous to reasonably high conversions exhibited classical free radical kinetics, regardless of the type and quality of radiation used. The kinetic features on which the free radical theory was based included a square-root dependence of polymerization rate on dose rate, an inverse square-root dependence of molecular weight on dose rate, an over-all temperature coefficient for the polymerization which was approximately the same as that for the photo-initiated reaction, inhibition by known free radical inhibitors, and finally, the behavior of monomer pairs in several copolymerization studies.

Although it was slightly disturbing to some investigators that ions produced either directly by interacting with the radiation or indirectly, following charge neutralization of an initially ionized molecule, appeared to be incapable of making their presence known in these and other hydro-

170

carbon systems, the reason was simple. After all, as Samuel and Magee (23) had shown by theoretical treatment, even in a medium of such high dielectric constant as water, few Compton-ejected electrons escaped their parent ions; rather, they were recaptured, followed by homolytic scission of the excited parent molecule into free radicals. The calculated lifetimes of the free ions were thus too short to allow for ionic processes. Platzman and Froehlich (20) predicted longer lifetimes, but experimental evidence, especially in liquid vinyl monomers, appeared to lend empirical proof of the shorter lifetimes of the ions.

In 1957 Davison, Pinner, and Worrall (8) published data on the radiation polymerization of isobutene, which could best be explained as an ionic process. These initial findings were further confirmed by subsequent investigations (7, 9, 26, 27). Needless to say, these disclosures prompted reinvestigation of the question of radiation-induced ionic polymerizations in other systems.

These investigations have proceeded, in general, along three separate but not necessarily unrelated paths. The rationales employed have been based on several assumptions. First, since free radical polymerization with near-zero activation energy for the initiation process should have over-all temperature coefficients of somewhere between 5 and 8 kcal. per mole (whereas ionic polymerizations generally have zero or small negative temperature coefficients) shouldn't low temperature studies reveal the existence of radiation-induced ionic polymerizations? Second, and allied with the first point, shouldn't the presence of solvents (needed in many instances to achieve low enough temperatures) of higher dielectric constant than the usual vinyl monomers enhance the possibility of favoring ionic propagation? Third, shouldn't the complete removal of impurities known to interfere strongly in conventional polymerizations—e.g., water—further promote the lifetime of any ions that might be formed? Fourth, might not the presence of (heterogeneously) distributed electron traps—e.g., various metal oxides—increase the lifetimes of any carbonium ions, once they were formed?

Thus the search began along the following three lines: (1) irradiation of common monomers, such as styrene (5, 14, 19) at low temperature in chlorinated solvents; (2) irradiation of common monomers in the presence of added solids (6); (3) irradiation of monomers that, like isobutene, do not normally polymerize by a free radical mechanism under conditions of high purity, including exhaustive drying. (2, 3, 10).

We became interested in this general area in 1959, prompted by the initial findings of Davison *et al.* (8, 9). From its inception, the study initiated in our laboratory was a twofold approach. In addition to adopting the approach characterized by Davison (8), using α-methylstyrene as the monomer, one of us also attempted to find and develop an instrumental technique that would detect and, hopefully, give at least a relative quantitative estimate of polymerizing ions in media of low dielectric constant. The latter aim was partially achieved a few years ago, insofar as we were able to detect the presence of polymerizing carbonium ions in a conventionally initiated styrene polymerization (15). While this technique has not yet been applied successfully to a radiation-induced polymerization, it has played an important role in the experimental findings discussed below. In fact, we believe it to be a classical example of cross fertilization between two independent investigations.

We wanted to be able to correct measurements of dielectric loss (conductance) and dielectric constant of polymerizing styrene solutions for whatever contribution arose from the dead polystyrene present in the solutions. What better way to make polystyrene that was free of all catalyst fragments and polar groups than to irradiate pure, dry styrene? Using the same exhaustive drying technique that we were developing for our α-methylstyrene studies, we prepared a batch of pure, dry styrene. This was then to be irradiated under such conditions that approximately 15% conversion to polymer would occur.

At the time this irradiation was to occur (1960) it was well-known that bulk styrene (dielectric constant ∼2.4), at room temperature (∼20°C.) and a dose rate of approximately $2 \times 10^5$ rads per hour, would polymerize at a rate of approximately 2 to 2.5% per Mrad. Thus, a 70-hour irradiation under the above conditions was considered adequate.

At the end of the irradiation, however, rather than having a slightly viscous solution of polystyrene in unreacted styrene monomer, we had a solid block of polystyrene!

What had happened to this sample to yield such unexpected results? The purity of the starting monomer, other than its water content, was probably no better or worse than that used in previous studies. The final degassing of the monomer had been conventional. Only one difference had been introduced in the preparative scheme—the monomer had been dried over baked silica gel, and the glassware of the vacuum apparatus had been flame-dried under vacuum. In other words, the irradiated styrene had been exhaustively dried.

An obvious question then arose: is this a phenomenon common to all vinyl monomers? In other words: is this exclusion of water sufficient to promote radiation-induced ionic polymerizations even in media of very low dielectric constant and at room temperature? We believe that the answer to both forms of the question is yes, although it may be difficult to achieve the proper conditions in some systems.

The greatest obstacle to be overcome in this area is the extreme sensitivity of the system to trace impurities and the concurrent irreproducibility in the experimental data. Most of the previous studies of styrene (*12, 16, 21, 24, 25*) and α-methylstyrene (*2, 3, 10*) have been plagued with irreproducibility.

We believe that we have developed a technique of sample preparation which practically eliminates this problem. Below is a description of our technique and some of the data which we have obtained on α-methylstyrene. Our results on styrene have appeared elsewhere (*21, 22*) and are mentioned here only by way of comparison.

## Experimental

**Purification.** α-Methylstyrene was purified by distillation through a 6-foot, Heli-grid-packed, modified Podbielniak column under a reduced pressure of dry helium. Purity of the distillate was established by vapor phase chromatographic analysis, using flame ionization detection and an appropriate column. Sample purity generally ranged from 99.90 to 99.98%.

A sample of approximately 15 to 20 ml. of monomer was collected in an ampoule (*A*, Figures 1 and 2), attached to the product take-off assembly of the still. There are no stopcocks between the column and vessel *A*, and hence no possibility of contamination with any stopcock lubricant. When sample collection is completed, the ampoule is isolated from the distillation apparatus by freezing a monomer-filled U-tube located between the distillation head and the collection vessel. The contents of the ampoule are then frozen, and vessel *A* is removed from the still by flame-sealing at point 1. The monomer in vessel *A* is kept frozen until the degassing step is reached.

Here it is necessary to describe in some detail two procedures: Procedure I and Procedure II. Procedure II is a modification of Procedure I, initiated to eliminate some of its shortcomings.

**Sample Preparation.** PROCEDURE I. Referring to Figure 1, vessel *A*, with its frozen monomer, is sealed onto the high vacuum manifold through the side arm containing breakseal 2. Vessel *B*, containing silica gel, and vessel *C*, a dilatometer, are enclosed in an electrically heated oven, indicated by the broken lines, and are heated to the desired temperature (500°C.) during the baking-out process. The remainder of the manifold and glass tubing are wrapped in heater tape. The bake-out is achieved by heating to the desired temperature for 36 to 48 hours. At the end of the bake-out period, the system is at a pressure of $10^{-8}$ to $10^{-7}$ torr.

After bake-out, the glassware is allowed to cool to room temperature. Breakseal 2 is broken, and monomer in *A* is degassed by successive freeze-pump-thaw cycles. The thoroughly degassed monomer is then distilled onto the silica gel in *B* by surrounding that vessel with an ice-water bath. When sufficient monomer has been transferred, the contents of *A* and *B* are frozen, and *A* is removed from the manifold by flame sealing.

Monomer is allowed to equilibrate with the silica gel in *B* at room temperature, after which it is distilled into *C* by surrounding that vessel

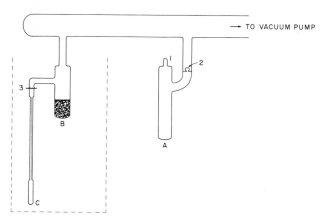

*Figure 1. Schematic arrangement of glass apparatus in Procedure 1*

with an ice-water bath. When sufficient monomer has been transferred to *C*, the monomer in both *B* and *C* is frozen by surrounding them with methanol–dry ice baths. Vessel *C* is then removed from the manifold by sealing at point 3. Samples thus prepared are used as soon as possible; if storage is necessary, they are kept at dry ice temperature until they are ready for irradiation.

PROCEDURE II. Referring to Figure 2, one sees that *A* is connected directly to the high vacuum manifold as before, but in addition, it is connected with the remainder of the vessels by a parallel "manifold" in which there is incorporated a second breakseal, 5. This arrangement allows us to isolate bake-out vessels *B*, *C*, and *D* completely from vessel *A* during the degassing operation.

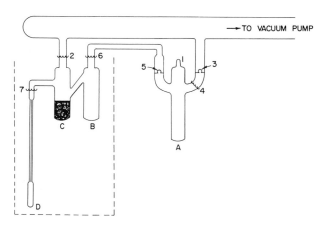

*Figure 2. Schematic arrangement of glass apparatus in Procedure II*

Thus, after attaching *A* to the apparatus as shown in Figure 2, bake-out is accomplished as before. When vessels *B*, *C*, and *D* cool to room temperature, they are isolated from the main manifold and *A* by flame-sealing at point 2. The monomer in *A* is then degassed, through breakseal 3, as before. After degassing is completed, monomer in *A* is frozen, and this vessel is removed from the main manifold at point 4.

Breakseal 5 is then broken, and monomer is distilled into *B*, which is at this point surrounded by an ice-water bath. When sufficient monomer has been transferred, *A* and *B* are placed in ice-methanol baths, and *A* is removed at point 6. The silica gel in *C* is poured into *B*.

After equilibration, some monomer is distilled directly into *D*, surrounded with an ice-water bath. At this point, both *C* and *D* are surrounded by methanol–dry ice baths, and *D* is removed by sealing at point 7.

**Irradiations and Dosimetry.** Dilatometers are irradiated in one of several dry cobalt-60 γ-ray facilities, which are viewed through periscopes. Temperature control is maintained by using either appropriate freezing mixtures or externally controlled constant temperature baths, from which the fluid is circulated into and out of the bath in the irradiation cell.

Dosimetry was based either directly on the Fricke Dosimeter (*1*) (using $G_{Fe^{3+}} = 15.5$) or on an *n*-on-*p* solar cell (*18*) that was frequently calibrated against the Fricke dosimeter.

**Rate of Polymerization.** The polymerization rate was assumed to be a linear function of the rate of contraction of the sample. Over the conversion range in which the experiments were performed (<15%) this was experimentally verified as a reasonable assumption by occasionally comparing the calculated total conversion with that determined gravimetrically. The two never varied by more than 5%.

To minimize the heat transfer problem occasioned by the high rates of polymerization encountered, the dilatometers were constructed with a surface-to-volume ratio (in the bulb) of approximately 6 to 1. This was achieved by constructing thin, long rectangular "paddle-like" bulbs, 8.5 cm. long by 2.5 cm. wide by 0.5 cm. thick. This design also assures uniformity of radiation dose rate from front to rear of the sample.

**Pulse Radiolysis.** Two samples were prepared to investigate transients by pulse radiolysis. The dilatometer was replaced by a cylinder (4 cm. long and 2 cm. in diameter) of Supracil, and filled. One sample was filled according to Procedure II, as outlined above; the other was prepared without any drying other than that accomplished by distillation through the fractionating column. The former sample is designated as the dry sample, the latter, as the wet sample.

Each pulse was of 1-microsecond duration and amounted to 160 ma. of electrons delivered by a 15-m.e.v. Linac. The analyzing light source was a 600-watt, high pressure xenon lamp. A single reflection of the analyzing light afforded a total optical path length within the sample of 8 cm. A series of monochromators was used to isolate a given wavelength, the transmitted light was detected and amplified by appropriate phototubes and associated electronics, and the final trace was displayed on an oscilloscope. This display was photographed, and the data were obtained by analyzing the transmitted light *vs.* time curves, at each wavelength investigated.

### Results

Earlier work, using individual ampoules of styrene and $\alpha$-methylstyrene (*12, 16*), had indicated a high degree of irreproducibility in the observed total conversion of monomer to polymer. For this reason we used dilatometers. By using a dilatometer of proper design and size, it is possible to study, with a given, inherently reproducible single sample, the dose rate dependence of the reaction.

Figure 3 shows typical experimental curves for a dilatometric sample of $\alpha$-methylstyrene at different dose rates (at 0°C.), in which the height

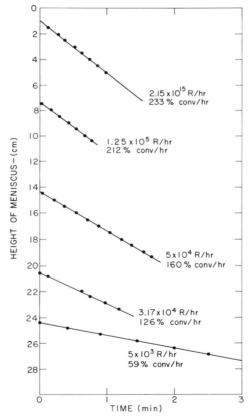

*Figure 3.    Typical height* vs. *time behavior*
*for dilatometer of $\alpha$-methylstyrene at 0°C.*
*and several dose rates*

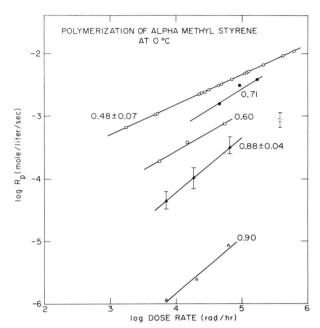

*Figure 4.    Rate of polymerization of α-methylstyrene at*
*0°C. as a function of dose rate, under various conditions*
*of sample preparation*

○    *Procedure II, 5 independent samples*
●    *Procedure I, single sample*
□    *Procedure I, single sample*
▲    *Procedure I, 5 independent samples*
△    *Procedure I, single sample (suspected leak)*
◌    *Ref. 3*

of the meniscus of the monomer in the dilatometer stem is plotted against time. There appears to be an induction period. After a short time (short compared with the duration of a given experiment), thermal equilibrium is reached, and the rate of meniscus fall becomes constant with time.

Data on the dose-rate dependence of the polymerization rate of α-methylstyrene at 0°C. are presented in Figure 4. The lowest curve represents data on a single dilatometer in which there was a suspected leak. The next higher curve represents data obtained on five separate dilatometers, each prepared according to Procedure I. Each of the dilatometers was irradiated at the same three dose rates, and the vertical bars through the data points give an approximate estimate of the degree of reproducibility from one dilatometer to another. The line itself is the least-squares line through the experimental points, and it has a slope of 0.88 ± 0.04. Extrapolating this line to higher dose rates, it passes very close to the point quoted by Williams (3) for the same monomer.

The two intermediate curves each represent a single dilatometer, each prepared according to Procedure I and irradiated at three dose rates. The slopes of these lines are 0.60 and 0.71, and the absolute values of the rates of polymerization are markedly higher than for the previous samples. Within experimental error, the slopes of these two lines are essentially the same and are less than the value given for the previously quoted, lower rates of polymerization.

The uppermost line is a least-square line drawn through the experimental data obtained on five separate dilatometer samples, each prepared by Procedure II and irradiated at three dose rates at least. The slope of this line is $0.48 \pm 0.07$, and again represents polymerization rates that are higher than any of the other values reported here or elsewhere (3, 16).

The spectrum obtained for the transients produced in $\alpha$-methylstyrene, between the wavelengths 315 to 480 m$\mu$, is shown in Figure 5. The arrows indicate the two maxima previously reported by Hirota (13) for this monomer. The lower end of the spectrum has been corrected for light scattered within the monochromator. Each point on these spectra represents the maximum absorption (all species) at zero time. There appears to be little difference in the spectra of the dry and the wet monomer.

Also included in this figure are several points that were obtained after opening the dry sample to the atmosphere and also after adding

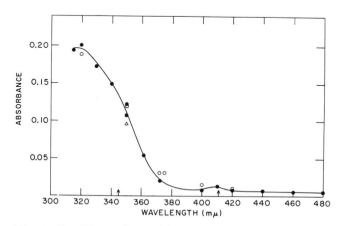

*Figure 5.    Ultraviolet-visible spectrum of transients observed in $\alpha$-methylstyrene after a 1-microsecond pulse of 160 ma. of 15-m.e.v. electrons*

    ○   *Dry sample (Procedure II)*
    ●   *Wet sample*
    △   *Dry sample opened to atmosphere*

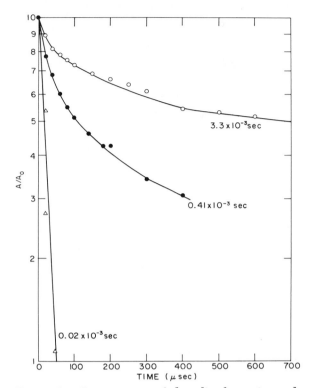

*Figure 6.   Decay curves of short-lived transients ob-
served in  α-methylstyrene  under  various  conditions*

    ○   *Dry sample (Procedure II)*
    ●   *Wet sample*
    △   *Dry sample opened to atmosphere*

sufficient water to ensure saturation of the monomer. In the first case, both oxygen and water have been introduced into the sample. The major effect appears to be a lowering of the absorbance, and hence the initial concentration of absorbing species, at the several points investigated.

The data at 350 m$\mu$ were further analyzed, and the decay curves are presented in Figures 6 and 7. In Figure 6 the decay curves of the shortest-lived species are shown, where a sweep time of 100 $\mu$sec. per cm. was employed. For both the dry and the wet samples, the decay curves, plotted as first-order decays, exhibit complex shapes. A similar complex behavior is shown by a second-order plot of the data. Although there is no basis for choosing one plot over the other, we have chosen the former for convenience. Further investigation may show this arbi- trary choice to have been wrong. We take this to indicate that there is more than one absorbing species, and the various components have different decay constants. The numbers shown along the far end of each of these curves represent calculated "apparent" half-lives over the latter part of the decay curves.

Also shown in this figure is what appears to be a single decay curve for the case in which the monomer was saturated with both water and air.

In Figure 7 the decay of the longer lived species is presented, again assuming first-order kinetics. Here the sweep time was 100 msec. per cm. There appears to be little difference, if any, in the behavior of the dry and the wet samples. The break in these two curves, yielding what appears to be a second component, is probably real. The slope of the line joining the points for the water- and air-saturated sample is essentially the same as that of the second region of the other curves.

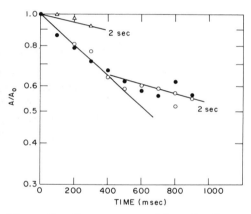

*Figure 7.   Decay curves of long-lived transients observed in α-methylstyrene under various conditions*

○   Dry sample (Procedure II)
●   Wet sample
△   Dry sample opened to atmosphere

### Discussion

The effects of minute traces of water on the kinetics of the radiation-induced polymerization of α-methylstyrene have been known and studied for some time by several workers (2, 3, 10, 16). Although these studies have shed much light on the subject, all have been handicapped by irreproducibility in the data from sample to sample. Williams (3) was the first to use dilatometers to eliminate some of the effects of irreproducibility, but even then a wide range in polymerization rates on different dilatometers was obtained. Perhaps then, one of the most significant conclusions to be drawn from the data in Figure 4 is that a method of reproducibly preparing samples has been developed.

The second important point is that the dependence of the polymerization rate on the dose rate varies from 0.90 to 0.48, going from lower to high relative rates at the same time. This behavior seems to be related to the exhaustiveness of the drying method employed.

Both Williams (3) and Hirota (13) have explained their results by postulating that the propagating species in this system, under their conditions of dryness, is either a carbonium ion or a radical anion. Based on the data in Figure 4, we believe that both species may propagate, depending on the state of dryness of the system.

In our laboratory we have observed similar behavior in the case of styrene. With styrene, a more detailed study of the effects of drying has been made, and all of the kinetic results can be readily explained by postulating the coexistence of more than one ionic process under the conditions of the most exhaustive purification and drying (21, 22), reverting to a single ionic species under the conditions of moderate dryness (22). This behavior reverts further to the "normal" free radical process when no extraordinary means of drying the monomer are employed (4, 21).

Since the sensitivity towards water in many organic reactions lies in the order carbanion > carbonium ion > free radical, it appears likely that as water is progressively removed from $\alpha$-methylstyrene—and, perhaps, other vinyl monomers—the free radical propagation is augmented or supplanted by a carbonium ion mechanism, which, in turn, is further enhanced at low water content, by a carbanion mechanism. Under the latter conditions, one would expect a termination mechanism which is bimolecular with regard to the total concentration of propagating species and hence a square-root dependence of the polymerization rate on the dose rate. This is the order dependence observed in $\alpha$-methylstyrene at the highest polymerization rates and lowest water content.

Turning to the pulse radiolysis data for further information, it is fairly obvious that any attempt to explain the radiation-induced polymerization of $\alpha$-methylstyrene on the basis of a single ionic species, be it a positive or a negative ion, is faulted by the data. Certainly several species are formed in detectable quantities. It is unfortunate that they all absorb in essentially the same region of the spectrum, but this is not unexpected (11). What it means, however, is that neither identities nor concentration can be established solely on the basis of the spectrum that one obtains. Thus, it would appear that ascribing the spectrum of $\alpha$-methylstyrene to the radical anion, as Hirota has done (13), is at best an oversimplification.

Without attempting to subject the data in Figures 6 and 7 to a more exhaustive analysis than is warranted, we feel that certain observations can be made, and several tentative conclusions can be drawn. The longer-lived species does not seem to show any great sensitivity toward sample preparation, and since the major difference between the dry and the wet sample was relative water content, we would tentatively denote this particular "millisecond" component a free radical. The appearance of a second species in the millisecond range is difficult to explain. Similar behavior has been observed in the case of styrene (17) and has been ascribed to the formation of $RO_2\cdot$. In the present case, however, only the water-saturated sample was known to contain appreciable quantities of oxygen. For this particular sample the single observed decay is suspiciously similar to that of the unknown second component in the dry and wet samples. Perhaps the latter was not as thoroughly degassed as we intended.

The several short-lived species, in the microsecond range, we believe are ions—either normal ions or radical ions. Their behavior is apparently a relatively strong function of the dryness of the system. This is evident from the marked difference in behavior of the decay curves of the dry and the wet samples in Figure 6. The drastic effect of water (in the presence of oxygen) is more dramatically shown in the behavior of the water-saturated sample.

Hirota (13) has reported that the equilibration of $\alpha$-methylstyrene with atmospheric water causes the absorption spectrum of this system practically to disappear. We find that although there is a marked decrease in the absorption spectrum under these conditions, it does not go to zero. In addition, the decay of the several transients is affected by oxygen and water in the manner discussed above.

### Conclusions

We would like to emphasize two main points. The suspected ionic polymerization of $\alpha$-methylstyrene under conditions of high purity and low water content probably cannot be explained on the basis of any one, single propagating species. Second, the sample-preparation technique described is capable of eliminating the problem of irreproducibility which has plagued all previous work with this monomer. The results we obtained using this new technique appear to indicate that both carbonium and carbanions—normal or radical—are simultaneously propagating in the system.

### Acknowledgment

The author is indebted to the Argonne National Laboratory, Chemistry Division, and especially to J. K. Thomas, who performed the pulse radiolysis experiments and whose helpful suggestions made that part of this work possible. Special thanks are due to C. L. Johnson, whose skill in designing and constructing the apparatus for sample preparation and in performing the kinetic experiments provided many of the data on which this presentation is based.

## Literature Cited

(1) A.S.T.M., "Standard Method of Test for Adsorbed Gamma Radiation Dose in the Fricke Dosimeter," D 1671–63.
(2) Bauman, C. G., Metz, D. J., *J. Polymer Sci.* 62, S141 (1962).
(3) Best, J. V. F., Bates, T. H., Williams, T. F., *Trans. Faraday Soc.* 58, 192 (1962).
(4) Chapiro, A., "Radiation Chemistry of Polymeric Systems," p. 164, Interscience, New York, 1962.
(5) Chapiro, A., Stannett, V., *J. Chim. Phys.* 56, 830 (1959).
(6) Charlesby, A., Morris, J., *J. Polymer Sci.* 4, Part C, 1127 (1963).
(7) Collinson, E., Dainton, F. S., Gillis, H. A., *J. Phys. Chem.* 63, 909 (1959).
(8) Davison, W. H. T., Pinner, S. H., Worrall, R., *Chem. Ind. (London)* 1957, 1274.
(9) Davison, W. H. T., Pinner, S. H., Worrall, R., *Proc. Roy. Soc. (London)* A252, 187 (1959).
(10) Hirota, K., Makino, K., Kuwata, K., Meshitsuka, G., *Bull. Chem. Soc. Japan* 33, 251 (1960).
(11) Jaffe, H. H., Orchin, M., "Theory and Applications of Ultraviolet Spectroscopy," pp. 462-463, Wiley, New York, 1962.
(12) Johnson, C. L., Metz, D. J., Division of Polymer Chemistry, ACS, Polymer Preprints 4, 440 (1963).
(13) Katayama, M., Hatada, M., Hirota, K., Yamazaki, H., Ozawa, Y., *Bull. Chem. Soc. Japan* 38, 851 (1965).
(14) Krongauz, V. A., Bagdassarian, K. S., *Dokl. Akad. Nauk USSR* 32, 1863 (1958).
(15) Metz, D. J., *J. Polymer Sci.* 50, 497 (1961).
(16) Metz, D. J., *Trans. Am. Nucl. Soc.* 7, 313 (1964).
(17) Metz, D. J., Thomas, J. K., Potter, R. C., IUPAC Macromolecular Chemistry Meeting, Tokyo-Kyoto, Japan. 1966.
(18) Muller, A. C., Rizzo, F. X., Glanter, L., *Nucl. Sci. Eng.* 19, 400 (1964).
(19) Okamura, S., Higashimura, T., Futami, S., *Isotopes and Radiation (Japan)* 1, 216 (1958).
(20) Platzman, R. L., Froehlich, H., *Phys. Rev.* 92, 1151 (1953).
(21) Potter, R. C., Bretton, R. H., Johnson, C. L., Metz, D. J., *J. Polymer Sci.,* in press.
(22) Potter, R. C., Bretton, R. H., Metz, D. J., *J. Polymer Sci.,* in press.
(23) Samuel, A. H., Magee, J. L., *J. Chem. Phys.* 21, 1080 (1953).
(24) Ueno, K., Hayashi, K., Okamura, S., *J. Polymer Sci.* B3, 363 (1965).
(25) Ueno, K., Hayashi, K., Okamura, S., *Polymer,* in press.
(26) Worrall, R., Charlesby, A., *Intern. J. Appl. Radn. Isotopes* 4, 84 (1958/9).
(27) Worrall, R., Pinner, S. H., *J. Polymer Sci.* 34, 229 (1959).

RECEIVED April 4, 1966. Research performed under auspices of the U.S. Atomic Energy Commission.

# 13

# Gamma-Radiation–Induced Polymerization of Some Vinyl Monomers in Emulsion Systems

GREGOR J. M. LEY, DIETER O. HUMMEL, and CHRISTEL SCHNEIDER

Institut für physikalische Chemie und Kolloidchemie, Universität Köln, Cologne, Germany

*A sensitive recording dilatometer capable of detecting a conversion as low as 0.07 mg. styrene per gram emulsion was used to study gamma-induced emulsion polymerization of 12 monomers. Relative maximum reaction rates of 11 monomers range from as low as 0.04 for methacrylonitrile to about 23 for methyl acrylate (styrene = 1.0). No simple correlation of this figure with the absolute values of $k_p$ given in the literature seems to exist. Curves of conversion rate vs. time for all systems up to high conversions are given. None shows exactly the classic form which is described and explained qualitatively by Harkins and quantitatively by the Smith-Ewart kinetics. It is concluded that all emulsion systems cannot be described in terms of this scheme.*

Numerous publications deal with the gamma-radiation–induced bulk- or solution-polymerization of vinyl monomers, but there are only a few investigations on the gamma-induced polymerization in emulsion systems. This is surprising, because as early as 1954 Ballantine (3) showed that this process under comparable conditions can be much faster and yields polymers of much higher molecular weight than the corresponding bulk or solution polymerization. Later, Okamura (9), Mezhirova *et al.* at the Karpov Institute (8), Vanderhoff *et al.* (13), Allen *et al.* (2), Acres and Dalton (1), Stannett (12), and we (7) reported on the same subject. There are also a few patents on gamma-initiated emulsion processes. Finally, Chapiro and Maeda (5) published a paper on gamma-induced suspension polymerization of styrene.

Most of the work reported was done on styrene and methyl methacrylate, but there is little information on other systems. It seemed therefore desirable to study the gamma-induced emulsion polymerization of some other monomers.

On the other hand, a number of qualified investigations on the emulsion polymerization initiated by chemical catalysts and on the experimental verification of the quantitative theory of Smith and Ewart were performed by van der Hoff (*14*) and Gerrens *et al.* (*4, 6*). The high experimental standard of these papers in determining the kinetic data is rarely met by papers on the gamma-induced emulsion polymerization.

The goal of our work was to study the gamma-radiation–induced emulsion polymerization of some less common vinyl monomers, and to obtain more reliable data by refining the experimental technique.

### Experimental

**Dilatometer.**   Reliable kinetic data on gamma-induced emulsion polymerization can be obtained only when the polymerization rate is measured continuously (*7*). The recording dilatometer used in our previous work had some disadvantages. A mercury meniscus traveled down a precision capillary, releasing a thin platinum wire within the capillary. The electrical resistance of this assembly was used as a measure for the

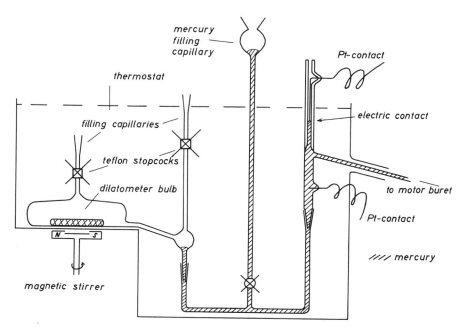

*Figure 1.   Dilatometer apparatus*

conversion of monomer into polymer. Capillary, platinum wire, and mercury had to be cleaned carefully; otherwise the migrating mercury tended to separate incompletely from the wire as well as from the walls of the capillary. We therefore changed the measuring principle as described below, and thus considerably increased the sensitivity and reliability of the apparatus.

The reaction vessel of the dilatometer (Figure 1) resembles the one used in our previous study and is based on a suggestion of Bartholomé *et al.* (*4, 6*). To guarantee a fast removal of the heat of polymerization as well as a thorough agitation of the system by the magnetic stirrer, the reaction vessel is disk-shaped and has a volume of 100 ml. The vessel is filled with the emulsion by using the inner capillary and is sealed off by two Teflon stopcocks. All other capillaries are filled with mercury. The outer capillary holds a T-shaped junction connected to a mercury-filled motor buret (Figure 2). The capillary on top of the junction narrows to an inner diameter of about 0.4 mm. and is open to the atmosphere. The mercury meniscus in this capillary is touched by a fine platinum tip, forming an electrical contact, which by means of an electronic relay, operates the reversible motor of the mercury buret. When the volume of the polymerizing emulsion contracts, the electrical circuit is interrupted; then the motor buret feeds mercury into the system until the previous position of the meniscus is re-established, and the mercury comes in contact with the platinum again. To prevent any oxidation or sticking of the mercury meniscus, two precautions were found necessary:

The amperage at the electrical contact must be kept low, and thus one should use an electronic relay.

The mercury meniscus should not stand still for any long period of time. Therefore the motor of the syringe is reversed immediately after the meniscus has reached the platinum tip. Hence, even if there is no change in volume, the motor buret is always working to and fro, thus keeping the meniscus oscillating around the contact–no contact position.

The whole dilatometer is immersed in an open bath thermostat, and the temperature is kept constant within $\pm 0.05°C$. The position of the motor buret syringe is converted into an electrical signal and scanned by a millivoltmeter installed in a neighboring laboratory (Siemens Kompensograph, maximum deflection 250 mm. with a signal of 5 mv.). When the pen reaches full deflection, the meter is compensated automatically back to zero, there resuming scanning. Thus, a considerable ordinate expansion can be achieved.

For a typical styrene experiment a polymer concentration of the dispersion of 293 mg. of polystyrene per gram of emulsion ($g_E$), and a total ordinate height of 41.68 meters was found. Consequently, a 10-mm. deflection of the meter corresponded to the conversion of:

$$\frac{2.93 \times 10^2}{4.168 \times 10^3} = 0.0702 \text{ mg. styrene per gram of emulsion.}$$

The conversion factor for absolute reaction rate, $f$, given for each reaction rate–time curve below also is defined as:

$$f = \frac{\text{moles of monomer}}{\text{kg.}_E \, \Sigma U}$$

where moles of monomer per kilogram of emulsion ($\text{kg.}_E$) is the concentration of polymerized monomer at the end of the experiment, and $\Sigma U$ is the total height of the ordinate of the original dilatometer record in arbitrary units. Therefore $f$ also is a direct measure of the sensitivity

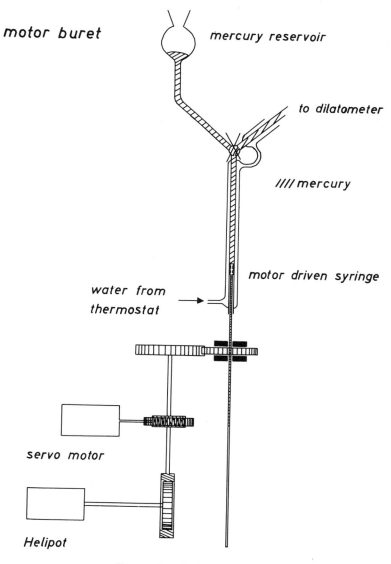

*Figure 2.   Automatic buret*

of the instrument used, and it differs from the value given above only in dimensions (moles per kilogram and milligrams per gram, respectively). The high sensitivity is normally not necessary but is sometimes very useful. One example is the quantitative determination of pre- and after-irradiation effects which will be described in our next paper.

**Chemicals.** WATER. Water was distilled three times, once in a normal still, twice in a quartz still. Before preparing the emulsion, this water was boiled 3 hours under a stream of purified argon.

MONOMERS. High grade monomers were carefully purified by chemical methods and dried. Before preparing each emulsion, the monomer was rectified by a column distillation in an argon atmosphere under reduced pressure, and then freed from traces of oxygen by a series of freeze-thaw cycles *in vacuo*. Purity of the monomers was checked by gas chromatography.

EMULSIFIER. For most of the experiments sodium dodecyl sulfate (SDS) was used as an emulsifier. A commercial product was recrystallized twice from alcohol.

ARGON. Commercial high grade argon was passed over BTS catalyst (BASF, Fluka) at 300°C. According to the literature, the oxygen content is thus reduced to a concentration of less than 0.1 p.p.m.

**Preparation of Emulsions.** Monomer, water, and emulsifier were mixed in an apparatus similar to that described by Bartholomé *et al.* (*4, 6*). However, instead of the Ultra-Turrax, a vibrating plate stirrer was used.

When preparing the emulsion, one precaution is crucial. A monomer can dissolve considerable amounts of argon or other inert gases. Since the monomer phase is disappearing during the reaction, at a certain conversion gaseous argon may be released eruptively from the emulsion. This process seems to be analogous to the known phenomenon of boiling delay, and can be identified by the sudden increase in volume, causing a sudden reversal of the dilatometer curve. Visual inspection of the dilatometer shows small gas bubbles undoubtedly produced by this process. Since experiments where gas evolution has happened cannot be evaluated quantitatively, it is necessary to avoid this phenomenon. Usually this can be done by preparing the emulsions at temperatures 30° to 40°C. higher than the polymerization temperature. The argon released by the disappearing monomer phase is then dissolved by the aqueous phase which at the lower temperature is not saturated with argon.

In each preparation two dilatometers are filled at the same time with the same emulsion and then are exposed to gamma irradiation, one immediately after the other. While the first dilatometer is being irradiated, the second is kept in a refrigerator.

A cobalt-60 source of about 40 curies was used for irradiation. The irradiation facility is of the shielded room type. Dosimetry of the highest dose rate level *(I)* was done using the Fricke dosimeter. Dose rate was adjusted by varying the distance between the source and the dilatometer or by partial shielding with lead. Relative ionization chamber measurements were used to adjust the lower dose rate levels to 0.5 and 0.25 *I*, respectively.

The reproducibility of the maximum reaction rate for styrene emulsions for parallel experiments (dilatometers filled with emulsion out of the same preparation) was within 2 to 3%, as compared with 8 to 10% for experiments with different preparations.

Handling of the dilatometer, determination of final conversion, and evaluation of the recordings of the millivoltmeter were described earlier *(1)*.

A careful purification of all substances used and rigorous exclusion of oxygen are important because at the low dose rates used even minute traces of inhibitors would cause long inhibition periods. Oxygen not only caused inhibition periods but also rendered reaction rate values irreproducible. Figure 3 shows the beginning of the original recording for a

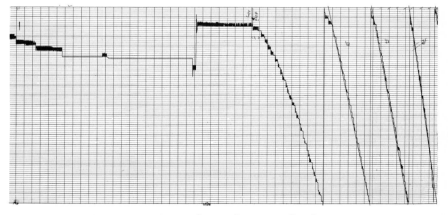

*Figure 3.   Original recording of millivoltmeter*

styrene emulsion polymerization. After constant temperature has been reached, the meter is set back, and after 7 minutes of constant reading, the source is elevated from the concrete shield. The polymerization starts immediately without an inhibition period. The noise of the record is caused by the oscillation of the mercury meniscus. The automatic setback to zero of the meter can be seen.

### Results and Discussion

**Properties and Behavior of Monomers.** Table I shows the physical data of the monomers used for our investigations. All of these monomers

Table I.   Physical

| Monomers | M.P., °C. | B.P., °C. (Torr) | |
|---|---|---|---|
| Styrene | −30.6 | 145.2 | (760) |
| Acrylonitrile | −84 | 77.3 | (760) |
| Methyl acrylate | below −75 | 80 | (760) |
| Ethyl acrylate | below −75 | 99.6 | (760) |
| Butyl acrylate | — | 35 | (8) |
| Methacrylonitrile | −35.8 | 90.3 | (760) |
| Methyl methacrylate | −48 | 101 | (760) |
| Butyl methacrylate | — | 52 | (11) |
| Decyl methacrylate | — | — | — |
| Vinylidene chloride | −122 | 31.7 | (760) |
| Chloroprene | — | 59.4 | (760) |
| Isoprene | −146.8 | 34.08 | (760) |

except isoprene could be polymerized in emulsion by low dose rates of gamma-radiation. Isoprene emulsions did not polymerize even with dose rates up to $10^5$ rads per hour.

In our experiments the monomer concentration was between about 150 and 200 grams per kg. of emulsion. Sodium dodecyl sulfate in a concentration of 5 to 15 grams per kg. of water was used as an emulsifier. The reaction temperature was generally 25°C. Only with vinylidene chloride and chloroprene a reaction temperature of 5°C. was used because of the low boiling point of these monomers. Dose rate ranged between about 500 and 2000 rads per hour but was kept constant during each experiment.

Table II shows the experimental data as well as the maximum overall reaction rates of the monomers studied. All figures are average values of at least two preparations—i.e., four dilatometric measurements. The last column gives the reaction rate relative to that of a comparable styrene emulsion under the same conditions of temperature and dose rate whose reaction rate was accepted as unity.

One can roughly distinguish three groups of monomers:

1. Monomers with relative reaction rates well below 1 (methacrylonitrile and decyl methacrylate).

2. Monomers with relative rates between 1 and 5 (acrylonitrile, vinylidene chloride, chloroprene, and short-chain methacrylates).

**Data of Monomers**

| Density, (25°C.) | Solubility | |
| --- | --- | --- |
| | % water in monomers | % monomers in water |
| 0.905 | — | 0.012 (20° C.) |
| 0.8004 | 3.4  (25° C.) | 7.4  (25° C.) |
| 0.952 | — | 5.2  (30° C.) |
| 0.919 | — | 1.82 (30° C.) |
| — | — | — |
| 0.8001 (20° C.) | 1.62 (20° C.) | 2.54 (25° C.) |
| 0.940 | — | 1.59 (20° C.) |
| — | — | — |
| — | — | — |
| 1.2129 (20° C.) | — | 0.01 (25° C.) |
| 0.9583 (20° C.) | — | — |
| 0.6805 (20° C.) | — | — |

3.  Monomers with relative rates of 10 to 23 (acrylic esters).

Methyl acrylate gave by far the highest absolute reaction rates of all monomers studied.

There seems to be no simple correlation between the absolute values of the propagation rate constants given in the literature and the relative reaction rate of the monomers.

**Reaction Rate—Time Curves.**  In papers on the emulsion polymerization of styrene generally the classic curve is shown.  The three reaction periods of this curve, according to Harkins, Smith, and Ewart (6) can be interpreted as:

1.  A period of particle formation characterized by a rapidly increasing reaction rate.

2.  A period of constant particle number and constant monomer concentration in the monomer-polymer particles, with constant reaction rate.

3.  A period of decreasing monomer concentration in a constant number of particles showing a reaction rate decreasing according to a first-order law.

The very informative semilogarithmic plot of over-all reaction rate *vs.* time was first published by Bartholomé *et al.* (4, 6).  Looking at the reaction rate–time curves given below one can see that even for the styrene system, which was shown to follow Smith-Ewart kinetics the best

Table II.

| Monomer | $T.$, °C. | Intensity, rads/hr. | Monomer Concn., moles/kg. emulsion |
|---|---|---|---|
| Methacrylonitrile | 25 | 1920 | 2.229 |
|  | 45 | 1920 | 2.229 |
| Decyl methacrylate | 25 | 1920 | 0.662 |
| Styrene | 25 | 1920 | 1.288 |
| Acrylo nitrile | 25 | 1920 | 2.890 |
| Vinylidene chloride | 5 | 1920 | 2.441 |
|  | 5 | 1920 | 2.436 |
| Methyl methacrylate | 25 | 960 | 1.449 |
| Butyl methacrylate | 25 | 960 | 1.095 |
|  | 25 | 960 | 1.0396 |
| Chloroprene | 5 | 1920 | 2.13 |
| Butyl acrylate | 25 | 480 | 1.578 |
| Ethyl acrylate | 25 | 480 | 2.032 |
| Methyl acrylate | 25 | 480 | 2.228 |

of all monomers, this scheme is highly idealized. Figures 4, 5, and 6 show reaction rate–time curves for the gamma-initiated emulsion polymerization of styrene at different emulsifier concentrations. In fact, none of them is completely classic in form.

At the lowest emulsifier concentration there is a long period of constant reaction rate which, however, is terminated at 70 to 80% conversion by a rather high maximum of the reaction rate owing to the strong gel effect (Trommsdorff effect) in the comparably large particles.

At intermediate concentrations of SDS the constancy of the reaction rate during the zero-order period is much lower, and a small but distinct gel effect is still modifying the first-order reaction period.

At the highest emulsifier concentration there is only a broad maximum instead of a zero-order period whereas the following long period corresponds satisfactorily with a first-order law. The curve of Figure 5 serves also as an example of the original form of all reaction rate–time functions. The values of the over-all reaction rate are determined from the millivoltmeter record for every minute and plotted on semilog paper. Sequences of identical rate readings give the impression of a line parallel to the abscissa.

## Experimental Data

| Concn. Sodium Dodecyl Sulfate moles/kg. water | Absolute Reaction Rate, g./min./kg. emulsion | Relative Reaction Rate (Styrene = 1) |
|---|---|---|
| 18.75 | 0.0127 | 0.0404 |
| 18.75 | 0.1384 | 0.234 |
| 17.5 | 0.281 | 0.310 |
| 50.76 | 0.963 | 1.0 |
| 17.8 | 0.287 | 1.335 |
| 18.3 | 0.3565 | 1.833 |
| 54.5 | 0.8476 | 1.829 |
| 53.4 | 1.892 | 2.316 |
| 53.16 | 2.655 | 2.475 |
| 17.8 | 1.652 | 4.464 |
| 54.8 | 1.267 | 2.67 |
| 18.75 | 5.749 | 11.20 |
| 18.72 | 6.769 | 16.90 |
| 18.75 | 7.944 | 23.06 |

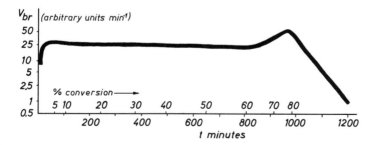

*Figure 4.  Reaction rate–time function for a styrene emulsion; low concentration of emulsifier*

[M]: *1.81 moles/kg. emulsion*
[SDS]: *8.73 × 10⁻³ mole/kg. water*
*Temperature: 25°C.*
*Dose rate: 1920 rads/hr.*
*Final conversion: 87.7%*
*Transformation factor of absolute reaction rate,* $f = 5.2 \times 10^{-5}$ *mole/kg. emulsion/unit*

Previously (7) we published a curve which was obtained at inter-mediate SDS concentration with a somewhat lower styrene concentration and roughly one-tenth of the dose rate. This curve showed a rather good classic form.

In that publication a dependence of the shape of the rate–time function on such parameters as initial monomer concentration, emulsifier concentration, and dose rate was shown for the methyl acrylate system. The behavior of this system tentatively was explained by assuming a strong gel effect even at low conversions, of prolonged particle formation, and some kind of interparticle radical termination—all factors which are included neither in the Harkins view nor in the classical Smith-Ewart theory.

High solvation of a high molecular weight polymer renders the monomer-polymer phase highly viscous and causes a gel effect at low conversions. A high solubility of the monomer in water, or a high con-centration of emulsifier, is likely to cause a prolonged particle formation. Finally the pre- and aftereffects observed during intermittent irradiation of emulsion systems led us to assume that radicals—by transfer or some other mechanism—can escape a monomer-polymer particle.

These nonclassical mechanisms have not yet been proved, though there is much evidence for them [see also Schulz and Romatowski (11)

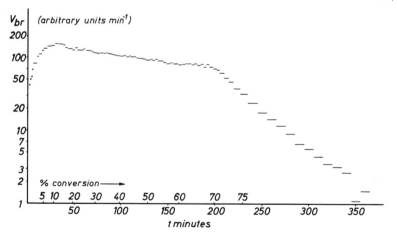

*Figure 5.    Reaction rate–time function for a styrene emulsion; medium concentration of emulsifier*

[M]: *1.65 moles/kg. emulsion*
[SDS]: *49.7 × 10⁻³ mole/kg. water*
*Temperature: 25°C.*
*Dose rate: 1920 rads/hr.*
*Final conversion: 79.2%*
*Transformation factor of absolute reaction rate, f = 5.6 × 10⁻⁵ mole/kg. emulsion/unit*

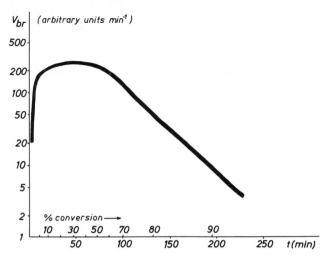

*Figure 6. Reaction rate–time function for a styrene emulsion; high concentration of emulsifier*

[M]: *1.96 moles/kg. emulsion*
[SDS]: *183.18 × 10⁻³ mole/kg. water*
*Temperature: 25°C.*
*Dose rate: 1920 rads/hr.*
*Final conversion: 92.7%*
*Transformation factor of absolute reaction rate, f = 5.9 × 10⁻⁵ mole/kg. emulsion/unit*

and Romatowski and Schulz (*10*)]. Despite these restrictions we shall try to describe the reaction rate–time functions observed for a number of vinyl monomers in terms of these variables influencing the behavior of the systems. This attempt is at the moment only tentative.

Vinylidene chloride and chloroprene (Figures 7 and 8) under the given conditions produce curves which more or less resemble the styrene curve. Vinylidene chloride especially shows a long period of a rather constant reaction rate. By the theory of Harkins and Smith-Ewart this would be interpreted as a period of constant particle number and of constant monomer concentration at the reaction site—*i.e.*, the monomer-polymer particles. The first assumption seems justified (*15*). The second assumption of constant monomer concentration at the reaction site can be true only in a modified sense because poly(vinylidene chloride) is insoluble in its monomer, and the monomer-polymer particles in this system therefore have a completely different structure as compared with the monomer-polymer particles in the styrene system.

After the period of almost constant reaction rate and at conversions higher than 60%, the decrease in reaction rate follows approximately first-order kinetics. A tentative explanation for this behavior of vinylidene chloride emulsion systems may be the following. Let us first assume that

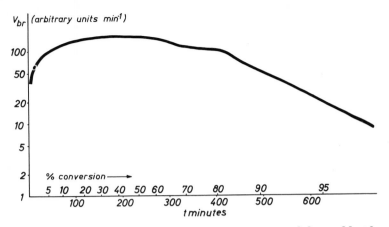

*Figure 7.   Reaction rate–time function for a vinylidene chloride emulsion*

[M]: *2.44 moles/kg. emulsion*
[SDS]: *53.69 × 10⁻³ mole/kg. water*
*Temperature: 5°C.*
*Dose rate: 1920 rads/hr.*
*Final conversion: 97.0%*
*Transformation factor of absolute reaction rate,* f = *4.2 × 10⁻⁵ moles/kg. emulsion/unit*

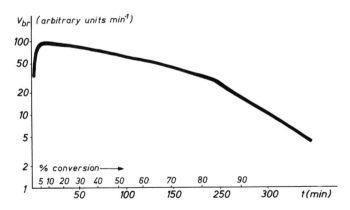

*Figure 8.   Reaction rate–time function for a chloroprene emulsion*

[M]: *2.13 moles/kg. emulsion*
[SDS]: *54.8 × 10⁻³ mole/kg. water*
*Temperature: 5°C.*
*Dose rate: 1920 rads/hr.*
*Final conversion: 97.5%*
*Transformation factor of absolute reaction rate,* f = *14.3 × 10⁻⁵ mole/kg. emulsion/unit*

the particle number after the first period is approximately constant and that the polymerization takes place in a layer of monomer surrounding each polymer particle.

The monomer concentration in this adsorbed layer is kept constant by diffusion from the monomer droplets. The growing surface of the polymer adsorbs more and more monomer, and at fairly high conversions the pure monomer phase disappears because all residual monomer is adsorbed. Further polymerization reduces the surface concentration of the monomer according to a first-order law.

The similarity of the reaction rate–time curve of chloroprene (Figure 8) to the styrene curve is possibly caused by the similar properties of these monomers with respect to water solubility, solubility of the polymer in the monomer, and the absolute reaction rate values.

Acrylonitrile (Figure 9) shows two periods of almost constant but different absolute reaction rates, followed by a period of first-order reaction rate at a high conversion. This monomer is somewhat similar to vinylidene chloride since it also does not swell in its own polymer. On the other hand acrylonitrile has a water solubility roughly three orders of magnitude higher than vinylidene chloride or styrene and even higher than methyl acrylate (*see* Table I). We therefore have to assume particle formation in the aqueous phase, as was done for methyl acrylate emulsions.

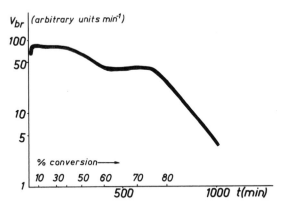

*Figure 9. Reaction rate–time function for an acrylonitrile emulsion*

[M]: 2.89 moles/kg. emulsion
[SDS]: $17.72 \times 10^{-3}$ mole/kg. water
Temperature: 25°C.
Dose rate: 1920 rads/hr.
Final conversion: 81.8%
Transformation factor of absolute reaction rate, f =
$5.9 \times 10^{-5}$ mole/kg. emulsion/unit

Methacrylonitrile (Figure 10) during the first period shows the normal rapid rate increase, followed by a long period of more slowly but steadily increasing rate. At about 20% conversion there seems to be a slight tendency to level off; shortly afterwards, though, the rate again sharply increases, reaching a maximum at about 60% conversion. After the maximum, the rate sharply decreases, not obeying a first-order law for any longer period of time.

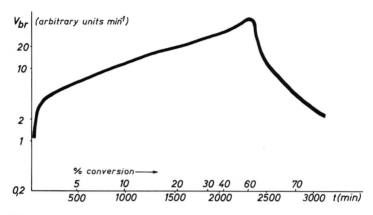

*Figure 10.    Reaction rate–time function for a methacrylonitrile emulsion*

[M]: *2.23 moles/kg. emulsion*
[SDS]: *18.64 × 10⁻³ mole/kg. water*
*Temperature: 45°C.*
*Dose rate: 1920 rads/hr.*
*Final conversion: 71.3%*
*Transformation factor of absolute reaction rate,* f = 3.8 × 10⁻⁵
  *mole/kg. emulsion/unit*

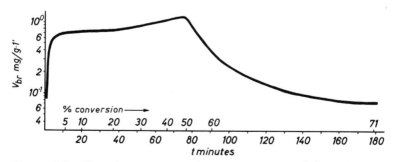

*Figure 11.    Reaction rate–time function for a methyl methacrylate emulsion*

[M]: *1.27 moles/kg. emulsion*
[SDS]: *4.57 × 10⁻² mole/kg. solution*
*Dose rate: 200 rads/hr.*
*Final conversion: 71%*

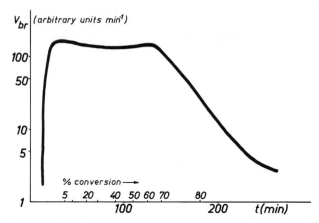

*Figure 12. Reaction rate–time function for a butyl methacrylate emulsion*

[M]: *1.40 moles/kg. emulsion*
[SDS]: *18.64 × 10⁻³ mole/kg. water*
*Temperature: 25°C.*
*Dose rate: 480 rads/hr.*
*Final conversion: 84.6%*
*Transformation factor of absolute reaction rate, f = 4.7 × 10⁻⁵ mole/kg. emulsion/unit*

The behavior of the system is somewhat similar to that of methyl methacrylate (Figure 11). Hence, it may be possible to describe both systems in terms of a pronounced gel effect at conversions higher than 25 to 30%, as generally accepted for the methyl methacrylate system.

The reaction rate–time function of butyl methacrylate (Figure 12) exhibits two distinct maxima followed by a period of rapidly decreasing reaction rate. The second maximum might be caused by the gel effect.

Decyl methacrylate (Figure 13) shows only one broad maximum. The reproducibility of the curve at high conversions was much lower than usual. This is partly caused by the low reaction rates in this range. The reaction time was approximately 40 hours at a dose rate of 1920 rads per hour.

Butyl acrylate (Figure 14) in its polymerization behavior resembles ethyl acrylate (Figure 15). All polymeric acrylic esters are excessively swollen by their monomers. Their solubility in water decreases rapidly with increasing length of the carbon chain of the alcoholic component. In all cases the pure monomer phase will disappear at relatively low conversion (MA and EA at about 15 to 20% conversion). This is probably the reason no zero-order period can be observed. Both ethyl and butyl acrylate show a long first-order period. Methyl acrylate (Figure 16) behaves differently. Because of its high water solubility a prolonged particle formation in the aqueous phase is likely.

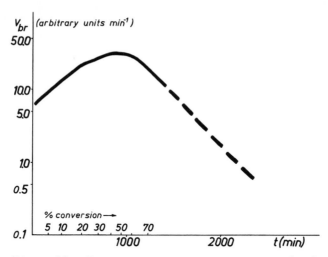

*Figure 13.    Reaction rate–time function for a decyl methacrylate emulsion*

[M]: *0.66 mole/kg. emulsion*
[SDS]: *17.37 × 10⁻³ mole/kg. water*
*Temperature: 25°C.*
*Dose rate: 1920 rads/hr.*
*Final conversion: 75.0%*
*Transformation factor of absolute reaction rate,* $f = 3.5 \times 10^{-5}$ *mole/kg. emulsion/unit*

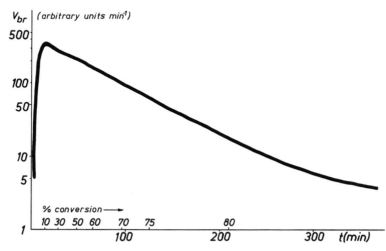

*Figure 14.    Reaction rate–time function for a butyl acrylate emulsion*

[M]: *1.58 moles/kg. emulsion*          [SDS]: *18.64 × 10⁻³ mole/kg. water*
*Temperature: 25°C.    Dose rate: 480 rads/hr.    Final conversion: 81.3%*
*Transformation factor of absolute reaction rate,* $f = 6.2 \times 10^{-5}$ *mole/kg. emulsion/unit*

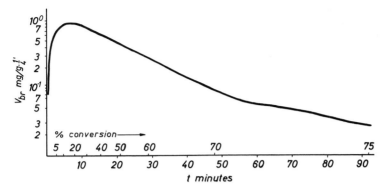

Figure 15.   Reaction rate–time function for an ethyl acrylate emulsion

[M]: *1.23 moles/kg. emulsion*
[SDS]: *4.5 × 10⁻² mole/kg. solution*
*Dose rate: 200 rads/hr.*
*Final conversion: 78.5%*

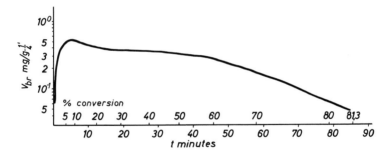

Figure 16.   Reaction rate–time function for a methyl acrylate emulsion

[M]: *1.3 moles/kg. emulsion*
[SDS]: *4.58 × 10⁻² mole/kg. solution*
*Dose rate: 50 rads/hr.*
*Final conversion: 81.3%*

## Conclusions

The above discussion of the polymerization rate *vs.* time curves of the different systems is descriptive rather than explanatory. Almost every system exhibits a characteristic behavior, and the authors feel that it is no longer possible to press the various systems into one scheme. In earlier times when just conversion-time curves were determined, the bulk of these curves was referred to as sigmoidal in shape, and only large deviations from the normal behavior could be observed. Consequently an equally generalized scheme has been used to explain this general behavior. The conversion rate–time curves meanwhile obtainable in high precision, reveal so many details in the behavior of the different systems that a generalized description seems no longer justified.

To present an explanation based on facts, we still lack a positive knowledge of the specific properties of each system. In this situation the above discussion merely can point to certain properties of each system which are likely to cause its specific behavior.

## Acknowledgment

We gratefully acknowledge the financial support of the Bundes-minister für wissenschaftliche Forschung and the valuable assistance of Christel Rüber in the experimental work.

## Literature Cited

(1)  Acres, G. J. K., Dalton, F. L., *J. Polymer Sci.* A1, 2419, 3009 (1963).
(2)  Allen, P. E. M., Downer, J. M., Hastings, G. M., Melville, H. W., Moly-neux, H. P., Urwin, J. R., *Nature* 177, 910 (1956); 182, 245 (1958); *Makromol. Chem.* 38, 72 (1960); 67, 157 (1963).
(3)  Ballantine, D. S., *Brookhaven Natl. Lab. Rept.* T-50, No. 294, 18; T-53, No. 317, 7 (1954).
(4)  Bartholomé, E., Gerrens, H., Herbeck, R., Weitz, H. M., *Z. Elektrochem.* 60, 334 (1956).
(5)  Chapiro, A., Maeda, N., *J. Chim. Phys.* 56 (2), 230 (1957).
(6)  Gerrens, H., "Fortschritte der Hochpolymeren-Forschung," Vol. 1, No. 2, Springer Verlag, Berlin, 1959.
(7)  Hummel, D. O., Ley, G. J. M., Schneider, Christel, ADVAN. CHEM. SER. 34, 60 (1962); *Angew. Chem.* 75, 330 (1963).
(8)  Mezhirova, L. P., Jakovleva, M. K., Matveeva, A. V., Abkin, A. O., Khomikovskii, P. M., Medvedev, S. S., *Vysokomolekulyarnye Soedineniya (Moscow)* 1, 68 (1959).
(9)  Okamura, S., International Conference on Application of Large Radiation Sources in Industry, Warsaw, Poland, Sept. 8 to 12, 1959.
(10)  Romatowski, J., Schulz, G. V., *Makromol. Chem.* 85, 227-248 (1965).
(11)  Schulz, G. V., Romatowski, J., *Makromol. Chem.* 85, 195-226 (1965).
(12)  Stannett, V. T., Research Triangle Inst., Rept. 874, 5, Contract AT (40-1)-2513 (1964).
(13)  Vanderhoff, J. W., Bradford, E. B., Tarkowski, H. L., Wilkinson, B. W., *J. Polymer Sci.* 50, 265 (1961).
(14)  van der Hoff, B. M. E., ADVAN. CHEM. SER. No. 34, 6 (1962).
(15)  Wiener, H., *J. Polymer Sci.* 7, 1 (1951).

RECEIVED May 2, 1966.

# Reaction Rates and Physical Properties in the Radiation Graft–Copolymer System: Poly(vinyl chloride)–Styrene

DAVID E. HARMER

The Dow Chemical Co., Midland, Mich.

*Gamma-radiation from cobalt-60 was used to effect the graft copolymerization of styrene monomer to poly(vinyl chloride) in a composition range of 10 to 30% styrene. In this range, the reaction occurs in the gel phase, and no excess of monomer is employed. To reach full conversion of monomer it was usually necessary to heat the system. Full conversion could also be gained when a short period of heat treatment followed irradiation, an observation which led to the conclusion that many radicals became trapped or buried at room temperature. Measurements of physical properties revealed that the material is fabricated easily before irradiation while the cured product has tensile strength, elongation, and flexural strength improved over pure poly(vinyl chloride) or pure polystyrene. These properties are at a maximum in the same composition range as a maximum in the density of the graft copolymer.*

The grafting of styrene monomer to a poly(vinyl chloride) [PVC] backbone results in a system in which the styrene monomer behaves as a temporary plasticizer for the PVC, allowing it to be molded under conditions not possible with ordinary rigid PVC. After fabrication, objects can be given a low radiation exposure, which effects the grafting reaction. The final product is then a rigid, rather than plasticized, PVC formulation. Such a process holds attractive possibilities for commercial use. In addition, it provides data for gel-phase graft copolymerizations.

One of the most suitable systems for grafting is a radiation-sensitive polymer in the presence of radiation-insensitive monomer. With this combination, the grafting of monomer to the polymer backbone is favored over homopolymerization of the monomer itself. Poly(vinyl chloride) in combination with monomeric styrene is an excellent example of such a system. Much of the previously reported work on this system has employed large excesses of the monomer phase surrounding a thin film of the polymer (2, 3, 5, 8, 9). In these cases, diffusion of monomer into the polymer was necessary and often had an important effect on the kinetics of the system. In the work reported here, the system consists of a semi-rigid gel-phase mixture of poly(vinyl chloride) and monomeric styrene. Under these conditions the polymerization is controlled by the reactions taking place within the gel rather than by diffusion of an excess of monomer from a separate phase.

## Experimental Procedure

**Preparation of Monomer-Polymer Mixture.** The poly(vinyl chloride) chosen for this work was a pure granulated polymer without additives. Styrene was obtained freshly distilled. To it was added 500 p.pm. of dinitro-o-cresol and a stabilizer (Thermalite RS-31 stabilizer, a sulfur-containing organotin compound) in amounts of 1% by weight based on PVC. The styrene containing the two dissolved additives was blended with the poly(vinyl chloride) powder, after which the mixture was extruded rapidly to effect a final mixing of the various components into a homogeneous material. The extruded material was then chopped into small pellets (3 to 4 mm.). No attempt was made to exclude oxygen during any of these operations.

**Analytical Procedures.** Figures for conversion are based on a method in which the graft copolymer was dissolved in o-dichlorobenzene and residual styrene monomer was determined by ultraviolet spectrophotometry.

**Irradiation Conditions and Dosimetry.** All irradiations were carried out in the gamma-radiation field of either a nominally 10 or 18 kilocurie cobalt-60 source. Dosimetry of the gamma-radiation field was carried out using the Fricke method (ASTM test D 1671-59). Since the effective mass absorption coefficient for $\gamma$-rays of this energy is nearly equal for the polymer and for the dosimetric solution, no correction was made for the change in media.

**Physical Testing Methods.** Specimens of the graft copolymer to be subjected to physical testing were prepared by molding, on a hot press, the original monomer–polymer powder. A steel frame formed an opening of the required shape and size for the desired test bar. The formulations were prepared in the usual manner, except that tert-butyl catechol was substituted for dinitro-o-cresol as the inhibitor. For the physical property work, mixtures of a 71-29 PVC–styrene composition were cured for 1 megarad at 50 kilorads per hour. The 80-20 mixtures were cured for 0.5 megarad at 100 kilorads per hour, and the 89-11 composition was cured for 0.3 megarad at 100 kilorads per hour. All samples were exposed within glass tubes to obviate monomer losses. The samples were heated for 10 minutes at 75°C. following irradiation.

### Reaction Rate Studies

The grafting of styrene to poly(vinyl chloride) was first investigated at room temperature, using compositions containing 9 and 23% styrene. Although the reaction appeared to be rapid during the initial stages, the rate eventually decreased, and conversion was complete only after a relatively long time. It is felt that this effect can be attributed to the increasing rigidity of the polymer–monomer mixture as conversion increases, making diffusion of monomer to reactive sites increasingly difficult.

**Irradiation at Elevated Temperatures.** If the extremely high viscosity of the medium is responsible for retarding the rate of reaction, an increase in temperature, with resulting decrease in viscosity, should result in increased reaction rates. With the 77-23 PVC–styrene composition, a slight increase in conversion was noted when the irradiation was carried out at 75°C., rather than at room temperature. However, in the 91-9 composition, as shown in Figure 1, the increase in rate of reaction was quite marked.

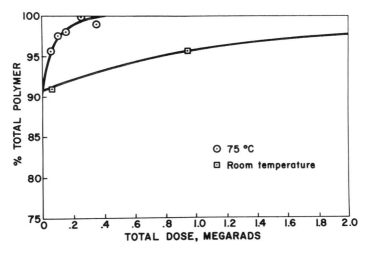

*Figure 1.   Effect of irradiation at elevated temperatures on grafting of 91-9 PVC–styrene*

Schultz (7) has studied the methyl methacrylate polymerization, which is interesting to compare with effects noted in the poly(vinyl chloride)–styrene graft polymerization. When his polymerizations were carried out well below the glassy transition temperature, the conversions reached limiting values. Monomer present in the system functioned as a plasticizing agent, allowing polymerization to occur up to the point

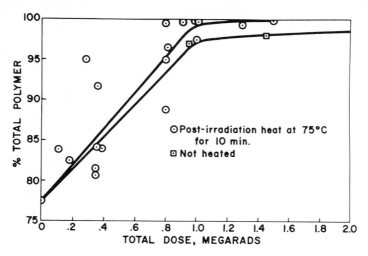

*Figure 2.   Effect of postirradiation heating on 77-23 PVC–styrene*

where the mixture became too rigid. Adding such solvents as benzene reduced the solidification temperature to a point where the polymerization could continue to completion. It seems probable that a similar effect is operative in the PVC–styrene system since polymerization at the elevated temperature, where diffusion of the monomer is facilitated, occurs far more readily.

**Postirradiation Heat Treatments.** The experiments have indicated that the efficiency of polymerization under constant irradiation depends

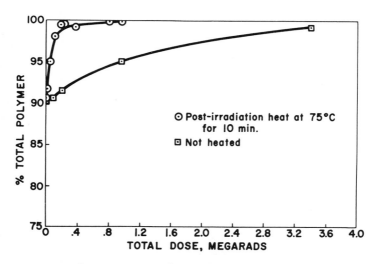

*Figure 3.   Effect of postirradiation heating on 91-9 PVC–styrene*

on the viscosity or diffusion rate within the system. Thus, many of the radicals produced at lower temperatures might be expected neither to polymerize nor to terminate. Hence, a certain amount of radicals should be present in the system even after it is withdrawn from the irradiation treatment.

A similar phenomenon was postulated by Thomas and Pellon ( *10* ) to account for data obtained in the kinetics of acrylonitrile polymerization. They felt that it was possible to obtain unimolecular chain termination by a process of "burial." This was conceived as a mechanism by which the growing chain became shielded from further growth by coiling or by embedding itself in the solid phase. At room temperatures we feel the

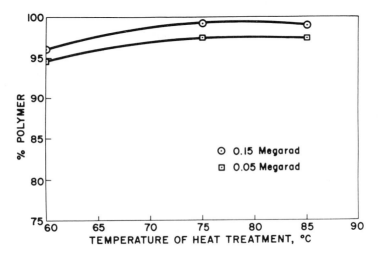

*Figure 4.    Effect of temperature during postirradiation heating of 91-9 PVC–styrene*

diffusion rate may become so low as to cause a similar process within the PVC–styrene system.

Evidence for such stable free radicals has been obtained from electron spin resonance measurements. A sample of the 77-23 PVC–styrene, which had been exposed to 0.8 megarad of gamma-radiation at room temperature, displayed resonance peaks comparable to $3 \times 10^{-8}$ mole per gram of free radicals (compared with a diphenyl picrylhydrazyl standard). When an identical sample was heated for 10 minutes at 75°C. following irradiation, the free radical population had fallen below detection limits. Heating evidently destroyed or decreased the free radical content by reaction or termination.

The effect of postirradiation heating on the course of the polymerization itself can be seen in Figures 2 and 3. Within the scatter of experimental data, an increase in conversion occurs in the postirradiation heat-treated 77-23 composition. The effect is especially important at high levels of conversion. For the 91-9 PVC–styrene composition, the effect is quite marked throughout the conversion range.

Since Schultz (7) found that ultimate conversion depended considerably on temperature (in a highly polymerized methyl methacrylate system), similar effects would be expected in the postirradiation-heating of the PVC–styrene system. Such effects have indeed been found. Figure 4 shows the effect of heating temperature on the conversion level at two different radiation doses. No increased conversion is found for a temperature higher than 75°C. This seems to indicate that a more or less definite "melting point" of the partially polymerized mixture exists. When this temperature is reached during the postirradiation treatment, the reaction runs to a point of termination and is unaffected by further temperature increases.

The glassy transition temperature for poly(vinyl chloride) has been reported as 75°C. (6) although other authors have indicated a somewhat higher value (4). The data indicate that it is necessary to approach the glassy transition temperature closely to facilitate diffusion within the system enough to cause maximum conversion of monomer at a given radiation dose.

The effect of radiation intensity was investigated for three compositions of PVC–styrene. The data for the 77-23 composition are shown in Figure 5. A radiation intensity effect is present even when postirradiation heating is used. When the 84-16 and 91-9 PVC-styrene compositions were similarly studied, no significant dose rate effect was found.

Since biradical termination of growing chains is associated with dependency of less than the first power with respect to radiation intensity (1), the absence of a dose rate effect may be taken to mean that biradical termination is not important. One may conclude that in the systems containing the lesser amounts of styrene, and thus having sharply decreased capability for internal diffusion, biradical termination is not significant during the actual irradiation.

## Determination of Homopolymer

In any graft copolymer system, the monomer can undergo homopolymerization as well as graft copolymerization. The relative proportion of monomer undergoing these two reactions was determined for the PVC–styrene system by extracting the pulverized polymer for 70 hours with boiling cyclohexane. Three polymer fractions were collected. The first (the major portion of the polymer) was the undissolved residue after the end of extraction. The second portion was obtained by cooling the cyclohexane and mixing it with five times its volume of ethanol. The

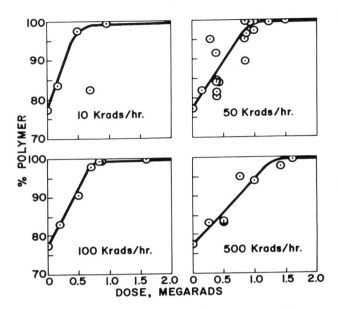

*Figure 5. Effect of radiation dose rate on grafting of 77-23 PVC–styrene using heat treatment*

final fraction was recovered by evaporating the total volume of combined solvents. The relative proportion of styrene and poly(vinyl chloride) in each fraction was determined by chlorine analysis (Table I). From these data, the total amount of homopolymer was calculated as 1.9% of the total copolymer, indicating a high degree of graft copolymerization in this system.

### Physical Properties of Grafted Polymer

**Melt Viscosity of Uncured Mixtures.** One of the attractive features of the PVC–styrene system is the fact that the styrene acts as a temporary

### Table I. Fractionation of PVC-Styrene Graft Copolymer by Extraction

| Cut | % of total | % PVC | % Polystyrene in Fraction (Grafted or Homopolymer) |
|---|---|---|---|
| Residue after extraction | 96.68 | 89.6 | 10.4 |
| Precipitation from solvent | 0.41 | 8.4 [a] | 91.6 [a] |
| Residue from evaporation of solvent | 1.71 | 8.4 | 91.6 |
| Unreacted styrene monomer | 0.45 | — | — |
| Stabilizer | 0.9 | — | — |

[a] No analysis, assumed to have same composition as residue from solvent.

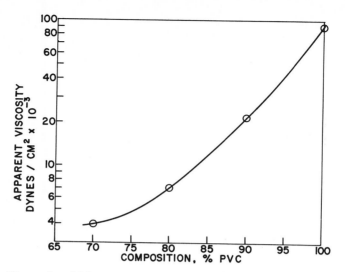

*Figure 6.    Melt viscosity of unirradiated PVC–styrene mixture at 180°C.*

plasticizer to make the mixture easily fabricated before irradiation. This effect can be illustrated by examining the melt viscosity of polymers containing varying amounts of styrene monomer. The tests were carried out on an Instron rheometer at 180°C. through a capillary of 0.026 inch diameter and 0.375 inch length (Figure 6). It is apparent that monomeric styrene renders the poly(vinyl chloride) much more free-flowing in its molten state.

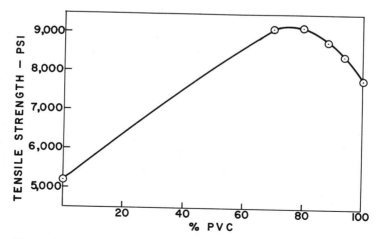

*Figure 7.    Tensile strength (yield) of grafted PVC–styrene compositions (compression-molded)*

**Tensile and Flexural Strength.** The tensile strength and elongation of various compositions of PVC–styrene, as well as pure poly(vinyl chloride) and pure polystyrene were determined, using ASTM test D 638-58T (Figures 7 and 8). In both cases, maxima in the physical properties are achieved in this grafted system. When flexural strengths of the compositions were tested by ASTM method D 790-58T, no failures resulted at the test limits in grafted compositions between 80 and 94% PVC in the composition. (This particular test is designed for a limiting fiber strain of 0.05 inch per inch.) These results are presented graphically in Figure 9.

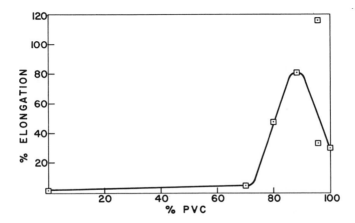

*Figure 8. Elongation (ultimate) of grafted PVC–styrene compositions (compression-molded)*

**Density of Graft Copolymer.** The densities of cured samples of varying compositions of PVC–styrene graft copolymer were measured by water displacement (Figure 10). Density goes through a maximum, in contrast to the work reported by Takamatsu (9), in which the density of a PVC–styrene graft copolymer was found to be a linear function of the degree of grafting. This difference may arise from the fact that Takamatsu exposed his poly(vinyl chloride) in film form to radiation in the presence of excess styrene and found dimensional changes in the film when grafting was finished. Our material undergoes little dimensional change during grafting (0.5% linear shrinkage in the case of the 90-10 composition).

The maximum density occurs in approximately the same composition range as the maxima of various physical properties described above. One may thus ask whether there could be a cause-and-effect relationship between the density and the physical properties. We postulate that this

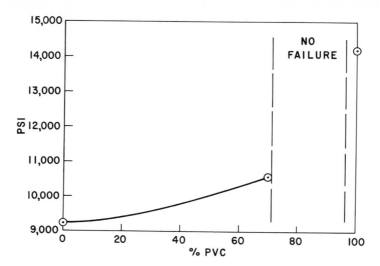

*Figure 9.    Flexural strength of grafted PVC–styrene composition
(compression-molded)*

may be the case.  The fact that adding styrene to PVC increases density
indicates that the styrene side chains must in some way occupy space,
within the solid polymer, which was not entirely taken by the base PVC.
In other words, the packing of atoms within the polymer must be closer
when a small percentage of styrene is grafted into this system.  It seems
plausible that at least part of the enhanced physical properties in this

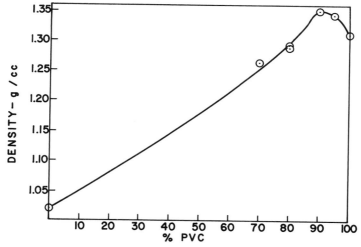

*Figure 10.    Density as a function of composition in PVC–styrene
system*

system arise from the physical relationship of styrene side chains within the matrix of the poly(vinyl chloride) backbone chains.

## Acknowledgment

The author acknowledges the work of M. D. Archambault, The Dow Chemical Co., who diligently carried out the numerous experiments necessary to generate and confirm the data reported. He also acknowledges the assistance of B. Loy, The Dow Chemical Co., who carried out the electron spin resonance studies. The helpful suggestions of A. Chapiro, Centre National de la Recherche Scientifique, are gratefully acknowledged.

## Literature Cited

(1)  Angier, D. J., Turner, D. T., *J. Polymer Sci.* **28**, 265 (1958).
(2)  Chapiro, A., Geothals, E., Bonamour, A. J., *J. Chim. Phys.* **57**, 787 (1960).
(3)  Chapiro, A., Matsumoto, A., *J. Polymer Sci.* **57**, 743 (1961).
(4)  Dannis, M. L., *J. Appl. Polymer Sci.* **4**, 249 (1960).
(5)  Hardy, G., Dobo, J., *Chem. Prumysl* **9**, 215 (1959).
(6)  Mark, H., Tobolsky, A. V., "Physical Chemistry of High Polymeric Systems," 2nd ed., p. 347, Interscience, New York, 1950.
(7)  Schultz, G. V., *Z. Phys. Chem. (Frankfurt Ed.)* **8**, 290 (1956).
(8)  Shinohara, K., Takamatsu, T., *Rikagaku Kenkyusho Hokoku* **36**, 652 (1960).
(9)  Takamatsu, T., *Rikagaku Kenkyusho Hokoku* **36**, 646 (1960).
(10) Thomas, W. M., Pellon, J. J., *J. Polymer Sci.* **13**, 329 (1954).

RECEIVED April 29, 1966.

# 15

# Radiation–Induced Graft Polymerization of Flexible Polyurethane Foam

WALTER J. SKRABA

Sterling Forest Research Center, Union Carbide Corp., Tuxedo, N. Y.

JOHN W. LYNN

Chemicals Division, Union Carbide Corp., South Charleston, W. Va.

*Flexible polyurethane foam pre-irradiated with ionizing radiation in the presence of air can be readily grafted with vinyl monomers. Relatively low radiation doses (3 to 10 megarads) are required to graft various polar vinyl monomers. Grafting of as little as 2% by weight of acrylamide, methacrylamide, or acrylic acid converts the normally hydrophobic polyurethane foam into a water-wettable sponge.*

Ionizing radiation has long been used to alter polymer properties, but only recently has it been able, in certain applications (grafting and crosslinking), to compete with or even improve on conventional methods. As a case in point, flexible polyurethane foam seems to be a good substitute for natural sea sponge; it is attractively soft when wet or dry, abrasion-resistant, and long-lasting. Unfortunately, conventional polyurethane foam does not soak up and hold water like a natural sponge. To make it more suitable for this application, its wettability must be improved.

This paper describes a method for improving hydrophilicity by using radiation-induced grafting of flexible polyurethane (polyether) foam with polar vinyl monomers. By this procedure, the normally hydrophobic material can be converted into a remarkably water-wettable sponge.

Other methods utilizing chemical initiators can be used to graft polymers—*e.g.*, polyurethane can be oxidized with ozone and then heated in the presence of vinyl monomers to produce a graft (2). Polyurethane can be immersed in an aqueous solution of ceric ammonium nitrate containing vinyl monomers to produce a graft following a redox grafting procedure described by Mino and Kaizerman (4). However, using chemical methods, the degree of grafting is difficult to control, and excessive amounts of homopolymer are formed.

## Radiation Methods of Grafting

The three principal irradiation techniques used to produce graft copolymers by irradiation are:

1. Direct Radiation Grafting of Polymer in the Presence of Vinyl Monomer. This leads to the formation of free radicals on both polymer and monomer, resulting in graft polymerization and homopolymerization. The extent of homopolymerization depends on the sensitivity of the monomer used.

2. Grafting of Vinyl Monomer by Trapped Radicals in Irradiated Polymer. The polymer is preirradiated *in vacuo* or in the presence of an inert gas and then immersed in monomer. The trapped free radicals in the irradiated polymer can then initiate graft polymerization.

3. Grafting of Vinyl Monomer on Radiation-Peroxidized Polymer. The polymer is irradiated in the presence of air or oxygen and then immersed in monomer. The peroxides in the irradiated polymer are decomposed by heat or catalysts to form free radicals, capable of initiating graft polymerization.

According to Chapiro (*1*), when a polymer, —P—P—P—P—, is subjected to ionizing radiation in the presence of air, Reactions 1–4 can occur.

$$—P—P—P—P— \rightsquigarrow \quad —P—\overset{\cdot}{P}—P—P— \;+\; H \tag{1}$$

$$—P—\overset{\cdot}{P}—P—P— \;+\; O_2 \quad \longrightarrow \quad \begin{array}{c} —P—P—P—P \\ | \\ O_2\cdot \end{array} \tag{2}$$

$$\begin{array}{c} —P—P—P—P \\ | \\ O_2\cdot \end{array} \;+\; —P—P—P—P— \quad \longrightarrow \quad \begin{array}{c} —P—P—P—\ P— \\ | \\ O_2 \\ | \\ H \end{array}$$

$$+\; —P—\overset{\cdot}{P}—P—P— \tag{3}$$

$$\begin{array}{c} —P—P—P—P— \\ | \\ O_2 \end{array} \;+\; —P—\overset{\cdot}{P}—P—P— \quad \longrightarrow \quad \begin{array}{c} —P—P—P—P— \\ | \\ O_2 \\ | \\ —P—P—P—P— \end{array} \tag{4}$$

These peroxide bonds, as shown in Equations 3 and 4, are stable at room temperature, but when the temperature is raised, the bonds undergo homolytic cleavage to form peroxy radicals (Reactions 5 and 6). Therefore, if a polymer is immersed in a vinyl monomer, M, and the temperature is increased, the peroxy radicals can initiate the grafting of monomer to the polymer backbone (Reaction 7). Homopolymerization also occurs during the grafting reaction and may arise as a result of chain initiation of monomer (Reaction 8) by the hydroxyl radical formed in the thermal cleavage of hydroperoxide.

$$
\begin{array}{c}
\text{—P—P—P—P—} \\
| \\
O_2 \quad \xrightarrow{\ \Delta\ } \quad 2 \ \text{—P—P—P—P—} \\
| \qquad\qquad\qquad\qquad | \\
\text{—P—P—P—P—} \qquad O\cdot
\end{array} \tag{5}
$$

$$
\begin{array}{c}
\text{—P—P—P—P—} \qquad \text{—P—P—P—P—} + OH \\
| \qquad\qquad\qquad\qquad\quad | \\
O_2 \qquad \xrightarrow{\ \Delta\ } \qquad O\cdot \\
| \\
H
\end{array} \tag{6}
$$

$$
\begin{array}{c}
\text{—P—P—P—P—} + xM \longrightarrow \text{—P—P—P—P—} \\
| \qquad\qquad\qquad\qquad\qquad\qquad | \\
O\cdot \qquad\qquad\qquad\qquad\qquad\quad O\text{—M}
\end{array} \tag{7}
$$

$$
OH\cdot + xM \longrightarrow OH\text{—M} \tag{8}
$$

However, in the presence of redox catalysts, such as cuprous and ferrous salts (3, 5), cleavage of the hydroperoxide can occur at room temperature (Reaction 9), but without the formation of hydroxyl radical, thereby minimizing the formation of homopolymer.

$$
\begin{array}{c}
\text{—P—P—P—P—} \\
| \\
O_2 \ + Fe^{2+} \text{ or } Cu^+ \longrightarrow \text{—P—P—P—P—} + OH^- + Fe^{3+} \text{ or } Cu^{2+} \\
| \qquad\qquad\qquad\qquad\qquad\qquad\quad | \\
H \qquad\qquad\qquad\qquad\qquad\qquad\qquad O\cdot
\end{array} \tag{9}
$$

If the reaction takes place in the presence of monomer, grafting occurs in the usual manner. The fact that some homopolymerization also occurs in the redox-catalyzed grafting system can be explained by a chain-transfer mechanism (Reaction 10). The growing polymer radicals can abstract hydrogen atoms from the monomer, forming monomer radicals and thereby initiating homopolymerization.

$$
\begin{array}{c}
\text{—P—P—P—P—} + HM \longrightarrow \text{—P—P—P—P—} + M\cdot \\
| \qquad\qquad\qquad\qquad\qquad\qquad\qquad | \\
OM\cdot \qquad\qquad\qquad\qquad\qquad\qquad OM\text{—H}
\end{array} \tag{10}
$$

$$
M\cdot + xM \longrightarrow MM
$$

In this work, all three methods had been evaluated and found to be capable of grafting polyurethane foam. Because of its simplicity and applicability to the present system, the peroxide method, using redox catalysts, was chosen for detailed experimental work.

## Experimental

**Materials.** The flexible polyurethane (polyether) foam, formulated from a polyol, tolylene diisocyanate, emulsifier, catalyst, and blowing agent, was obtained from the Nopco Chemical Co. It had a density of about 1.5 pounds per cubic foot (0.02 gram per cc.) and contained approximately 40 open cells per linear inch. The foam samples were washed in detergent, dried, and weighed before being irradiated.

The monomers (acrylamide, acrylic acid, and methacrylamide) and the redox activators (ferrous ammonium sulfate and cuprous chloride) were used as received.

**Radiation Sources.** Two types of ionizing radiation sources were used: cobalt-60 and a 2-m.e.v. van de Graaff accelerator. The 1200-curie, cobalt-60 gamma source consisted of 39 stainless steel–clad pencils, ½ inch in diameter by 10½ inches long. In this study, the pencils were grouped in a circle inside a basket so that the highest flux was obtained in the center of a circle 5½ inches in diameter. The basket was mounted on an elevator that could be controlled electrically. When not in use, the source was lowered into 12 feet of water—enough shielding so that the radiation room could be entered safely. Entrance to the radiation room is by a labyrinthine passageway, and the entire facility is enclosed with concrete walls 48 inches thick. Experiments were viewed by closed-circuit television.

The samples of polyurethane foam to be irradiated were suspended from a rack so that when the source was raised, the samples were surrounded by the cobalt-60 pencils. The total dose received by the foam was 3 or 10 megarads at a dose rate of about 100,000 rads per hour.

The electron source was a 2-m.e.v. van de Graaff accelerator equipped with a 15-inch beam scanner. Samples of foam, $2 \times 3\frac{1}{2} \times 5\frac{1}{2}$ inches, were placed on a shuttle and passed 10 times under the electron beam of the machine operating at 60 $\mu$a. and 2 m.e.v. Each pass delivered about 1,000,000 rads, so the total dose to the foam was about 10 megarads. All of the irradiations were carried out in air at room temperature.

**Grafting Procedures.** In the grafting experiments, two procedures were followed.

1. A sample of preirradiated foam was immersed in a 10% aqueous monomer solution containing 0.01% of ferrous ammonium sulfate or an equivalent amount of cuprous chloride. It had been established that ferrous ion and cuprous ion were equally effective in catalyzing the grafting reaction at room temperature. While the solution was being purged with nitrogen, the foam was squeezed and relaxed several times to remove occluded air and then allowed to stand in the monomer solution under a blanket of nitrogen at room temperature. After 15 to 30 minutes, the foam was removed, washed in water, dried, and weighed. The washing procedure was repeated until constant weight was obtained, and the percent monomer grafted was calculated from the weight increase. Since the homopolymers of acrylamide, methacrylamide, and acrylic acid are readily soluble in water, it was assumed that the weight increase of

polyurethane foam was caused by grafted monomer rather than embedded homopolymer.

2. The preirradiated foam was treated with monomer solution containing ferrous ammonium sulfate catalyst under the conditions described above, but the nitrogen purge was omitted. The samples were removed from the monomer solution and passed between rubber rollers to remove excess monomer and then placed in an air-tight container. The container was evacuated, and grafting of the monomer-wetted polymer was allowed to proceed *in vacuo* for about 16 hours at room temperature.

In the absence of redox catalysts, no grafting was observed even after 24 hours' contact of the polyurethane foam with the monomer.

### Results and Discussion

The grafting results are summarized in Tables I and II for polyurethane foam preirradiated in air, with cobalt-60 radiation, to a dose of 3 megarads. Table I shows the degree of grafting of preirradiated foam immersed in monomer solution containing ferrous ammonium sulfate catalyst; with 5% aqueous solutions of acrylic acid, acrylamide, and methacrylamide, 4 to 7% grafting occurs in 30 minutes. Increasing the monomer concentration to 10% decreases the time to achieve grafting of 4 to 7% of monomer to 15 minutes. Table II shows the effect of grafting foam wetted with monomer solution in the presence of ferrous ammonium sulfate. As expected, more time was required to graft in the

**Table I.   Grafting of Preirradiated Foam Immersed in Monomer**[a]

| Monomer | | | |
|---|---|---|---|
| Type | Concn., % | Time, min. | Graft, % |
| Acrylic acid | 5 | 30 | 4 |
| Acrylic acid | 10 | 15 | 5 |
| Acrylamide | 5 | 30 | 5 |
| Acrylamide | 10 | 15 | 4 |
| Methacrylamide | 5 | 30 | 7 |
| Acrylic acid | 10 | 60 | 25 |

[a] Gamma-radiation: 3 megarads in air. Redox catalyst: 0.01% $Fe^{2+}$. Grafting temperature: 25°C.

**Table II.   Grafting of Preirradiated Foam Wetted with Monomer**[a]
(10% concentration, 16 hours)

| Type | Graft, % |
|---|---|
| Acrylic acid | 6 |
| Acrylamide | 8 |
| Methacrylamide | 8 |

[a] Gamma-radiation: 3 megarads in air. Redox catalyst: 0.01%. Grafting temperature: 25°C.

**Table III.  Effect of Dose Rate on Grafting of Preirradiated Foam Immersed in Monomer** [a]

| Type | Concn., % | Dose Rate, rads/hr. | Dose, megarads | Graft, % | Grafting Rate, %/megarad |
|---|---|---|---|---|---|
| Acrylamide | 10 | $10^5$ | 3 | 4 | 1.3 |
| Acrylamide | 10 | $10^8$ | 10 | 2 | 0.2 |
| Acrylic acid | 10 | $10^5$ | 3 | 5 | 1.7 |
| Acrylic acid | 10 | $10^8$ | 10 | 3 | 0.3 |
| Methacrylamide | 10 | $10^5$ | 3 | 7 | 2.3 |
| Methacrylamide | 10 | $10^8$ | 10 | 3 | 0.3 |

[a] Grafting time: 15 minutes.

semidry state; approximately 16 hours were required to obtain grafts comparable to the solution method of grafting.

Homopolymer was formed by both methods of grafting; however, the amount was considerably greater with the immersion method. When the time of grafting in solution was increased beyond 30 minutes, the extent of grafting continued to increase, but there was a tendency for the homopolymer to crosslink and become embedded in the foam. When this occurred, beads of crosslinked homopolymer were trapped in the cells of the foam, and they could not be removed by subsequent washing.

An appreciable dose-rate effect on grafting was observed (Table III). At the cobalt-60 dose rate of 0.1 megarad per hour, the extent of grafting was about seven times greater than with the accelerator dose rate of about 100 megarads per hour.

This behavior is probably related to the concentration of oxygen in the foam before irradiation and to the rate of diffusion of oxygen into the foam during irradiation. In cobalt-60 irradiations, the rate of radical formation is probably lower than the rate of oxygen diffusion into the polymer so that most of the polymer radicals can react with oxygen to form peroxidized polymer. However, at the much higher rate of radical formation in the accelerator irradiations, the oxygen is used up faster than it can diffuse to the radical sites in the polymer. Under these conditions, competing radical reactions such as recombination, degradation, and crosslinking can also take place, resulting in less peroxidized polymer per megarad of radiation.

Despite the higher dose required to peroxidize polyurethane foam with the electron accelerator (about 10 megarads), it is considered to be the best method for irradiating large quantities. In treating low-density material, such as polyurethane foam (0.02 gram per cc.), the penetration of high-energy electrons is appreciable. For example, electrons from the 2-m.e.v. van de Graaff accelerator can effectively penetrate foam to a depth of about 6 to 8 inches, thereby permitting irradiation of pound

Table IV.   Physical Testing Data on Flexible Polyurethane Foam

| Dose, megarads | Monomer Grafted | Graft, % | Tensile, p.s.i.g. | Elonga- tion, % | Compres- sion Set, 90% | Rebound, % |
|---|---|---|---|---|---|---|
| — | — | — | 22.7 | 409 | 9.6 | 56.5 |
| 10 | — | — | 21.6 | 430 | 5.3 | 44.0 |
| 10 | Acrylamide | 6 | 24.5 | 428 | 14.2 | 39.0 |
| 10 | Acrylic acid | 8 | 25.2 | 410 | 19.0 | 37.5 |

quantities of foam per hour. Cobalt-60, however, has an advantage over particle accelerators in providing low dose, high volume radiation processing where deep penetration is required.

*Properties of Grafted Foam*

There was no significant radiation damage in the flexible polyurethane foam as shown in Table IV, and the formation of graft did not greatly affect the basic properties of tensile, elongation, and rebound with the possible exception of the high compression set. However, foam that had been grafted to the extent of 2 to 5 weight % with acrylamide, acrylic acid, and methacrylamide showed striking hydrophilic properties. Conventional flexible foam is hydrophobic and will float in water, but grafted foam absorbs water so effectively that it sinks. The grafted foam holds more water per cubic inch than a cellulose sponge and absorbs water from a surface more completely and with less streaking properties that are well suited to applications in home and industry. These properties were retained by the grafted foam even after storage for one year.

*Conclusions*

The radiation-induced peroxidation of polyurethane foam and subsequent grafting in monomer solution containing redox catalysts, either by immersion or in the wetted state, offer advantages over other radiation methods. The peroxidized foam appears to be stable at room temperature; after irradiation, grafting can be done at any convenient location and time. Moreover, with this method, the extent of grafting can be readily controlled. Grafting can be done at room temperature without forming excessive amounts of unwanted homopolymer, thus resulting in higher grafting efficiency.

*Literature Cited*

(1)  Chapiro, A., *J. Polymer Sci.* **29**, 321 (1958).
(2)  Kreisler, A. V., *et al.*, German Patent **1,109,877** (June 29, 1961).
(3)  Manson, J. A., Cragg, L. H., *Can. J. Chem.* **36**, 858 (1958).
(4)  Mino, G., Kaizerman, S., *J. Polymer Sci.* **31**, 242 (1958).
(5)  Orr, R. J., Williams, A. L., *J. Am. Chem. Soc.* **79**, 3137 (1957).

RECEIVED May 24, 1966.

# Radiation Grafting of Vinyl Monomers to Wool

DANIEL CAMPBELL, J. L. WILLIAMS, and VIVIAN STANNETT

Camille Dreyfus Laboratory, Research Triangle Institute, Durham, N. C.

*Further details of the mutual radiation grafting of styrene to wool have been elucidated. Substantial grafting takes place in air. Mainly postirradiation effects were found with machine irradiation. The grafting was diffusion controlled, and the grafted side chains and in situ homopolymer have molecular weights between 25,000 and 100,000, believed to be caused by chain transfer. A brief discussion of the grafting kinetics is presented. ESR spectroscopy was used to determine second-order radical decay constants as 0.03, 1.9, and 4.8 $\times$ $10^{-22}$ radical$^{-1}$ gram seconds$^{-1}$ for the dry wool, 10% methanol, and 18% methanol-monomer solutions, respectively. The G(radical) values were found to be 0.8 for dry wool and 0.4 for the monomer solutions after correcting for the different decay rates.*

Some general features of the mutual radiation grafting of vinyl monomers to wool were described earlier (9). Styrene was chosen for study in detail in an attempt to ascertain the kinetic features of the process. To achieve measurable levels of grafting, it was necessary to have a swelling agent such as water or methanol present in the monomer solution. A typical set of grafting-dose curves is presented in Figure 1. The amounts of grafting increase greatly with increasing methanol content. Similar results were obtained by substituting water for methanol. On the other hand, the yield of homopolymer produced in the free solution was found to be unaffected, within the experimental error. It is believed that adding water or methanol is necessary to swell the wool fibers and increase the rate of diffusion of monomer to the active centers (free radicals) formed by the irradiation. All the experiments reported previously (9) were performed under high vacuum and at a constant dose rate. Further details of the styrene-wool grafting system have now

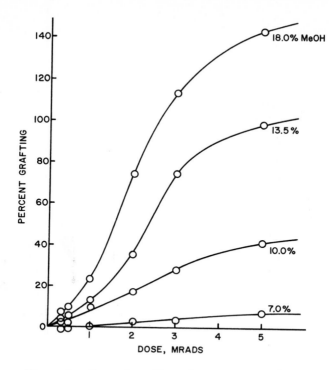

*Figure 1.   Percent grafting of styrene to wool vs. radiation dose at various methanol concentrations in monomer–dioxane solution*

been investigated. In particular, a combination of electron spin resonance (ESR) and grafting data has been used to elucidate additional features of the mutual process.

### Experimental

Details of the wool used and the grafting techniques have been described (9). The irradiations were carried out in a 1500-curie cobalt-60 room type source. The dose rate could be varied continuously by changing the distance from the source.

After removing any residual homopolymer by benzene extraction, the grafted polystyrene was separated from the wool by treating with a two-phase toluene–5% sodium hypochlorite solution. Two separate 24-hour treatments were necessary to dissolve the polystyrene completely and render it soluble in benzene. The technique previously used (5% potassium hydroxide and benzene) left about half the polystyrene insoluble in benzene because of attached amino acid residues.

**ESR Measurements.** Samples were sealed in 3-mm. o.d. Suprasil quartz tubes after thorough degassing of both the wool and monomer solutions. They were then irradiated at room temperature with a dose rate of 0.3 Mrad per hour for varying lengths of time. ESR measurements were carried out at room temperature, but at all other times the samples were maintained at liquid nitrogen temperature to prevent decay of the free radicals. Radiation-induced paramagnetic centers in the quartz were removed by flame-annealing one end of the tube in the usual manner. ESR spectra were recorded with a Varian V.4502-10 spectrometer and were presented either as first or second derivatives of the resonance absorption curve. The number of free radicals was determined by integrating the first-derivative curve and by comparing with $\alpha$-$\alpha'$-diphenyl-$\beta$-picryl hydrazyl.

### Results and Discussion

The previous study was confined to only one dose rate and a limited range of methanol contents. Furthermore, the effects of oxygen and post-irradiation were examined only briefly. These aspects of the grafting process were investigated before embarking on the more detailed ESR study.

**Postirradiation Effects.** Several experiments were conducted in which parallel runs were made. In one case the tubes were frozen in

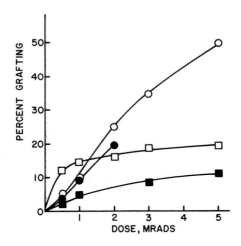

Figure 2. Postirradiation effects in grafting of styrene to wool; 3.06M styrene in dioxane containing 10% methanol

○ 0.05 Mrad per hour, left 24 hours before opening
● 0.05 Mrad per hour, opened immediately after irradiation
□ 0.20 Mrad per hour, left 24 hours
■ 0.20 Mrad per hour, opened immediately

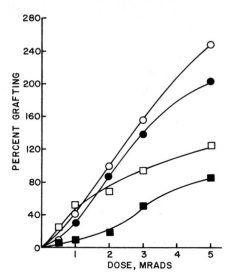

Figure 3. Postirradiation effects in grafting of styrene to wool; 3.06M styrene in dioxane containing 18% methanol

○ 0.05 Mrad per hour, left 24 hours before opening
● 0.05 Mrad per hour, opened immediately after irradiation
□ 0.20 Mrad per hour, left 24 hours
■ 0.20 Mrad per hour, opened immediately

liquid nitrogen immediately after irradiation and then cut open and poured into methanol; in the other, the tubes were left overnight at room temperature and then opened. The results of these experiments at two swelling levels and two dose rates are shown in Figures 2 and 3. At the higher dose rate considerable postpolymerization can be seen at both swelling degrees. At the low dose rate the postpolymerization effects are much less pronounced although still present. Most of the postpolymerization occurs at low total doses; at higher doses the amounts of grafting are parallel—*i.e.*, most of the postpolymerization effect takes place early in the irradiation process. This is presumably when the monomer content in the fibers is still high and the radical content low, leading to the uninterrupted growth of the chains. At low intensities the radicals do not build up as fast, and the residual radical population is low, after the radiation is stopped, leading to only a small post effect. All the subsequent experiments were conducted in such a way as to minimize the post effect—*i.e.*, by opening immediately after irradiation. It has been shown (9) that air can effectively inhibit the post effect in the case of cobalt-60 irradiation.

**Effect of Dose Rate and Swelling.** Grafting experiments were conducted with the 10 and 18% methanol content monomer solution with dose rates ranging from $7.5 \times 10^{-4}$ to 0.2 Mrad per hour (Figures 4 and 5). The grafting yields per megarad continued to increase as the dose rate decreased, even at the highest methanol content, showing that the rate is diffusion controlled at all the dose rates used.

The effect of increasing the methanol content beyond the 18% previously reported was also studied (Figure 6). At the dose rate of 0.1 Mrad per hour the grafting yield per megarad continued to increase up to 40% methanol content; beyond this, polymer started to precipitate in the free solution, and the results became erratic. The results again demonstrate the diffusion-controlled nature of the grafting process. Changes in the methanol and dioxane concentrations would also change the rate of radical production by the direct radiolysis of these solvents. However, it has been shown (9) that the yield of homopolymer formed in the free solution did not change within the experimental error on changing the methanol concentration from 0 to 18%. It is clear therefore that the effect of increasing the methanol concentration is not caused by changes in the radical yield by radiolysis of the solvent system.

A few experiments were conducted in which pure styrene or styrene in cyclohexane and in benzene were used at the low dose rate of 0.003 Mrad per hour. Grafting of a few percent was achieved in cyclohexane with 2 Mrads, but the others gave essentially zero grafting within the experimental error. A number of experiments were conducted at high dose rates, using the 3-m.e.v. Van de Graaff accelerator at the High Voltage Engineering Corp., Burlington, Mass. The maximum dose rate used was 1.0 Mrad per pass of 1.5 seconds with a 40-second pause between passes. Dose rates of 0.5 and 0.25 Mrad per pass were also used. All the results obtained are summarized in Table I. In the case of radiation under vacuum much of the eventual grafting is caused by post-irradiation grafting. However, reasonable amounts were also grafted directly in the few minutes available before opening the tubes. It was also surprising and interesting that even in air substantial grafting occurs. Decreasing the dose rate by a factor of 4 to enable a larger waiting period per total dose had little effect on the amount grafted. In the case of the low swelling (10% methanol) grafting medium there was virtually no difference between the results obtained in air and in vacuum.

**Effect of Air.** The comparatively small effect of air on the Van de Graaff grafting experiments led to a few similar experiments with cobalt-60 radiation (Table II). In all cases substantial grafting took place in the presence of air. In many cases there was no difference within the

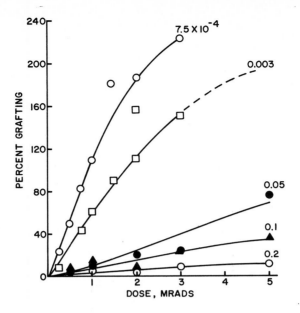

Figure 4. *Effect of dose rate on grafting of styrene to wool; 10% MeOH, 30% styrene, 60% dioxane. Figures refer to dose rate in Mrads per hour*

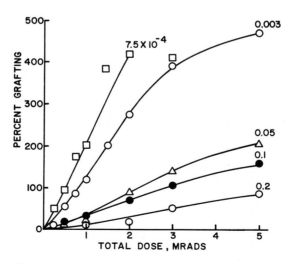

Figure 5. *Effect of dose rate on grafting of styrene to wool; 18% MeOH, 30% styrene, 52% dioxane. Figures refer to dose rate in Mrads per hour*

experimental error between air and vacuum grafting. These results confirm those reported previously. The reason for an occasional low result in air is not known, but it may be caused by excessive air in the wool structure—*i.e.*, insufficient wetting of the wool with the grafting solution.

The lack of an oxygen effect is surprising, particularly at the lower dose rates. It could be caused by its consumption by easily oxidized groups in the wool produced by the radiolysis. However, it seems more

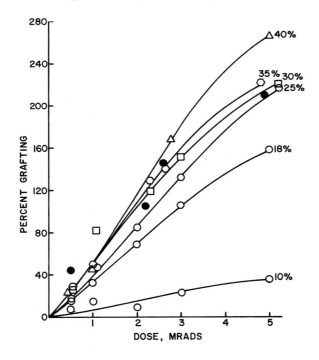

*Figure 6. Effect of methanol content on grafting of styrene to wool. Styrene, 3.06M in dioxane; dose rate, 0.1 Mrads per hour. Figures refer to % MeOH.*

● –45% MeOH

likely that the styrene monomer is able to compete satisfactorily with oxygen in its rate of diffusion to and reaction with the active centers (free radicals) produced in the wool by the radiation. It was shown earlier (9) that air does inhibit the postirradiation grafting in mutually irradiated systems using cobalt-60. However, for the Van de Graaff-irradiated samples air does not inhibit the postpolymerization, probably because of the much higher concentration of radicals in the wool at the time the radiation ceases. Hence, a large excess of radicals would be available to continue the postpolymerization process despite of the presence of air.

### Table I.  Grafting with Van de Graaff Accelerator[a]

| Dose Rate per Pass, Mrad | Total Dose, Mrads | % MeOH | Conditions | % Graft |
|---|---|---|---|---|
| 1.0 | 2.0 | 18 | Left 3 days | 38.3 |
|  | 5.0 |  | in vacuum | 52.5 |
|  | 2.0 |  | Opened | 11.5 |
|  | 5.0 |  | immediately | 15.4 |
|  | 2.0 |  | Left 3 days | 49.9 |
|  | 5.0 |  | in air | 47.3 |
| 0.5 | 2.0 |  | Opened | 12.6 |
|  | 5.0 |  | immediately | 14.9 |
| 0.25 | 2.0 |  |  | 11.5 |
|  | 5.0 |  |  | 15.8 |
| 1.0 | 2.0 | 10 | Left 3 days | 18.3 |
|  | 5.0 |  | in vacuum | 26.3 |
|  | 2.0 |  | Left 3 days | 18.1 |
|  | 5.0 |  | in air | 29.3 |

[a] 3.06$M$ Styrene in dioxane; 40-second interval between passes plus 40 seconds at end of radiation.

In the cobalt-60 system, on the other hand, the radical population is low, and sufficient air is available to diffuse in to terminate the growing chains.

**Molecular Weight of Grafted Side Chains.** In previous work the wool had been hydrolyzed away from the grafted material in order to isolate the polystyrene side chains. Sodium hydroxide was used with good results; however, about one-half of the polystyrene was soluble in only such solvents as dimethyl formamide and benzene–methanol mixtures. Infrared examination showed the presence of groupings charac-

### Table II.  Effect of Air in Mutual Grafting of Polystyrene to Wool at 10 and 18% MeOH Content

|  | Dose Rate | Dose, Mrads | % Graft | |
|---|---|---|---|---|
|  |  |  | Vacuum | Air |
| 10% MeOH | 0.2 | 5 | 17.2 | 8.6 |
|  | 0.1 | 2.3 | 30.5 | 27.3 |
|  | 0.1 | 5 | 61.0 | 18.7 |
|  | 0.02 | 2 | 31.6 | 32.2 |
|  | 0.02 | 5 | 216.5 | 152.5 |
| 18% MeOH | 0.2 | 5 | 76.3 | 78.4 |
|  | 0.1 | 2.3 | 49.2 | 48.9 |
|  | 0.1 | 2.4 | 66.9 | 47.4 |
|  | 0.02 | 1 | 50.2 | 48.4 |
|  | 0.02 | 5 | 342.6 | 309.6 |

teristic of amide and carbonyl groups, and the lack of benzene solubility was undoubtedly caused by the presence of some amino acid residues. These experiments were valuable in establishing the presence of actual grafting and giving a good indication of the approximate molecular weights. However, for a more precise examination of the molecular weight dependence this incomplete hydrolysis was unsatisfactory. Repeated acid or alkaline hydrolysis also failed to render the grafted polystyrene side chains benzene- or toluene-soluble.

Cold aqueous sodium hypochlorite solution was investigated (*10*). Two separate treatments of the grafted wool with a two-phase toluene–5% aqueous sodium hypochlorite, each for about 24 hours, removed the wool and rendered the polystyrene completely soluble in benzene and toluene. Several samples of grafted wools prepared at both 10 and 18% methanol contents and at a range of dose rates were treated this way,

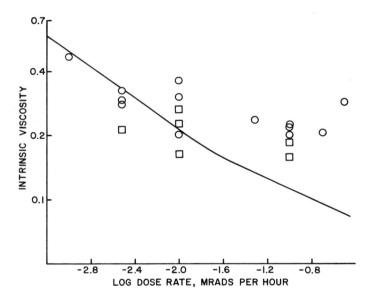

*Figure 7. Intrinsic* Viscosity *of polystyrene graft as a function of dose rate. Solid Line Represents Homopolymer.*

□ *–10% MeOH;* ○ *–18% MeOH*

and the intrinsic viscosity of the polystyrene was measured. The results are shown in Figure 7 together with the curve obtained for the polymer obtained from the free grafting solution. Little difference in the intrinsic viscosities was found between the 10 and 18% methanol contents for the free solution, confirming previous results (*9*).

The viscosity-average molecular weights in the free solution were found to be proportional to the square root of the dose rate up to about 0.02 megarad per hour and then to drop off to about a 0.4 power. This agrees with the literature results as discussed, for example, by Chapiro (3).

The molecular weights of the grafted polymer followed a different pattern. There was little change in the molecular weights with dose rate, and they were only a few times higher than those from the corresponding free solution. The molecular weights consistently varied with increasing amount of grafting and at low dose rates were, if anything, less than those of the corresponding free solution polymer. The 18% methanol grafts were of higher chain length than the 10% methanol.

The actual viscosity-average molecular weights ranged from about 25,000 to 100,000. Under similar conditions cellulose and cellulose acetate form grafts with molecular weights of about one million (6). This difference was unexpected and is apparently unique to wool grafting. It means in principle that there are many short grafted side chains in the case of wool even under heterogeneous grafting conditions. These are known from earlier results to be highly diffusion controlled. The comparatively low molecular weight side chains could arise from two causes: either there is heavy chain transfer in the case of wool compared with the cellulosics, or the grafting is in local monomer solution clusters leading to low molecular weights. The latter is highly unlikely, considering the large effect of swelling on the grafting rates and the lack of a square root dependence of molecular weight on the dose rate. Furthermore, the low molecular weights lead to G(graft initiation) values of 20 to 60, even assuming a viscosity to number average molecular weight ratio of only 2. This is an unlikely G value, especially since the G(radical) value for dry wool is less than unity. The evidence, therefore, suggests that the chain transfer mechanism is responsible. Assuming the chains are mainly terminated by chain transfer, the molecular weight would be given by:

$$MW \approx \frac{k_p(R\cdot)(M)}{k_{tr}(R\cdot)(\text{wool})} \approx \frac{k_p(M)}{k_{tr}(\text{wool})}$$

where $k_p$ and $k_{tr}$ are the propagation and chain transfer rate constants, respectively. The low monomer content in the wool and the low effective $k_p$ value owing to diffusion control make a high rate of chain transfer highly likely. As the grafting increases, the monomer concentration increases, the wool becomes diluted, and $k_p$ increases, leading to the higher molecular weights observed. Similarly, the higher methanol content would lead also to higher monomer concentration and $k_p$; again this should lead to higher molecular weights, as observed. There appears to be a tendency towards higher molecular weights at lower dose rates, indicating some contribution to the termination process by radical combination, which would lead to the observed higher molecular weights at the lower dose rates. Wool contains many functional groups which have high chain transfer constants, including disulfides and some thiol groups. It is reasonable, therefore, that the low molecular weights are caused by the chain transfer effects discussed above.

**Kinetics of Mutual Radiation Grafting.** The shape of the grafting dose curves shown in Figure 1 are typical of many heterogeneous fiber systems such as styrene to rayon (4), poly(vinyl alcohol) (8), and nylon (7). For the wool–styrene system additional experiments were carried out to find the reasons for the type of curve found. The details of these experiments have been described (9). When the radiation was stopped, there was a very large posteffect, often amounting to more than 100% additional grafting. When the tubes were opened to air, this effect was largely eliminated, mainly because of the inhibiting effect of oxygen. When such a system was again degassed, sealed under vacuum, and re-irradiated, the grafting-dose curve was similar to the initial one. This process could be repeated again. It is known from the effect on the grafting rate of swelling agents, thickness of the fibers, and the dose rate that the grafting reaction is diffusion controlled. The large post-irradiation effects demonstrate that the growing chains are long-lived. It is believed, therefore, that the grafting reaction is largely a non-steady-state process.

In an earlier paper (1) equations were developed to describe the grafting-dose process incorporating the two ideas of (a) a slow buildup of the free radical population during the grafting process, and (b) the gradual consumption of the monomer initially present in the fiber, thereby reducing the concentration to a smaller diffusion-controlled value (similar analyses could be made for films).

The rate of polymerization in the fiber, $R_p$, is equal to $k_p\,(R\cdot)(M_f)$, where $k_p$ is the propagation rate constant, $(R\cdot)$ is the concentration of growing chains, and $M_f$ is the concentration of monomer in the fiber averaged across its diameter. Both $(R\cdot)$ and $(M_f)$ are time-dependent until a final steady state is eventually reached.

The details of the kinetics are presented elsewhere (4), but the final rate equation was derived as:

$$R_p = \alpha\gamma M_i e^{-\gamma t}(\cosh t/\beta)^{-\alpha\beta}\left[\int_0^t e^{\gamma t}(\cosh t/\beta)^{\alpha\beta}\,dt + 1/\gamma\right]\tanh t/\beta$$

where $\alpha = k_p(k_1 I^{1/2}/k_t)$, $\beta = (k_1 k_t I)^{-1/2}$, $\gamma = 2D/fr_o$, and $M_i =$ initial concentration of monomer in the fiber, and $k_1$, $k_t$, and $I$ are the initiation rate constant, second-order termination rate constant, and radiation intensity—*i.e.*, the dose rate—respectively.

The values of $\alpha$, $\beta$, and $\gamma$ can be estimated by analyzing the rates at small and infinite times. These were evaluated for the grafting of styrene to wool in 3.0$M$ styrene in dioxane containing 18% methanol at a dose rate of 0.3 megarad per hour. The grafting rates could then be calculated and the rate-dose curve constructed, followed by further refining the values by trial and error. The final curve is presented in Figure 8 together with the experimental points; good agreement between theory and experiment can be seen. It is not sufficient, however, for the kinetic equations

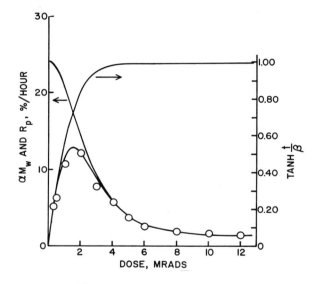

*Figure 8.    Change of average monomer concentration term and radical concentration term with dose and calculated rates of grafting. Open Circles are the experimental points*

to reproduce the experimental rates by choosing appropriate numbers for the adjustable parameters. The values chosen must also be physically realistic, and if possible, independent checks should be made of the various features of the kinetic scheme.

For the present case the values of $\alpha$, $\beta$, and $\gamma$ were found to be realistic, but the value of $M_f$ was 1.51 grams per gram of wool. This value appears high; however, it represents an average between the grafted and ungrafted wool. $M_f$ was estimated by soaking grafted and ungrafted wool in the monomer solution, allowing the samples to drain overnight, and polymerizing to 100% conversion by radiation. An average value of about 0.6 gram per gram of wool was found, not too far from the estimated value. ESR enables one to determine the radical concentration under actual grafting conditions. This has been done in the case where the kinetics were analyzed as discussed above (Figure 12). The steady state of radical population is reached at about 3 Mrads, in good agreement with the dose predicted by kinetic analysis. These experiments led to a more extensive study of the free radical population in wool under both dry and grafting conditions. The former studies were also of interest in the pre-irradiation grafting to wool, which is being studied in these laboratories.

**ESR Studies with Dry Untreated Wool.** The first derivative spectrum obtained by γ-irradiation of the dry wool is shown in Figure 9, *a* and is similar to that reported by Kenny and Nicholls (5). The spectrum is asymmetric and was shown to consist of at least two separate component spectra. This is illustrated in Figure 9, *a* and *b*, where the change of the

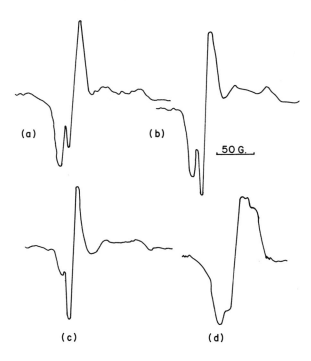

*Figure 9.    First Derivative E.S.R. Spectra of γ-Irradiated Wool Samples*

(a) *Dry wool*
(b) *Dry wool at high incident microwave power*
(c) *Dry wool after 14 days in vacuo at room teperature. Amp. 1.6 × (a)*
(d) *Wool-styrene-dioxane-methanol system*

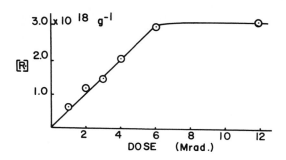

*Figure 10. Variation of free radical concentration with dose for dry wool*

signal shape with increasing incident microwave power shows saturation of one of the peaks relative to the other.

The variation of free radical concentration with dose for the untreated wool is shown in Figure 10. From the initial slope of the curve a $G(R\cdot)$ value is calculated to be 0.8, in good agreement with that calculated from curves in the literature. The free radicals produced in dry wool show some decay with time (Figure 11), and the spectrum decreased in intensity non-uniformly. This is shown in Figure 9, $c$, and it is again concluded that more than one type of free radical species is produced in the wool. This is also in good agreement with results previously reported (5).

**ESR Studies of Wool in Styrene Grafting Solution.** The variation of free radical concentration of wool irradiated in styrene–dioxane contain-

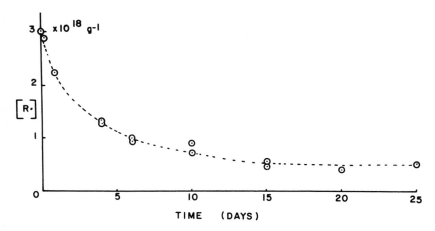

*Figure 11. Decay of free radicals with time in vacuo at room temperature for dry wool*

ing various amounts of methanol solutions is given in Figure 12. With increasing methanol concentration there is a decrease in the maximum radical concentration and the rate at which the maximum is attained. However, with the solution containing 0% methanol a lower free radical concentration is obtained relative to the dry wool, even though the postirradiation decay is relatively slow.

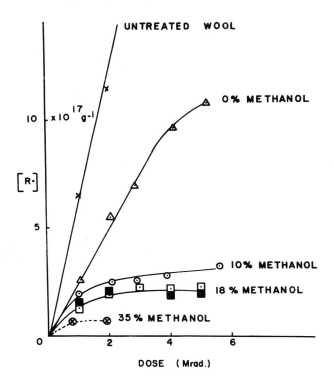

*Figure 12.   Variation of free radical concentration with dose for the wool-monomer solutions. 3.06M styrene in dioxane*

The spectrum for the 0% methanol solution is similar to that obtained for the dry wool, indicating little interaction of the styrene with the radicals. This is to be expected since no grafting of the styrene to wool takes place in the methanol-free solution.

For the 10, 18, and 35% methanol solution, however, the spectra are similar to each other but are distinctly different from that of the dry wool (Figure 9, *d*), and more closely resemble that of the polystyrene radical previously observed—for example, in the growth of the styrene–popcorn copolymer (*2*). It is likely, of course, that there will be some

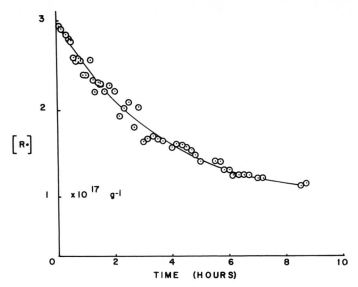

Figure 13.   *Decay of free radicals with time at room temperature for 10% methanol solution*

contribution of unreacted wool radicals to the total signal, but this is presumably small relative to the polystyryl radicals.

The postirradiation decay of the radical concentration at room temperature has been followed for the 10 and 18% methanol solutions. The actual rates of decay are shown in Figures 13 and 14, and the values plotted as a second-order decay reaction are shown graphically in Figure

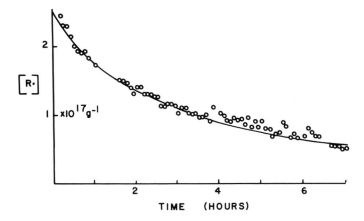

Figure 14.   *Decay of free radicals with time at room temperature for 18% methanol solution*

15. Although there is some scatter of the points, the decay is seen to be close to second-order over most of the range of values.  The values of the over-all rate of radical production and the second-order rate constant for their decay can be found from the slopes of the relevant curves.

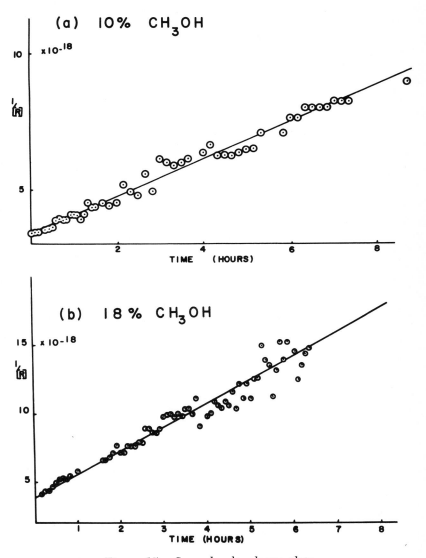

*Figure 15.   Second-order decay plots*

*(a) 10% methanol solution*
*(b) 18% methanol solution*

The actual rate of radical buildup can be expressed by the simple kinetic expression,

$$d(R\cdot)/dt = k_1 I - k_t(R\cdot)^2$$

where $k_1$ is the rate constant for radical formation and is closely related to the $G$(radical) value, $I$ is the radiation intensity, and $k_t$ is the rate constant for the second-order decay process.

This equation can be integrated to give:

$$(R\cdot) = (k_1 I/k_t)^{1/2} \tanh (k_1 k_t I)^{1/2}$$

In the steady-state condition, $(R\cdot)_{ss} = (k_1 I/k_t)^{1/2}$

Values for $k_t$ were found directly from the second-order decay plots for the 10 and 18% methanol solutions. With 0% methanol and with the dry wool the decay rate was negligibly slow compared with the rate of radical formation, and $k_1$ was determined directly, without correcting for termination. The decay of the free radicals produced in the dry wool did not fit a second-order decay curve very closely over the whole range of values, but a value for $k_t$ was determined to be $3 \pm 1 \times 10^{-24}$ gram per second, which is two orders of magnitude less than that found with the 10% methanol solution. In the other two solutions the rate of decay had to be taken into account to calculate $k_1$; when the concentration terms are expressed as numbers of radicals per gram of wool and the intensity as electron volts per gram per second, $G(R\cdot) = 100\ k_1$. The values obtained in this way are given in Table III.

### Table III.  Radical Yields and Decay Rates

|  | $G(R\cdot)$ | $K_t$, G. Radicals$^{-1}$ Sec.$^{-1}$ |
|---|---|---|
| Dry wool | 0.80 | $3 \pm 1 \times 10^{-24}$ |
| Wool in 30/70 styrene-dioxane | 0.38 | — |
| +10% $CH_3OH$ | $0.35 \pm 0.1$ | $1.9 \pm 0.2 \times 10^{-22}$ |
| +18% $CH_3OH$ | $0.37 \pm 0.1$ | $4.8 \pm 0.2 \times 10^{-22}$ |

Increasing the methanol content from 10 to 18% increases the rate of decay of the radicals by 2.5 times. The grafting yield, however, increases greatly in 18% methanol compared with 10% methanol, as shown in Figure 1, in spite of the faster termination rate. The increased grafting is caused by the much faster rate of diffusion of monomer in the more swollen fiber. Undoubtedly, the equilibrium monomer concentration in the fiber is also greater in the presence of the increased methanol concentration, but the strong dose rate dependence shown in Figure 5 shows clearly the diffusion-controlled nature of the growth process.

Despite the changes in the $k_t$ values the $G(R\cdot)$ are in excellent agreement in all cases where monomer solution is present. It is surprising that the value for dry wool is about twice the other values. It is known from the shape of the ESR spectra and from the grafting results that styrene does not react with the radicals in the case of zero methanol content. Even so, the $G(R \cdot)$ value is similar to that obtained under the higher swelling conditions. There is undoubtedly some sorption of dioxane. This could explain the lower $G(R \cdot)$ value as caused by an energy transfer process. Another possibility is that in the dry wool any hydrogen atoms or small fragments produced by the radiation could transfer to the wool before diffusing out of the fiber. In the presence of even a small amount of sorbed liquid, however, such fragments could diffuse rapidly out before transferring, leading to the drop in radical yield. Additional experiments would need to be devised and carried out before a clear-cut answer to this problem could be found.

### Acknowledgment

We thank the Camille and Henry Dreyfus Foundation for financial support.

The ESR spectrometer used is the property of The National Aeronautics and Space Administration and was kindly made available by the Langley Research Center.

### Literature Cited

(1) Araki, K., Kiho, H., Stannett, V., *Makromol. Chem.*, in press.
(2) Breitenbach, J. W., Campbell, D., Schindler, A., *Polymer Letters* **3**, 1017 (1965).
(3) Chapiro, A., "Radiation Chemistry of Polymeric Systems," Chap. 5, Interscience, New York, 1962.
(4) Huang, R. Y. M., Rapson, W. H., *J. Polymer Sci.* **C2**, 169 (1963).
(5) Kenny, P., Nicholls, C. H., Proceedings of International Wool Conference, Paris, July 1965.
(6) Krassig, H. A., Stannett, V., *Fortschr. Hochpolymer. Forsch.* **4**, 111 (1965).
(7) Odian, G., Sobel, M., Rossi, A., Klein, R., Acker, T., *J. Polymer Sci.* **A1**, 639 (1963).
(8) Sakurada, I., Okada, T., Kugo, E., *Isotopes Radiation (Japan)* **4**, 296 (1959).
(9) Stannett, V., Araki, K., Gervasi, J. A., McLeskey, S. W., *J. Polymer Sci.* **3**, 3763 (1965).
(10) Whitfield, R. E., private communication.

RECEIVED April 11, 1966. Conducted in part under contract with the U.S. Department of Agriculture, authorized by the Research and Marketing Act of 1946. Contract supervised by the Wool and Mohair Laboratory, Western Utilization Research and Development Division, Agricultural Research Service.

# 17

# Photolytic Degradation of Cellulose Triacetate

CATHERINE S. HSIA CHEN, STANLEY JANKOWSKI, and
ALLEN BROTHER

Celanese Corp. of America, Summit Research Laboratories, Summit, N. J.

*The degradation of cellulose triacetate induced by ultraviolet radiation was investigated in air and in vacuum, using mercury lamps. Volatile products were ascertained by mass spectrometry as formed during irradiation, and the resulting polymers were characterized by viscosity measurements and functional group analysis. After a small radiation dose, in vacuum, anhydrous cellulose triacetate yielded carbon monoxide and ketene as volatile products. In air, oxygen uptake was the main initial reaction; virtually no volatile material was detected even after a large total dose. Both in vacuum and in air, residual moisture in the polymer influenced degradation. The photolysis of related monomeric compounds (cellobiose octaacetate and glucose pentaacetate) was studied, and the reaction products were characterized.*

Photolysis of cellulose, cellulose acetate, and cellulose nitrate, and thermal pyrolysis of cellulosic materials, including cellulose triacetate, have been investigated (*1, 2, 3, 4, 7, 8, 9, 10, 11*), in the case of photolysis of cellulose, rather extensively (*1, 2, 3, 4, 8, 11*). In connection with a study of outdoor degradation of cellulose triacetate in the solid state induced by sunlight, we have investigated the photolytic degradation of this material both in vacuum and in the presence of oxygen. Cellulose triacetate in dilute solutions does not absorb ultraviolet radiation above wavelength 250 m$\mu$ (Figure 1, *c*). However, in a condensed phase, such as in the form of films, absorption above this wavelength becomes appreciable (Figure 1, *a* and *b*, for films of 5.8- and 1.3-mil thickness, respectively); therefore, photolytic changes can be induced by the ultraviolet region of the absorbed radiation. In this investigation such effects have been ascertained by using ultraviolet radiation at 253.7 and 313 m$\mu$.

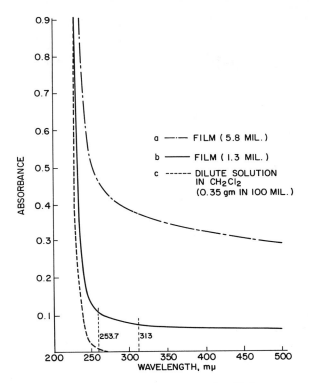

Figure 1.  *Absorption spectra of cellulose
triacetate*

While 253.7 mμ is of higher energy and more strongly absorbed by solid
cellulose triacetate, it is below the cutoff of the sun spectrum received
on the earth's surface (290 mμ). On the other hand, 313 mμ falls in the
most damaging region of the sun spectrum; its photolytic effects should
have practical importance.

The degradation has been followed with emphasis on identifying
the volatile products formed during irradiation by qualitative mass spectrometry. The resulting polymers have been characterized by viscosity
measurements and functional group analysis. The primary active species
have been examined by electron spin resonance spectroscopy. For a
more definitive elucidation of the photolytic degradation of cellulose
triacetate, comparative studies of photolysis of related monomeric compounds, cellobiose octaacetate, cellobiose, glucose pentaacetate, and
glucose were undertaken. This communication describes the results and
offers some discussion and conclusions.

*Experimental*

**Materials.** CELLULOSE TRIACETATE. Celanese cellulose triacetate was purified by dissolution in reagent grade methylene chloride, followed by filtration and reprecipitation into an excess of reagent grade 2-propanol. The polymer was collected on a Büchner funnel, washed with 2-propanol, and dried. Clear films of ∼ 5-mil thickness were cast from methylene chloride solution and used for the photolytic studies.

CELLOBIOSE OCTAACETATE AND GLUCOSE PENTAACETATE. Eastman White Label materials were purified by recrystallization from a methylene chloride–methanol mixture.

CELLOBIOSE AND GLUCOSE. These were Eastman White Label.

**Photolysis Reactors and Ultraviolet Sources.** For 253.7-m$\mu$ irradiation, a modified irradiation apparatus purchased from Delmar Co. was used. The reactor was a 2-necked, 500-ml., round-bottomed flask. One neck was an O-ring joint, and the other was a 24/40 joint. A 4- × 1-inch coiled low pressure mercury quartz lamp was placed inside the flask through the O-ring neck, and the joint was sealed with removable O-rings. The reactor was connected directly to the mass spectrometer by the 24/40 joint. The samples were placed inside the flask and irradiated internally. The O-ring was shielded from direct radiation so as not to induce degradation. The estimated output of the lamp was 30 watts, and the ambient temperature within the reactor during irradiation was 70°C.

For irradiation at 313 m$\mu$, the reactor consisted of a 6- × 2-inch o.d. cylindrical borosilicate glass tube fitted directly to the mass spectrometer by a 24/40 joint. A Hanovia analytical lamp, having an estimated output of 325 watts, was mounted externally alongside the tube. The radiation received by the samples inside the tube was filtered through borosilicate glass and was essentially 313 m$\mu$. The ambient temperature within the reactor during irradiation was 25°C. Some comparative experiments were carried out at 70°C. with additional heating. There was no detectable temperature effect between 25° and 70°C., and the results reported here are for 25°C.

**Irradiation and Mass Analysis.** The reactor was connected to a Bendix Time-of-Flight mass spectrometer using vacuum-tight Swagelok fittings. A variable leak allowed continuous monitoring of all volatile products generated. Mass spectra were recorded with a Honeywell ultraviolet oscillographic recorder, model 906B. Three high impedance electrometers were used to record the mass range from mass 1 to mass 250 in approximately 1 minute. Qualitative identification was based on molecular ions, ion fragmentation patterns, and empirical formula studies. The differentiation of CO (mass 28) and $N_2$ (mass 28) was initially established by ionization potential measurement and the molecular ion and a high pressure negative ion analysis for CO. Only CO, under the conditions employed, could produce the negative ion observed.

Samples were irradiated in the following manner: Cellulose triacetate, 2- × 2-inch film, was placed under the ultraviolet source for irradiation. The monomeric compounds were dissolved in suitable solvents and slurried along the reactor walls. Residual solvent was removed under vacuum. The complete removal of solvent, in all cases, was established by mass spectrometric analysis at a vacuum of $10^{-5}$ torr prior to irradiation. When free of background, the source was activated, and mass recordings were started after the first 30 seconds. All samples were irradiated for a total of 24 hours. During the first 5 minutes, recordings were made at 1-minute intervals. Then the oscilloscopic readout was monitored, with periodic mass recordings being made during the remainder of the 24 hours.

It took 20 minutes to detect the volatiles generated by irradiation in air at 760 torr. Hence, it was impossible to determine the volatiles during the initial stages of irradiation. Therefore, pure oxygen at 150 torr was used in place of air. By this system, mass detection of the volatiles could be made within 30 seconds to 2 minutes. An oxygen atmosphere was therefore used in place of air.

Because of the rapid changes in sample pressure and other problems such as differential pumping of the sample, quantitative measurements were extremely difficult, and the results were obtained on a qualitative basis. However, the order of formation of the volatiles could be detected with certainty.

**Infrared Examination of Samples after Irradiation.** Surface effects on the irradiated side of the cellulose triacetate films were examined employing a Perkin Elmer 521 using the ATR technique (5, 6), which allowed a comparison of both sides of an irradiated film. Monomeric compounds were examined in a KBr disk employing a Perkin-Elmer 21. In many cases remaining acetate groups were removed by treating with NaOH. The regenerated materials were examined to assess other groups, whose infrared absorptions occurred at the same wavelengths as the strong ester carbonyl absorptions.

**Solution Viscosity and Acetyl Value.** For cellulose triacetate, the values of $[\ln\eta_r/C]$ $C = 0.1\%$ in a 90 to 10 volume mixture of methylene chloride–methanol at 25°C. were measured and denoted as inherent viscosity (I. V.) (deciliters per gram).

Acetyl values were determined by base hydrolysis of the acetyl groups of a weighed sample, followed by back-titration to determine the number of milliequivalents of acetic acid.

$$\text{Acetyl value} = \frac{\text{No. of meq. of CH}_3\text{COOH} \times 0.06005 \times 100}{\text{wt. of sample}}$$

## Results

**Mass Spectrometric Analysis of Volatiles during Photolysis.** Samples investigated were cellulose triacetate, cellobiose octaacetate, glucose pentaacetate, cellobiose, and glucose.

IN THE PRESENCE OF OXYGEN. At 253.7 m$\mu$ (70°C.): In all cases, no volatile products were observed other than a small amount of $CO_2$.

A significant change was the decrease of the mass 16 and mass 32 ions, indicating a decrease of oxygen in the system.

At 313 m$\mu$ (25°C.): In all cases, no measurable volatile material was produced and no decrease in the oxygen content of the system could be detected.

IN VACUUM. At 313 m$\mu$ (25°C.): None of the samples produced any measurable volatile material.

At 253.7 m$\mu$ (70°C.): *Cellulose Triacetate.* Irradiation of cellulose triacetate film generated six volatile products which were identified as $CH_2=C=O$ (ketene), CO, $H_2$, $CO_2$, $H_2O$, and $CH_3COOH$. Ketene was the first component observed while CO was the second. After several minutes, the ketene concentration decreased, and CO became the major product generated during the remaining irradiation period. Total sample pressure appeared to reach a maximum after 10 minutes and dropped off gradually during the remaining 24 hours.

*Cellobiose Octaacetate and Glucose Pentaacetate.* In both cases the major component observed at 2 to 5 minutes was $CH_2=C=O$, with lesser amounts of CO, $CO_2$, $CH_3COOH$, and $H_2O$. $H_2$ was not observed.

*Cellobiose and Glucose.* The major product generated at 3 minutes was $H_2O$, with lesser amounts of CO, $CO_2$, and $H_2$. Both $CH_2=C=O$ and $CH_3COOH$ were totally absent.

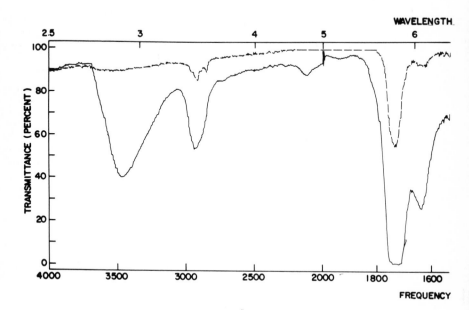

*Figure 2.    ATR infrared spectra of a cellulose triacetate film (~5-mil) irra broken curve:*

**Infrared Examination of the Residues.** CELLULOSE TRIACETATE FILM. ATR infrared spectra of the films irradiated at 313 mμ both in vacuum and in the presence of oxygen showed no change from those before irradiation. ATR infrared spectra of the films after irradiation at 253.7 mμ, both in vacuum and in the presence of oxygen, showed additional absorptions at 5.8 and 7.85 microns, which were attributable to carboxylic acids. In some cases absorptions at 6, 10.4, 11.5, and 12.4 microns were observed, indicating the presence of unsaturation.

Figure 2 compares ATR spectra of the irradiated and unirradiated sides of a cellulose triacetate film after 24-hour radiation at 253.7 mμ in vacuum. The ATR spectrum of a control cellulose triacetate film, which is identical with that of the unirradiated side in Figure 2, is given in Figure 3. Figure 4 shows the change of infrared absorptions of a cellulose film cast on a NaCl plate upon irradiation at 253.7 mμ in vaccum. The spectra were recorded at 90°C. An increase in OH (3 microns) and a decrease in carbonyl (5.7 microns) absorption were noted.

CELLOBIOSE OCTAACETATE AND GLUCOSE PENTAACETATE. The results on both compounds were similar. Samples irradiated at 253.7 and 313 mμ, both in the presence of oxygen and in vacuum, were saponified. Infrared analysis of the saponified residues showed that all samples had carbonyl absorption at 5.76 to 5.78 microns, owing to lactones, ketones,

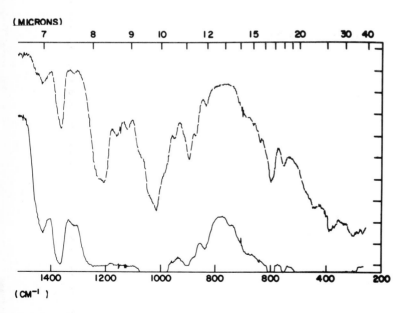

*diated in vacuum at 253.7 mμ. Solid curve: irradiated side; unirradiated side*

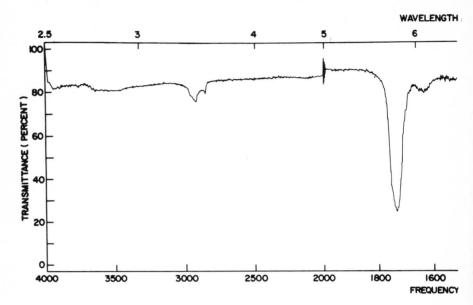

Figure 3.    ATR infrared spectrum

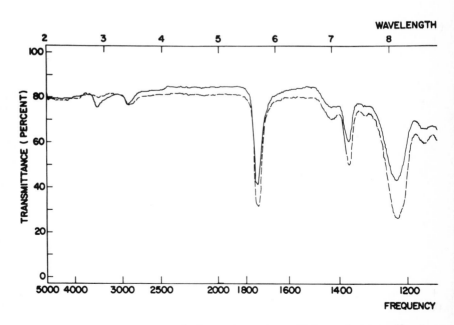

Figure 4.    Change of infrared absorptions of a cellulose triacetate film (cast
curve: original spectrum; solid curve:

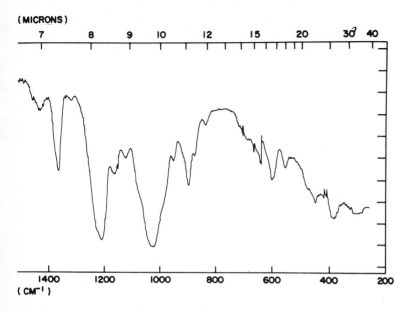

*of cellulose triacetate film (~ 5-mil)*

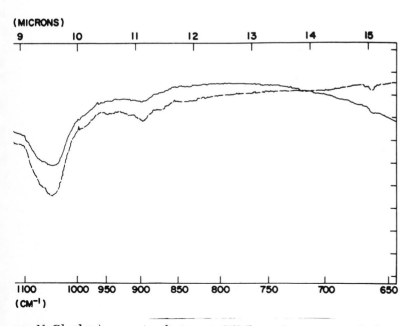

*on NaCl plate) upon irradiation at 253.7 mμ in vacuum. Broken spectrum after 5.5 hours' radiation*

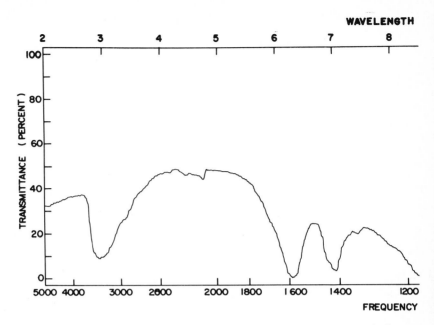

*Figure 5.    Infrared absorption spectrum of a saponified glucose*

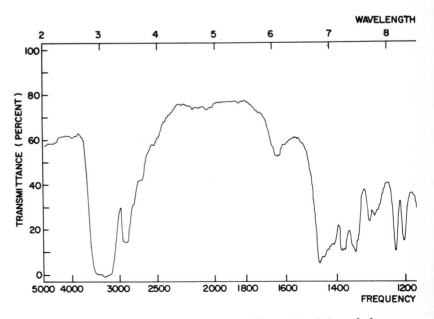

*Figure 6.    Infrared absorption*

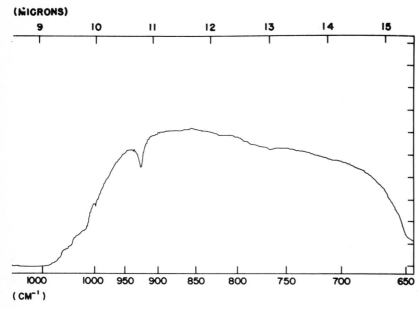

*pentaacetate sample after irradiation at 253.7 m$\mu$*

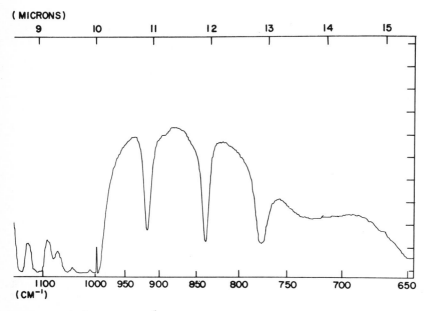

*spectrum of glucose*

and/or aldehydes. Carbonyl absorption at 5.85 microns, owing to acids or ketones, was also observed.

Figure 5 depicts the infrared absorption spectrum of a saponified glucose pentaacetate sample after irradiation at 253.7 m$\mu$. This spectrum differed greatly from that of glucose (Figure 6), which is the saponified product from the original glucose pentaacetate. In Figure 5, a strong carbonyl absorption at 6.3 microns is almost certainly caused by a carboxylic acid salt. The intensity of this absorption, relative to the 3-micron hydroxyl absorption, indicates that the ratio of the carbonyl group content to the hydroxyl group content is higher than 1 to 1. Intense absorption at 9 microns indicates a high ether content. The ether content is high relative to the hydroxyl content, the group ratio being higher than 2 to 1.

**Acetyl Values and Solution Viscosities of the Residues.** Acetyl values are summarized in Table I. In nearly all cases the irradiated samples had higher acetyl values than the original ones.

The inherent viscosity values of cellulose triacetate samples are summarized in Table II. In all the irradiated samples insoluble materials were also obtained.

Glucose pentaacetate and cellobiose octaacetate also yielded a fraction which was insoluble in methylene chloride and which appeared polymeric and amorphous.

*Discussion*

**Photolytic Effect of 313-m$\mu$ Radiation.** The results of mass spectrometric analysis during irradiation, infrared examination of the irradiated

### Table I. Acetyl Values

| Sample | Atmosphere | Radiation, m$\mu$ | Acetyl Value | Change |
|---|---|---|---|---|
| Glucose pentaacetate | Control | | 81.8 | |
| | Vacuum | 253.7 | 84.4 | +2.6 |
| | O$_2$ | 253.7 | 85.1 | +3.3 |
| | Vacuum | 313 | 82.3 | +0.5 |
| | O$_2$ | 313 | 81.4 | —0.4 |
| Cellobiose octaacetate | Control | | 72.6 | |
| | Vacuum | 253.7 | 74.0 | +1.4 |
| | O$_2$ | 253.7 | 75.5 | +2.9 |
| | Vacuum | 313 | 73.2 | +0.6 |
| | O$_2$ | 313 | 73.4 | +0.8 |
| Cellulose triacetate | Control | | 61.7 | |
| | Vacuum | 253.7 | 63.7 | +2.0 |
| | O$_2$ | 253.7 | 64.8 | +3.1 |
| | Vacuum | 313 | 61.9 | +0.2 |
| | O$_2$ | 313 | 62.2 | +0.5 |

## Table II. Inherent Viscosities of Cellulose Triacetate

| Radiation, $m\mu$ | Atmosphere | I. V.$^a$ (dl./gram) | Comment |
|---|---|---|---|
| Control Sample | | 1.80–1.80 | |
| 253.7 | Vacuum | — | Insoluble |
| 253.7 | $O_2$ | 0.14–0.18 | |
| 313 | Vacuum | 1.68–1.71 | Some insoluble material |
| 313 | $O_2$ | 1.73–1.75 | |

$^a$ I.V. denotes $(\ln\eta_r/C)$ $C = 0.1\%$ at 25°C. in 90–10% by volume of $CH_2Cl_2$—$CH_3OH$.

materials, acetyl value determination, and viscosity measurement indicate little effect when cellulose triacetate, cellobiose octaacetate, and glucose pentaacetate were irradiated with 313 m$\mu$ at 25°C. As shown in Figure 1, 313-m$\mu$ ultraviolet radiation is absorbed by solid cellulose triacetate, and the energy is sufficient to cleave C—O and C—C bonds (one quantum light energy at 313 m$\mu$ is equivalent to 91 kcal./mole thermal energy). The observed stability of cellulose triacetate and related model compounds toward 313-m$\mu$ radiation warrants further investigation, especially as regards energy dissipation. The excitation and fluorescence characteristics of cellulose triacetate and related model compounds currently are being investigated in these laboratories. The ESR studies on photolysis of glucose pentaacetate, cellobiose octaacetate, and cellulose triacetate with both 253.7- and 313-m$\mu$ radiation have been undertaken by Dan Campbell at the Research Triangle Institute. Essentially the same radical species were observed with either 253.7- or 313-m$\mu$ ultraviolet radiation. Detailed results will be reported when Campbell's work is completed.

**Photolytic Effect of 253.7-m$\mu$ Radiation.** IN THE PRESENCE OF OXYGEN. Upon irradiation the samples took up oxygen. Oxygen could be consumed in forming hydroperoxides or peracetates with cellulose triacetate and related compounds. The nature of the peroxy groups formed is currently being identified. Subsequent decomposition of these newly formed groups could lead to formation of carboxylic acid groups which were present in the irradiated material, as indicated by infrared absorptions and increase in acetyl values. Chain scission also resulted (lower inherent viscosity); however, deacetylation was not evident since no volatile product was detected.

IN VACUUM. Based on the results described above, the photolytic effects of 253.7 m$\mu$ (at 70°C.) can be summarized as deacetylation, chain scission, and crosslinking.

Possible mechanisms for deacetylation and crosslinking are represented in Figure 7. Since ketene was the first and major volatile product,

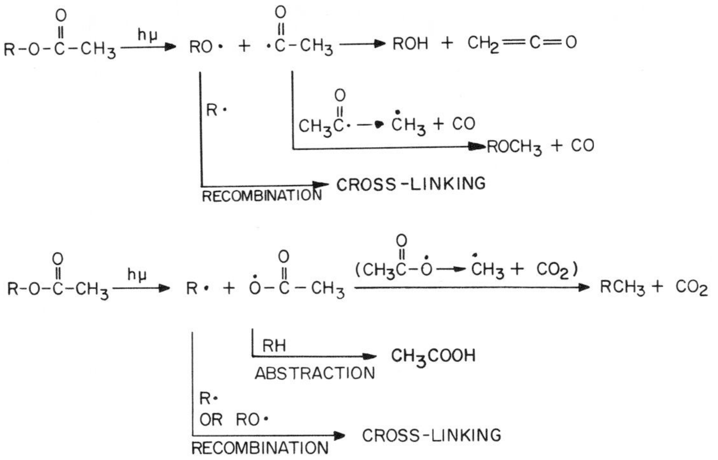

*Figure 7.   Possible mechanisms for deacetylation and crosslinking*

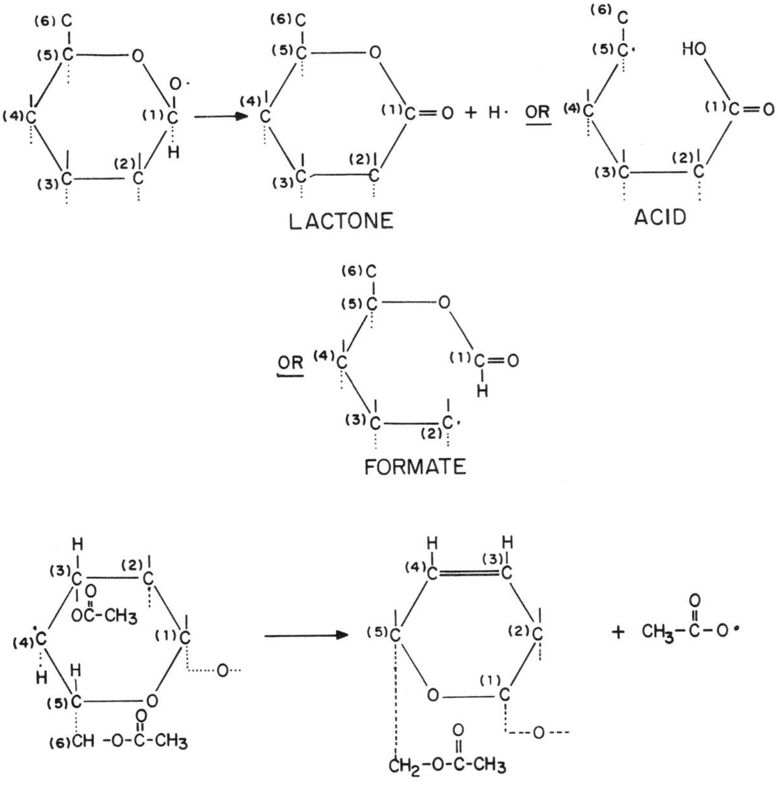

*Figure 8.   Type of functional groups from cleavage*

the first equation probably dominates the second. Acetoxy radicals ($CH_3COO\cdot$) could also possibly be derived from trans elimination of acetyl groups (represented in Figures 8, 9, and 10), thus offering another route to the acetic acid observed. It was further proved that ketene and

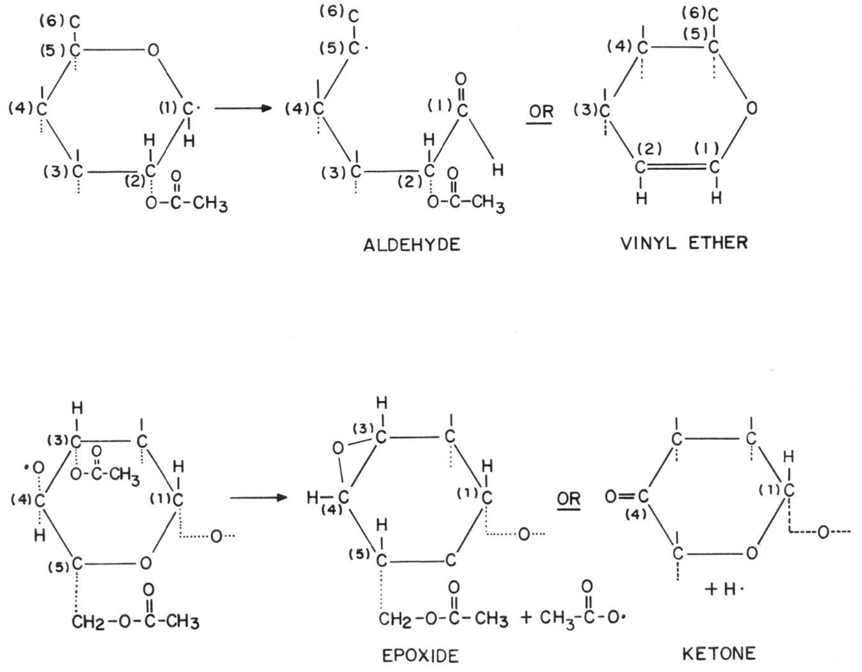
ALDEHYDE
OR
VINYL ETHER
OR
EPOXIDE
KETONE

*Figure 9. Type of functional groups from cleavage*

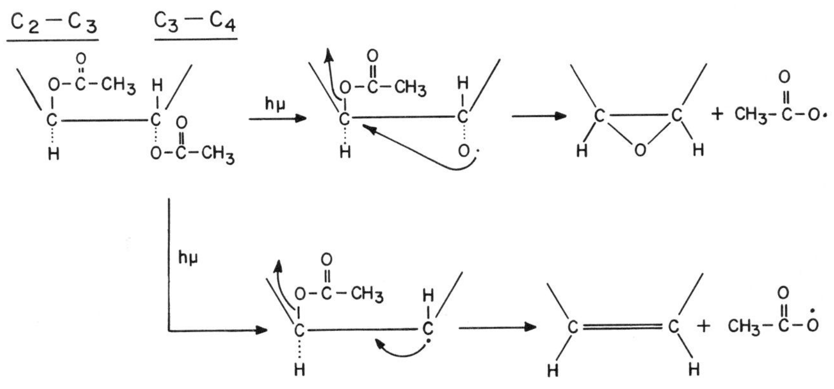
C2 — C3
C3 — C4
hμ
hμ

*Figure 10. Possible trans elimination of acetyl groups*

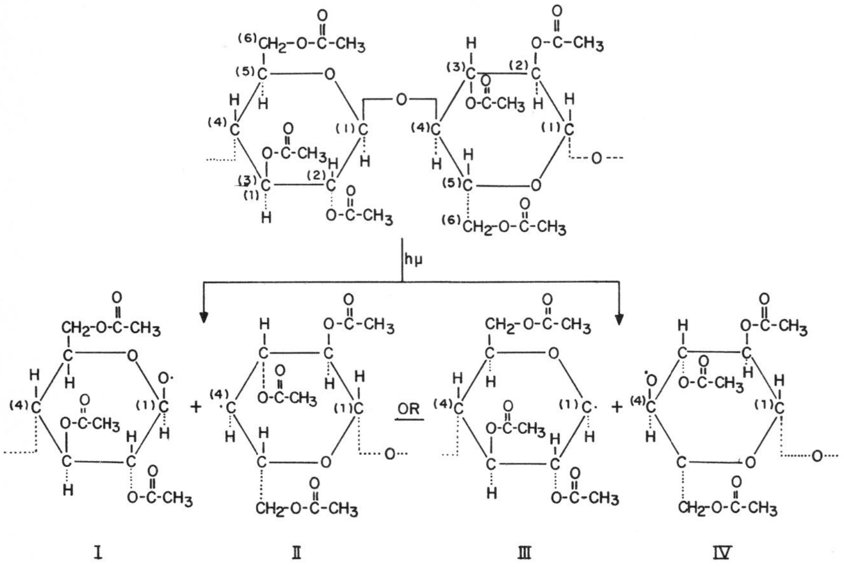

*Figure 11.   Two possible cleavage mechanisms*

acetic acid could be derived only from the acetyl groups since glucose and cellobiose did not produce these volatile products.

Chain scission most probably results from homolytic cleavage of the glucosidic linkages. Figure 11 represents the two possible ways of cleavage, while Figures 8 and 9 represent the type of functional groups which might be derived subsequently. Most of these groups were possibly present in the irradiated residues as indicated by infrared absorptions and acetyl values (higher acetyl values could be derived from acid, ester, and lactone groups).

## Conclusions

Cellulose triacetate undergoes photolytic degradation when irradiated with 253.7-mμ ultraviolet radiation both in the presence of oxygen and in vacuum. In the presence of oxygen, uptake of oxygen is the first step, followed by chain scission, oxidation, and crosslinking. Deacetylation is not apparent. In vacuum, the photolytic changes involve deacetylation, chain scission, and crosslinking. Irradiation with 313 mμ produces little change in cellulose triacetate, both in the presence of oxygen and in vacuum, although free radicals are produced when irradiation is carried out in vacuum.

Comparative investigations with related monomeric compounds, glucose pentaacetate, and cellobiose octaacetate indicate that, on a qualitative basis, these materials undergo photolytic changes in a manner similar to cellulose triacetate. These materials may serve as model compounds for future quantitative investigations of cellulose triacetate.

## Acknowledgment

The authors express their thanks to D. Young of these laboratories for his helpful infrared interpretations and to D. Campbell of the Research Triangle Institute for his contribution to the ESR studies.

## Literature Cited

(1) Beelik, A., Hamilton, J. H., *Chem. Ind. (London)* **1965**, 1341.
(2) Bera, B. C., *Chem. Ind. (London)* **1965**, 2068.
(3) Flynn, J. H., Morrow, W. L., *J. Polymer Sci.* **A2**, 81, 91 (1964).
(4) Flynn, J. H., Wilson, W. K., Morrow, W. L., *J. Res. Natl. Bur. Std.* **60**, 229 (1958).
(5) Gedemer, T. J., *Appl. Spectry.* **19**, 141 (1965).
(6) Harrick, N. J., *J. Opt. Soc. Am.* **55**, 851 (1965).
(7) Jortner, J., *J. Polymer Sci.* **14**, 199 (1959).
(8) Launer, H. F., Wilson, W. K., *J. Am. Chem. Soc.* **71**, 958 (1949).
(9) Lawton, T. S., Jr., Nason, H. K., *Ind. Eng. Chem.* **36**, 1128 (1944).
(10) Madorsky, S. L., Hart, V. E., Straus, S., *J. Res. Natl. Bur. Std.* **60**, 343 (1958).
(11) Stillings, R. A., Van Nostrand, R. J., *J. Am. Chem. Soc.* **66**, 753 (1944).

RECEIVED May 2, 1966.

# 18

# Free Radicals in Polyolefins Initiated with Ultraviolet and Ionizing Radiation

BENGT RÅNBY and PETER CARSTENSEN

Department of Polymer Technology, The Royal Institute of Technology, Stockholm, Sweden

*The radical structures formed by high energy radiation and ultraviolet light in some bulk polyolefins are compared. Polyethylene, polypropylene, polyisobutylene, poly(1-butene), and poly(4-methyl-1-pentene) have all been studied by the ESR technique after irradiation in vacuo with ionizing radiation and ultraviolet light, respectively. There are essential differences between the two types of radical-producing irradiations. After ultraviolet irradiation chain scission radicals and small fragments such as methyl and ethyl radicals are observed, while in the case of high energy radiation, no C—C bond scission radicals have been positively detected. Based on energy considerations, the probable reasons for these differences are discussed.*

The basic mode of interaction of high energy radiation with matter is fairly well understood, but several unstable intermediates must be involved before the observed chemical changes are reached. A better understanding of the structure and the reactions of these intermediates is important and can furthermore indicate how radiation-induced changes may be hindered or beneficially modified, either by the prevailing physical conditions or by using additives. High energy irradiation of polymers has been studied extensively. We have found that a comparison of the free radicals formed by high energy radiation with those initiated by ultraviolet radiation can contribute to a better understanding and assignment of the radical structures. In addition, ultraviolet effects on polymers are of great technical importance in commercial applications.

Free radicals—*i.e.,* molecules or parts of molecules in which the normal chemical binding has been modified so that an unpaired electron is left—are usually quite reactive, and their concentrations in chemical reactions are therefore extremely low. Until recently the presence of free radicals in a reacting system could only be detected indirectly by studying the reaction path, by means of intermediate and end products. The development of the electron spin resonance (ESR) method (*18*) has been an important, general tool for free radical research. It can be used to study the concentration and structure of free radicals, but it is not without limitations, the most obvious problem being sensitivity. Several attempts have been made to increase the number of radicals in the samples by increasing their lifetimes. This is often done by trapping the radicals in a solid matrix in which their lifetimes are increased because of their reduced mobility. In the case of solid polymers below their glass transition temperature, the concentration of radicals can reach measurable levels. The most commonly used methods of forming radicals in solid polymers are radiolysis by ionizing radiation (usually an electron beam or γ-rays from a cobalt-60 cell), photolysis, and mechanical degradation.

In addition to ESR spectroscopy, which is a general method for detecting radicals, Dole *et al.* (*9, 10, 11, 12*) have developed a method of ultraviolet spectroscopy at low temperatures, which is specific for allylic and polyenylic radicals. Numerous papers have dealt with changes in polymers on irradiation, and all of these conclude that the reactions, in one way or another, arise from the formation of free radicals. Only a few papers describe experiments in which the radicals have been observed directly by ESR or ultraviolet spectroscopy at low temperatures. This article merely summarizes the present knowledge of the nature of radicals formed in polyolefins by irradiation in vacuum (ionizing radiation and ultraviolet light) and discusses some new trends in studying these radicals.

### Radical Production by Ionizing and Ultraviolet Radiation

Most studies of free radicals in polymers have been made with ionizing radiation as initiators; in particular γ-rays from cobalt-60 cells have been used (*3, 7, 8*). The γ-quanta have energies of about 1 m.e.v., which is several hundred thousand times higher than the energies of normal chemical bonds. Bond scissions can therefore be expected to occur more or less randomly and multiple bond scissions to occur in a single radiation event. High energy radiation studies lead to the conclusion that, in most cases, equal amounts of absorbed energy produce equal changes in polymer properties, regardless of the type of radiation used.

With photolysis, on the other hand, the energy of the radiation quanta is of the same magnitude as the energy of common chemical bonds. Usually the light sources used in photolysis of polymers are mercury lamps, which have strong spectral lines at wavelengths of 2537, 3130, and 3655 A., corresponding to the energies 4.88, 3.95, and 3.39 e.v., respectively. The common chemical bonds in polymers are C—H, C—C, and C—O, which have bond strengths of 4.28, 3.44, and 3.45 e.v., respectively. Therefore it may be expected that ultraviolet quanta will break chemical bonds (33) and that the breaks will occur more selectively than with ionizing radiation. This suggests that only one bond scission occurs in a single radiation event and that bond scissions occur only where the strength of the bonds is less than the energy of the photons. If high pressure mercury lamps are used in the photolysis experiments, because of the spectral distribution (42), the number of C—C bond scissions would be expected to be about twice the number of C—H bond scissions.

It is often suggested that small fragments (hydrogen atoms, methyl and ethyl radicals, etc.), which are expelled from the polymer chains by high energy radiation, have a kinetic energy high enough to overcome the energy barrier corresponding to a hydrogen abstraction from a neighboring chain, leading to formation of a small molecule and another polymer radical. The small radicals could also diffuse quickly through the sample and be quenched by interaction with other radicals, or by collision with the walls of the container. These reactions are quite fast, and the small radicals would not be expected to be observed in high energy-irradiated polymers. On the other hand, the ultraviolet photons contain only slightly more energy than required to break the C—C and C—H bonds. Therefore, only little excess energy is transferred to the fragments produced by ultraviolet light, and the small radicals, while still mobile, should not be lost in the system. Consequently, they can be detected by means of ESR spectroscopy as first demonstrated for ultraviolet-irradiated polypropylene (51).

### Free Radicals in Bulk Polymers

**Polyethylene.** Polyethylene is without doubt the polymer which has been studied most extensively by ESR spectroscopy. The irradiation has been carried out with all sorts of high energy radiation at different temperatures, *in vacuo,* and under air or other gases. Since reviews of this subject exist (19, 36), a comprehensive discussion of the radicals formed is not attempted, and emphasis is given here only to the more recent advances. From the reviews (19, 35) it is evident that the spectra mainly observed are caused by three different radicals.

When polyethylene is irradiated at liquid nitrogen temperatures with low doses of ionizing radiation, the ESR spectrum mainly shows a sextet shape, which is interpreted as being caused by radicals formed by hydrogen abstraction from the polymer chains (I):

$$—CH_2—\overset{\cdot}{C}H—CH_2—$$

(I)

This spectrum, with an almost binominal intensity distribution, has been observed by several authors (*1, 19, 21, 22, 27, 32, 36, 37, 45*). The hyperfine splitting constant is about 30 gauss ($\alpha$- and $\beta$-protons are equal) while the line width varies between 15 and 25 gauss because of the different orientations of the $\alpha$-protons with respect to the magnetic field. Samples in which the polymer chains are oriented by stretching give two different spectra after irradiation (*29*). The one attributed to polymer chains oriented perpendicular to the magnetic field shows a 10-line spectrum with a hyperfine splitting constant of 15 gauss and a line width of 11.5 gauss. The other, with chains parallel to the magnetic field, shows a sharp sextet spectrum with a hyperfine splitting constant of 32.5 gauss. Here an interesting correlation between the degree of orientation and the hyperfine splitting constant of the $\alpha$-proton has been found (*23*). A recent advance in the experimental technique of measuring on oriented samples was made by Solovey and Yager (*46*), who used solution-crystallized polyethylene for their experiments. The ESR spectra were clearly resolved, because of high crystallinity and excellent orientation of the polyethylene chains at right angles to the lamellar crystals. All these data agree with the interpretation of the sextet spectrum as caused by radicals (I).

If polyethylene is irradiated at higher temperatures—*e.g.*, at room temperature—a new spectrum containing seven lines, with the hyperfine splitting constant of 21 gauss, is obtained (*39*). This spectrum is attributed to the allylic radicals (II):

$$—CH_2—\overset{\cdot}{C}H—CH=CH—CH_2— \longleftrightarrow —CH_2—CH=CH—\overset{\cdot}{C}H—CH_2—$$

(II)

Under these conditions radical I will not contribute to the spectrum because of its short lifetime at this temperature, but radical II has a rather long lifetime owing to its resonance stabilization. Even in this case, spectra of oriented samples have been recorded (*20, 39*). The spectra are rather complicated, containing a septet (splitting 21.3 gauss) with a doublet structure (splitting 5.5 gauss), but nevertheless are easily interpreted as being caused by radicals of type II.

After irradiation with high doses, the recorded spectrum is of singlet outline (*27, 37, 38*), and this signal has been interpreted as caused by polyenylic radicals (III):

$$—CH_2—\overset{.}{C}H—(CH=CH)_n—CH_2—$$

(III)

The line width of this singlet converges towards 17 gauss ($\Delta H_{msl}$) with increasing doses (27, 38). Similar effects have been observed in ESR studies of polyene acids (15, 16); the line narrowing is therefore explained by assuming that the length of the conjugated system increases. The long lifetime (half-life of several days at 150°C.) of the radicals which produce this spectrum further supports this interpretation.

The reactions of polyethylene radicals (3, 7, 8) are quite complex and not yet fully understood. We therefore deal only with certain aspects in the present paper. One interesting feature is the change of radical structure on irradiation with ultraviolet light. After irradiation of a sample containing allylic radicals (II), the spectrum changed from the original septet to a sextet (34, 40)—i.e., alkylic radicals (I) were produced. Furthermore, the total radical concentration was unchanged, and the spectrum consisted of 43% sextet and 57% septet; these results indicate that the free spin migrates along the polymer chain under the influence of ultraviolet light and that an equilibrium between alkylic (I) and allylic (II) radicals will be established.

Dole et al. (9, 10, 11, 12) have found by ultraviolet spectroscopy at liquid nitrogen temperature that ultraviolet irradiation of the allylic radicals (II) in polyethylene even give rise to formation of dienylic radicals—i.e., radical III with $n = 2$.

Few ESR studies concerning the radicals formed in polyethylene by ultraviolet light (4, 5, 44) have been reported. Rånby and Yoshida (44) obtained, after irradiating polyethylene with ultraviolet light in vacuo at liquid nitrogen temperature, a spectrum which contained a diffuse sextet with a hyperfine splitting constant of 33 gauss and traces of a quintet spectrum with a hyperfine splitting constant of 30 gauss. The sextet was interpreted, in accordance with the results from high energy radiation, as being caused by the alkylic radicals (I), while the quintet, which has not been observed when using ionizing radiation, was thought to be caused by radicals formed by chain scissions (IV):

$$—CH_2—CH_2 \cdot$$

(IV)

In radical IV the $\alpha$- and $\beta$-protons are thought to give the same hyperfine splitting constants. The quintet spectrum was observed even in the oriented samples and, in accordance with the interpretation, showed no anisotropy. Until further evidence is found, the interpretation of the quintet spectrum must be regarded as inconclusive.

After the sample had been heated to −95°C. for 10 minutes, the spectrum was quantitatively transferred into a singlet with the line width of 17 gauss ($\Delta H_{msl}$). This spectrum was interpreted as caused by polyenylic radicals (III). After heating to room temperature, no detectable concentration of radicals was found. In another study (*4, 5*) of ultraviolet-irradiated polyethylene, the sextet spectrum was also observed together with a singlet. The singlet spectrum was ascribed to peroxy radicals formed by the air present in the sample tube.

**Polypropylene.** In the reported studies of radicals formed in polypropylene by ionizing radiation, several different radical structures have been proposed—*i.e.*, V to IX—but no agreement has been reached so far (*13, 14, 28, 30, 31, 37, 41, 49, 50*). Almost all ESR spectra seem to have an even number of lines, which is possible with all the radical structures proposed here.

$$—CH_2—\overset{\cdot}{C}H—CH_2—$$

(V)

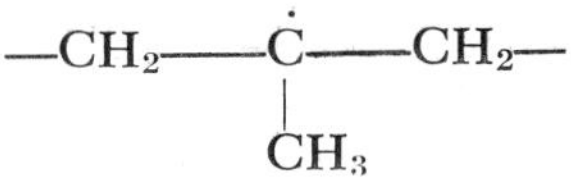

$$—CH_2—\overset{\cdot}{C}—CH_2—$$
$$\qquad\quad|$$
$$\qquad\quad CH_3$$

(VI)

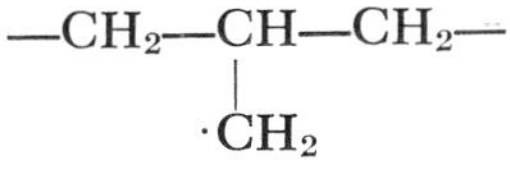

$$—CH_2—CH—CH_2—$$
$$\qquad\quad|$$
$$\qquad\;\cdot CH_2$$

(VII)

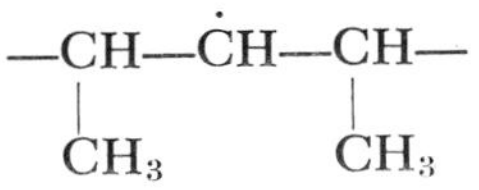

$$—CH—\overset{\cdot}{C}H—CH—$$
$$\quad|\qquad\qquad|$$
$$\;CH_3\qquad\;\;CH_3$$

(VIII)

$$—CH—\overset{\cdot}{C}H—C{=\!=}CH—CH—$$
$$\quad|\qquad\qquad|\qquad\qquad|$$
$$\;CH_3\qquad\;\;CH_3\qquad CH_3$$

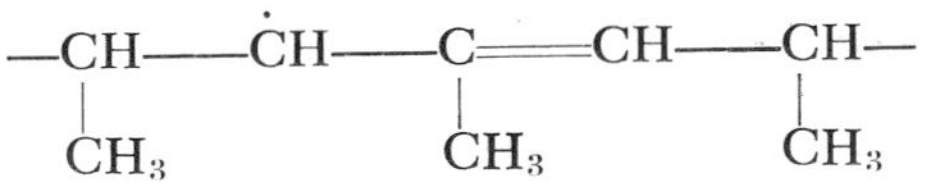

(IX)

Radical X, which would give an odd line spectrum, has also been proposed (*37*):

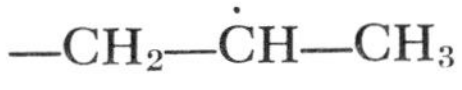

$$—CH_2—\overset{\cdot}{C}H—CH_3$$

(X)

There is still some doubt as to the validity of the assignments of the ESR spectra for high energy-irradiated polypropylene. It is difficult for us to evaluate the probability of the different interpretations, even though these problems have been treated previously in this laboratory (*50*).

Tsvetkov, Molin, and Voyevodskiĭ (28, 49) found that the ESR spectrum of irradiated polypropylene at −150°C. consisted of eight lines with a splitting of 21 gauss. They attributed this spectrum to radical VI. In later work by Libby, Ormerod, and Charlesby (30) the spectrum for the irradiated polymer at −196°C. was described as a sextet with the hyperfine splitting of 20 gauss. This spectrum was assigned to radical V. Ohnishi, Ikeda, Kashiwagi, and Nitta (37) found that the spectrum of polypropylene, irradiated and measured at −78°C., consisted of four different components, which could be characterized as eight-, seven-, six-, and one-line spectra. No attempt was made to assign these spectra to specific radicals.

Fischer and Hellwege (13) assigned the low temperature spectrum of oriented polypropylene to radicals (VI) and found that the spectrum showed no anisotropy, as expected from the structure of radical VI. Measurements at room temperature for oriented samples gave good evidence for assigning the spectra to allylic radicals (IX), which are resonance-stabilized. Yoshida and Rånby (50) analyzed the low temperature spectrum of oriented polypropylene as a sum of a quartet owing to the free radicals VII and/or VIII and an anisotropic spectrum owing to free radical IX. Measurements of the room temperature spectrum were in accordance with the interpretation given by Fischer and Hellwege (13). Forrestal and Hodgson (14), on the other hand, interpreted their low temperature spectra as composed of equal amounts of eight-line and four-line spectra, which were assigned to radical VI, and radical VII and/or VIII, respectively. Loy (31) reported that an irradiated sample gave a nonet spectrum owing to free radical VI, and that this spectrum was distorted by the quartet still remaining after warming to room temperature. Ayscough and Munari (2) re-examined the ESR spectra obtained at room temperature with stretched and unstretched polypropylene. They compared these spectra with those of an irradiated model hydrocarbon at liquid nitrogen temperature, which gave an allylic radical, with a spectrum different from that of the proposed radical (IX). From these experiments, in which the polypropylene spectra were similar to those reported by Fischer and Hellwege (13) it was concluded that the polypropylene spectra at room temperature probably arose from alkylic radicals with structure VI.

It is obvious from this review that there is still a great deal of uncertainty in interpreting the ESR spectra of irradiated polypropylene. We believe that applying ultraviolet absorption measurements to polypropylene—a method which Dole et al. (9, 10, 11, 12) have used for irradiated polyethylene—could determine whether allylic radicals (IX) are present or not, which is one of the basic questions.

Irradiation of polypropylene with ultraviolet light (*4, 5, 44, 51*) gave no evidence of any of the interpretations mentioned. Instead, ESR spectra of new types were obtained. One component was a quartet with sharp lines, interpreted as arising from methyl radicals (XI). The other components of the spectra (*4, 5, 44*), containing broad lines, were assigned to radicals V, which are the counterparts of the methyl radicals, and to VII and/or VIII.

$$\overset{\cdot}{C}H_3$$

(XI)

In addition, Yoshida and Rånby (*44*) suggested that the broad line quartet could also be caused by radicals XII formed by main chain scissions, analogous with the interpretation of spectra for ultraviolet-irradiated polyethylene.

$$-CH_2-\underset{\underset{CH_3}{|}}{CH}-CH_2\cdot$$

(XII)

**Polyisobutylene.** The polymers which we have dealt with until now are of the type which mainly crosslink under the influence of radiation *in vacuo.* Polyisobutylene with one tetrasubstituted carbon in each repeat unit can be considered as the simplest hydrocarbon polymer of the other type—*i.e.,* the polymers degraded by radiation.

The reported ESR spectra of polyisobutylene, irradiated with high energy radiation and measured at low temperatures (*31, 35, 47, 48, 49, 52*) are similar in form, showing a broad doublet with a hyperfine splitting constant of 20 gauss. These spectra have been interpreted as caused by radicals (XIII) formed by hydrogen abstraction from the main chain methylene groups:

$$-\underset{\underset{CH_3}{|}}{\overset{\overset{CH_3}{|}}{C}}-\overset{\cdot}{C}H-\underset{\underset{CH_3}{|}}{\overset{\overset{CH_3}{|}}{C}}-$$

(XIII)

On warming the irradiated sample to −60°C. and exposing it to ultraviolet light, a complex spectrum was recorded (*47, 48*), described as containing seven basic lines with additional weak lines. This spectrum was reversibly converted to the initial doublet on standing and was assigned to the radical (XIV):

$$\begin{array}{c} CH_3 \\ | \\ -CH_2-C\cdot \\ | \\ CH_3 \end{array}$$

(XIV)

The ESR spectra of polyisobutylene after irradiation with ultraviolet light (6) are different from those obtained after irradiation with ionizing radiation. The spectra consists mainly of two components; one, a sharp quartet which has a half life of 1½ hours at liquid nitrogen temperature, has been attributed to free methyl radicals (XI), in analogy with ultraviolet-irradiated polypropylene (51). The broad component is composed of many superimposed lines and was interpreted as caused by three different radicals, all stable at liquid nitrogen temperature. One of these radicals (XV) is the counterpart to the methyl radical (XI) while the others are the two radicals (XIII and XVI) which can both be formed by hydrogen abstraction.

$$\begin{array}{c} \phantom{-CH_2-}\dot{\phantom{C}} \\ -CH_2-C-CH_2- \\ | \\ CH_3 \end{array}$$
(XV)

$$\begin{array}{c} \cdot CH_2 \\ | \\ -CH_2-C-CH_2 \\ | \\ CH_3 \end{array}$$
(XVI)

Although it is well established that polyisobutylene degrades under radiation, the main-chain scission radicals were never observed as primary radicals in any of these ESR studies. A possible explanation is that the two free radicals formed by chain scission are unable to migrate from the reaction site. The two end-group radicals are then likely to react with each other by either recombination or disproportionation.

**Poly(1-butene).** Loy (31) reported that the spectrum of high energy–irradiated poly(1-butene) at −190°C. gave a poorly resolved six-line spectrum, with a hyperfine splitting constant of 21 gauss, indicating that the radicals formed have the structure (XVI):

$$\begin{array}{c} -CH_2-CH-CH_2- \\ | \\ \cdot CH-CH_3 \end{array}$$
(XVI)

After the sample had been warmed to −28°C. for 3 minutes, only a doublet spectrum was observed, which was not assigned any specific radical structure.

In more extensive studies carried out by Hukuda, Kusumoto, Kawano, and Takayanagi (17, 26, 43) three different samples of isotactic poly(1-butene) were used: one amorphous, one of low crystallinity ("semicrystalline"), and one highly crystalline (single crystals). After irradiation with γ-rays at −196°C., a sextet spectrum similar to the spectrum observed by Loy (*31*) was obtained. Above −70°C. the spectra of the amorphous and the semicrystalline samples changed to a quartet and an octet, respectively. Further experiments with oriented samples showed anisotropy in the octet spectrum. Accordingly, the octet was interpreted as arising from an allylic radical with the structure (XVII):

$$—CH_2——\overset{\cdot}{C}H——CH\!=\!=\!C——CH_2—$$
$$\underset{\displaystyle CH_2—CH_3}{\mid}$$

(XVII)

The hyperfine splitting constants (20 and 7 gauss) found for this radical agree well with the splitting constants found for the allylic radical (III) in polyethylene. The sextet spectrum observed at −196°C. is thought to arise from radicals of the structure XVI and/or XVIII, which could be formed by C—H bond scission in the side chain and by abstraction of ethyl side groups, respectively.

$$—CH_2—\overset{\cdot}{C}H—CH_2—$$

(XVIII)

The quartet spectrum observed for the amorphous samples at temperatures higher than −70°C. was thought to be caused by rearrangement of radical XVI, giving the radical structure XIX and a chain scission.

$$\underset{\displaystyle CH_2—CH_3}{\overset{\displaystyle —CH—CH_2\cdot}{\mid}} \quad + \quad \underset{\displaystyle CH—CH_3}{\overset{\displaystyle CH—CH_2—}{\|\|}}$$

(XIX)

Only one ESR study on the radicals formed by ultraviolet light in poly(1-butene) has been reported (*4, 5*). In this work ethyl radicals giving a sextet spectrum with a hyperfine splitting constant of 27 gauss (XX) were observed for the first time from poly(1-butene).

$$\cdot CH_2—CH_3$$

(XX)

The spectrum of the ethyl radicals (XX) was distorted by a superimposed spectrum of polymer radicals (XVIII), the counterparts of the ethyl radicals. In a more recent study, Ruben and Huber [*Polymer Letters* **4**, 337 (1966)] also obtained an octet spectrum of the γ-irradiated hexagonally crystallized polymorphic sample. They suggested that this spectrum is more likely caused by alkylic radicals of structure XXVI, a structure initially suggested by Hukuda *et al.* [Kusumoto, N., Hukuda, K., Kawano, I., Takayanagi, M., *Kogyo Kagaku Zasshi* **68**, 825 (1965)].

$$-CH_2\!-\!-\!-\overset{\displaystyle\cdot}{\underset{\displaystyle \underset{\displaystyle CH_2\!-\!-\!-CH_3}{|}}{C}}\!-\!-\!-CH_2-$$

(XXVI)

As in the case of polypropylene, the question is whether the complex spectrum recorded should be interpreted as arising from alkylic or allylic radicals—*i.e.*, structures XVII and XXVI, respectively. This basic problem could probably be solved by using ultraviolet absorption spectroscopy at liquid nitrogen temperature (*9, 10, 11, 12*).

**Poly(4-methyl-1-pentene).** Poly(4-methyl-1-pentene) has not yet drawn much attention in radiation chemistry. As far as we know, only one study on high energy-irradiated poly(4-methyl-1-pentene) has been published (*25*), and this was in the form of a short communication. The ESR spectrum at liquid nitrogen temperature was a sextet with a hyperfine splitting constant of 23 gauss. The radicals producing this spectrum were supposed to have structure XXI—*i.e.*, radicals formed by side-chain scission.

$$-\underset{\displaystyle\underset{\displaystyle C_4H_9}{|}}{CH}\!-\!-\!CH_2\!-\!-\!\overset{\displaystyle\cdot}{CH}\!-\!-\!CH_2\!-\!-\!\underset{\displaystyle\underset{\displaystyle C_4H_9}{|}}{CH}-$$

(XXI)

On warming to $-30°C.$, the spectrum of the crystalline samples changed to a sextet with a doublet substructure. By analogy with poly(1-butene) this spectrum was interpreted as arising from allylic radicals (XXII), but this assignment needs further justification.

$$-\underset{\displaystyle\underset{\displaystyle C_4H_9}{|}}{CH}\!-\!-\!\overset{\displaystyle\cdot}{CH}\!-\!-\!CH\!=\!=\!CH\!-\!-\!\underset{\displaystyle\underset{\displaystyle C_4H_9}{|}}{CH}-$$

(XXII)

The ESR spectrum of radicals in poly(4-methyl-1-pentene) induced by ultraviolet light (*4, 5*) is composed of a sharp quartet with the hyperfine splitting constant of 22.5 gauss and a broad quartet. The sharp component has been attributed to methyl radicals (XI) while the broad component could be caused by polymer radicals of structures XXIII and/or XXIV.

$$—CH_2——CH—$$
$$\quad\quad\quad\quad |$$
$$\quad\quad\quad CH_2$$
$$\quad\quad\quad\quad |$$
$$\quad\quad\quad CH—CH_3$$
$$\quad\quad\quad\quad |$$
$$\quad\quad\quad ·CH_2$$
$$(XXIII)$$

$$—CH——\overset{·}{C}H——CH—$$
$$\quad |\quad\quad\quad\quad\quad |$$
$$\quad C_4H_9\quad\quad\quad C_4H_9$$
$$(XXIV)$$

$$—CH_2——CH—$$
$$\quad\quad\quad\quad |$$
$$\quad\quad\quad CH_2$$
$$\quad\quad\quad\quad |$$
$$\quad\quad\quad ·CH—CH_3$$
$$(XXV)$$

The counterpart radical (XXV) to the methyl radical, which would give rise to a seven-line spectrum, was not found in this case. The analogous counterpart radicals for polypropylene and polyisobutylene were reported (4, 5, 6, 43). For poly(4-methyl-1-pentene) these radicals would be located in a side group and therefore more easily rearranged because of higher mobility. In addition to the short communication (25), Kusumoto *et al.* published a paper on high energy irradiated poly(4-methyl-1-pentene) [Kusumoto, N., Shirano, K., Takayanagi, M., *Kogyo Kagaku Zasshi* 68, 1553 (1965)]. They report that in addition to the sextet, an octet and odd number hyperfine structures (5, 7, and 9 lines) were observed at liquid nitrogen temperature. By increasing the temperature to about $-20°C.$, the octet splits clearly into a doublet substructure, which by cooling to liquid nitrogen temperature is reversed to the original octet. The octet spectrum was suggested as being caused by the allylic radical XXVII in the main chain

$$—CH_2——\overset{·}{C}——CH═══C——CH_2—$$
$$\quad\quad\quad\quad |\quad\quad\quad\quad\quad\quad |$$
$$\quad\quad\quad\quad C_4H_9\quad\quad\quad\quad C_4H_9$$
$$(XXVII)$$

or to the alkylic radical XXVIII in the side chain

$$—CH_2——CH——CH_2—$$
$$\quad\quad\quad\quad\quad |$$
$$\quad\quad\quad\quad\quad CH_2$$
$$\quad\quad\quad\quad\quad |$$
$$CH_3——\overset{·}{C}——CH_3$$
$$(XXVIII)$$

While warming the sample, the intensity of the odd number hyperfine structures increased relative to the octet, but no definite assignments of these odd line spectra to specific radical structures were attempted.

## Mechanism and Efficiency of Free Radical Formation

There is good evidence that the free radicals in polyethylene and polypropylene (44) are formed by direct interaction of ultraviolet light quanta with the polymers. Repeated purification of polyethylene and polypropylene did not change the rate of radical formation. The initial absorption of ultraviolet light may be caused by chemical groups, such as keto groups or double bonds in the polymers. No evidence has been found that gaseous oxygen takes part in the primary reaction of radical formation in polyethylene irradiated with ultraviolet light (44). The rate and efficiency of radical formation are, however, larger in polypropylene than in polyethylene by a factor of 5 to 10.

It is usually accepted that the initial radicals formed in the polyolefins by ionizing radiations are the result of C—H bond scissions. Radicals which can positively be attributed to direct C—C bond scissions have not been observed with ionizing radiations. Ultraviolet light can give hydrogen abstraction in the same way as ionizing radiations. In addition, primary radicals in polyolefins initiated with ultraviolet light can be formed by C—C bond scissions, both in side groups and in the main chain. The occurrence of main-chain scissions in polyethylene may be related to the expected preference of ultraviolet effects in the noncrystalline parts of the polymers. The energy of each quantum would not be sufficient for breakage or opening of more than one chemical bond for each event. The formation of methyl radicals in polypropylene, polyisobutylene, and poly(4-methyl-1-pentene) and ethyl radicals in poly(1-butene) may also be a specific effect with ultraviolet light. The concentration of methyl radicals is comparatively low during the ultraviolet irradiation, at the most only 10% of the total amount of radicals formed (6, 44). The methyl radicals probably disappear by abstracting hydrogen from the polymer, a first-order reaction giving methane (6).

It is evident from the data presented that ultraviolet light has different and more specific effects on forming radicals in polyolefins than those previously found for ionizing radiation. Furthermore, hydrogen atoms have been observed in the ESR spectra from ultraviolet experiments (6, 24). The hydrogen radicals, however, are not believed to be located in the polymer matrix but to be formed in the glass or adsorbed on the glass surface of the sample cell (6).

The efficiency of free radical production in polyolefins with ultraviolet light is quite low. Yoshida and Rånby (44) found, from the spectral energy distribution of the mercury lamp used and from measurements of the initial rate of free radical production, that 110,000 and 17,000 e.v. of ultraviolet light quanta hitting the samples produced one free radical in polyethylene and polypropylene, respectively. Not all the ultraviolet light is absorbed by the polymer samples; some is scattered. Usually the G values of radical production by ionizing radiation are in the range 1 to 6, corresponding to 100 to 15 e.v. per radical produced.

The number of lines in the ESR spectra, their distance (hyperfine splitting), and their intensity ratio can be used to determine the structure of free radicals. However, for bulk polymers the lines of the ESR spectra often are not fully resolved, their considerable line width causing overlap to occur. Thus, it is often difficult to determine the exact hyperfine splitting and the intensity ratio, making radical-structure determination rather uncertain. One of the biggest advances in ESR technique is using oriented polymer samples to study radiation-induced radicals. This technique is based on the fact that the $\alpha$-hydrogen splitting changes by rotation of the sample in the magnetic field. The effect causes changes in spectral shape, which facilitate the identification of the hyperfine lines. However, difficulties met with polypropylene radicals have shown that this method of preparing and measuring the samples is not sufficient to allow fully consistent interpretations of the spectra. We therefore conclude that the ESR technique is a powerful method for detecting radicals, but the radical structures should be interpreted with caution until further evidence for the proposed structures has been obtained from additional data.

## Acknowledgment

The authors are indebted to K. Takakura for translating the Japanese papers mentioned, to G. Mälhammar for helpful discussions and suggestions, and to C. R. Gore for reading the text.

## Literature Cited

(1)  Abraham, R. J., Whiffen, D. H., *Trans. Faraday Soc.* **54**, 1291 (1957).
(2)  Ayscough, P. B., Munari, S., *Polymer Letters* **4**, 503 (1966).
(3)  Bovey, F. A., "Effects of Ionizing Radiation on Natural and Synthetic High Polymers," "Polymer Reviews," Vol. 1, Interscience, New York, 1958.
(4)  Browning, H. L., Ackerman, H. D., Patton, H. W., Division of Polymer Chemistry, 150th Meeting, ACS, September 1965, Preprint p. 1014.
(5)  Browning, H. L., Ackerman, H. D., Patton, H. W., *J. Polymer Sci.* **A1, 4**, 1433 (1966).
(6)  Carstensen, P., Rånby, B., Proceedings of Third International Congress of Radiation Research, Cortina d'Ampezzo, Italy, June 1966.
(7)  Chapiro, A., "Radiation Chemistry of Polymeric Systems," "High Polymers," Vol. 15, Interscience, New York, 1962.
(8)  Charlesby, A., "Atomic Radiation and Polymers," Pergamon Press, London, 1960.
(9)  Dole, M., Bodily, D. M., "Abstracts of Papers," 151st Meeting, ACS, March 1966, G027.
(10) Dole, H., Bodily, D. M., IUPAC Symposium, Prague, 1965, Preprint 103.
(11) Dole, M., Bodily, D. M., Proceedings of Third International Congress of Radiation Research, Cortina d'Ampezzo, Italy, June 1966, in press.
(12) Fallgatter, M. B., Dole, M., *J. Phys. Chem.* **68**, 1988 (1964).
(13) Fischer, H., Hellwege, K. H., *J. Polymer Sci.* **56**, 33 (1962).

270                                                               IRRADIATION OF POLYMERS

(14) Forrestal, L. J., Hodgson, W. G., *J. Polymer Sci.* **A2**, 1275 (1964).
(15) Hanna, M. W., McConnell, H. M., *J. Chem. Phys.* **37**, 3008 (1962).
(16) Hanna, M. W., McLachlan, A. D., Dearman, H. H., McConnell, H. M., *J. Chem. Phys.* **37**, 361 (1962).
(17) Hukuda, K., Kusumoto, N., Kawano, I., Takayanagi, M., *Kogyo Kagaku Zasshi* **67** (12), 2163 (1964).
(18) Ingram, D. J. E., "Free Radicals as Studied by Electron Spin Resonance," Butterworth & Co., London, 1958.
(19) Kashiwabara, H., *Japan J. Appl. Phys.* **2**, 523 (1963).
(20) Kashiwabara, H., *J. Phys. Soc. Japan* **16**, 2494 (1961).
(21) *Ibid.*, **17**, 567 (1962).
(22) Kashiwabara, H., Shionara, K., *J. Phys. Soc. Japan* **15**, 1129 (1960).
(23) Kashiwagi, M., *J. Chem. Phys.* **36**, 575 (1962).
(24) Komatsu, T., Sohma, L., IUPAC Symposium, Prague, 1965, Preprint 82.
(25) Kusumoto, N., Hukuda, K., Takayanagi, M., *Rept. Progr. Polymer Phys. Japan* **8**, 315 (1965).
(26) *Ibid.*, p. 317.
(27) Lawton, E. J., Balwit, J. S., Powell, R. S., *J. Chem. Phys.* **33**, 395, 405 (1960).
(28) Lebedev, Ya. S., Tsvetkov, Yu. D., *Zh. Strukt. Khim.* **2**, 607 (1961).
(29) Libby, D., Ormerod, M. G., *J. Phys. Chem. Solids* **18**, 316 (1961).
(30) Libby, D., Ormerod, M. G., Charlesby, A., *Polymer* **1**, 212 (1960).
(31) Loy, B. R., *J. Polymer Sci.* **A1**, 2251 (1963).
(32) *Ibid.*, **44**, 341 (1960).
(33) Maas, K. A., Volman, D. H., *Trans. Faraday Soc.* **60**, 1202 (1964).
(34) Milinchuk, V. K., Pshezhetskii, S. Ya., *Vsokomol. Soedin* **5**, 946 (1963).
(35) Nitta, I., Ohnishi, S., *Ann. Rept. JARRP* **3**, 287 (1961), in Japanese.
(36) Ohnishi, S., *Bull. Chem. Soc. Japan.* **35**, 254 (1962).
(37) Ohnishi, S., Ikeda, Y., Kashiwagi, M., Nitta, *J. Polymer* **2**, 119 (1961).
(38) Ohnishi, S., Ikeda, Y., Sugimoto, S., Nitta, I., *J. Polymer Sci.* **47**, 503 (1960).
(39) Ohnishi, S., Sugimoto, S., Nitta, I., *J. Chem. Phys.* **37**, 1283 (1962).
(40) *Ibid.*, **39**, 2647 (1963).
(41) Ormerod, M. C., "Advances in Nuclear Science and Technology," Vol. 2, p. 107, Academic Press, New York, 1964.
(42) Philips' Technical Documentation "Light," high pressure mercury quartz burner HPK 125 W of 27.4.1955, p. 1.
(43) *Polymer Letters* **3**, 743 (1965).
(44) Rånby, B., Yoshida, H., *J. Polymer Sci.* **C12**, 263 (1966).
(45) Smaller, B., Matheson, M. S., *J. Chem. Phys.* **28**, 1169 (1958).
(46) Solovey, R., Yager, W. A., *J. Polymer Sci.* **A2**, 219 (1964).
(47) Teleshov, E. N., Pravednikov, A. N., Medvedev, S. S., *Dokl. Akad. Nauk SSSR* **156**, 1395 (1964).
(48) Teleshov, E. N., Sharptyi, V. A., Pravednikov, A. N., Medvedev, S. S., *Zh. Strukt. Khim.* **5**, 627 (1964).
(49) Tsvetkov, Yu. D., Molin, Yu. N., Voevodskiĭ, V. V., *Vysokomol. Soedin.* **1**, 1805 (1959).
(50) Yoshida, H., Rånby, B., *Acta Chem. Scand.* **19**, 72 (1965).
(51) Yoshida, H., Rånby, B., *J. Polymer Sci.* **B2**, 1155 (1964).
(52) Zhidomirov, G. M., Tsvetkov, Yu. D., Lebedev, Ya. S., *Zh. Strukt. Khim.* **2**, 696 (1961).

RECEIVED May 16, 1966.

# INDEX

## A

Absorption spectra of cellulose
   triacetate ................. 241
Acetyl values ................. 250
Acrylonitrile ................. 190
Air effect in wool grafting ....... 225
Aliphatic free radicals ......... 36
Alkyl acrylate copolymers
   amorphous ethylene .......... 76
   ethylene- ................. 71
Alkyl free radicals ............. 36
Allyl free radical growth, kinetics
   of the ................... 38
Allyl free radicals ............. 37
Allylic radicals .............257, 260
Alpha and gamma radiation ...... 17
Alpha radiation ............... 5
Amorphous ethylene–alkyl acrylate
   copolymers ............... 76
Antioxidant
   phenolic ................... 142
   thiobisphenolic .............. 142
Atomic hydrogen ............. 35

## B

Beam current on creep of glassy
   polymer, effect of .......... 86
Beer-Lambert law .............. 60
Biological macromolecules, irradia-
   tion of .................. 14
Biological material, reactivity trans-
   fer in ................... 19
Biological systems, irradiation of .. 14
Bulk viscosity ................. 117
Butyl acrylate ................. 190
Butyl methacrylate ............. 190

## C

Carbanions ................... 31
Carbon black .................. 77
Carbonium ion ................34, 41
Carbowax .................... 113
Catalysts, heavy metal .......... 113
Cellobiose octaacetate .......... 242
Cellulose triacetate
   absorption spectra of .......... 241
   infrared spectra of ............ 244
   inherent viscosities of ......... 251
   photolytic degradation of ...... 240
Chain reaction ................. 135
Chemical migration ............ 26
Chloroprene .................. 190
Cis groups, isomerization of ...... 63
Cost of irradiation ............. xi
Creep of glassy polymers ........ 79
Creep rates of polymers, transient
   acceleration of ............ 79
Crosslinked films, properties of ... 73
Crosslinked ionomers, radiation ... 139
Crosslinked polyethylenes, radiation 139

Crosslinking .................... 2, 57
   electron beam-initiated irradia-
    tion ..................... 156
   of ethylene copolymers, radiation 156
   in irradiated polystyrene ...... 98
   mechanism of .............. 3
   of polyethylene .............. 24
   radiation- ................. 44
   in polystyrene, $G$-values for .... 97
Crosslinks .................... 133
Crystalline bonds ............. 63
Cyclic structures ............... 69
Cyclohexane .................. 33

## D

Decay curves ................. 179
Decay of vinyl groups .......... 139
Decyl methacrylate ............. 190
Degradation of cellulose triacetate,
   photolytic ................ 240
Delayed stress application on creep
   of glassy polymer, effect of .. 86
Density of graft copolymer ...... 211
DFD 6040 ................... 142
Dienyl free radicals, kinetics of
   growth of ................ 42
Dienylic radicals .............. 260
Diffusible intermediates ........ 35
Dilatometer, recording .......... 185
Dioxane ..................... 33
Dioxene ..................... 33
Dose, dependence of product yields
   on ...................... 128
Dose rate effect in wool grafting .. 225
Dosimetry ................... 175
Dynamitron electron beam accel-
   erators ................... 168

## E

Elastic modulus $vs.$ radiation dose . 144
Elastomers ................... 57
   extensibility of ............... 140
   radicals in irradiated ......... 8
Electron accelerators .......... x
   grafting to wool .............. 228
Electron beam-initiated irradiation
   crosslinking .............. 156
Electron spin resonance .......128, 257
Electrons .................... 34
   super excited ................ 3
   trapped .................... 35
Elongation
   of PVC-styrene .............. 211
   at rupture $vs.$ radiation dose ... 144
Embrittlement, low temperature .. 75
Emulsion polybutadiene ......... 62
Emulsion polymerization ........ 185
End linking .................. 154
Energy of common chemical bonds 257–8
Energy transfer ................ 69

Environmental stress crack resistance .................... 74
ESR ....................128, 257
of aqueous solutions .......... 13
studies on irradiated polystyrene 83, 92
studies of wool grafting ....... 233
Ethane ........................ 34
Ethyl acrylate ................ 190
Ethylene–alkyl acrylate copolymers 71
amorphous ................ 76
Ethylene–butadiene
copolymers ................ 166
polymer .................... 156
Ethylene copolymers, radiation
crosslinking of ............. 156
Ethylene–ethyl acrylate ......... 162
Ethylene methacrylic acid ionomer
resins .................156, 157
Ethylene oxide ................ 113
Ethylene–vinyl acetate .......... 161
copolymers ................ 156
Ethyl radicals ................ 265
Evolution of hydrogen from PET . 132
Excited molecules .............. 23
Expansion of glassy polymers .... 94
Extensibility of an elastomer ..... 140
Extinction coefficients for trans-
vinylene unsaturation ....... 143

F

Films, properties of crosslinked ... 73
Flexible polyurethane foam ...... 214
Flexural strength of PVC–styrene . 211
Foam
flexible polyurethane .......... 214
grafting of vinyl monomer on
polyurethane ............. 215
radiation-induced graft polymerization of polyurethane .... 214
Fractures .................... 133
Free ions .................... 34
Free radicals .................25, 128
in polyolefins ................ 256

G

Gamma photons ............... 59
Gamma radiation ............. 5, 17
-induced polymerization of vinyl
monomers .............. 184
Gas evolution in glassy polymers,
G-values for ............. 99
Gelation
in irradiated polymers ........ 13
of PET .................... 133
Glassy polymers
creep of ................... 79
expansion of ............... 94
G-values for gas evolution in ... 99
Glucose ...................... 242
infrared absorption spectrum of.248–9
pentaacetate ............... 242
infrared absorption spectrum
of ...................248–9

Graft copolymer
density of ................... 211
styrene-poly(vinyl chloride) ... 203
Graft polymerization of polyurethane foam, radiation-induced 214
Grafted side chains, molecular
weight of ................ 228
Grafting of vinyl monomer
on polyurethane foam ........ 215
to wool, radiation ........... 221
Grafting to wool, electron accelerator ................... 228
G-values
for crosslinking in polystyrene .. 97
for gas evolution in glassy
polymers ............... 99
for scission in polystyrene ..... 97

H

Heat-shrinkable film ............ 74
Heavy metal catalysts .......... 113
n-Hexa-1-decane .............. 34
High temperature performance ... 74
Homopolymer ................. 208
Homopolymerization .......... 215
Hot blown plastic films ......... 73
Hydrocarbon polymers in nitrous
oxide atmosphere .......... 44
Hydrogen abstraction ..........5, 259
Hydrogen atom abstraction ...... 27
Hydrogen migration .......... 40
Hydrogen from PET, evolution of . 132
Hydrophilic monomers .......... 214

I

Infrared absorption spectrum
of glucose .................248–9
pentaacetate ............... 248
Infrared spectra of cellulose triacetate .................... 244
Inherent viscosities of cellulose triacetate ................... 251
Intermittent stress application on
creep of glassy polymers,
effect of ................. 89
Ionic
intermediates ................ 31
polymerization .............3, 171
species .................... 23
Ionization in solids ............. 2
Ionizing radiation .............. 256
Ion-molecule reactions ......... 32
Ionomer resins, ethylene methacrylic acid ............... 156
Ionomers, radiation crosslinked ... 139
Irradiated polymers, gelation in .. 13
Irradiation
advantages of .............. vii
of biological systems .......... 14
crosslinking, electron beam-
initiated ................ 156
of polymeric and biological
molecules .............. 14
of polymer solutions .......... 12

Isomerization of cis groups ...... 63
Isoprene .................... 190

**K**

Ketene ...................... 244
Kinetics .................... 130
  of the allyl free radical growth .. 38
  of grafting ................ 231
  of growth of dienyl and trienyl
    free radicals ............ 42

**L**

LET ....................17, 67
Lichtenberg discharge effect ..... 161
Linear accelerator ............. 81
Linear energy transfer .......... 17
Liquid vinyl monomers ......... 170
Lorentz band shape ............ 62
Low temperature embrittlement .. 75
Luminescent impurities ......... 10

**M**

Mass spectra ................. 242
Mechanism of crosslinking ....... 3
Mechanisms in polymers, radiation 1
Mechanisms of radiation-initiated
  transformations ............ 22
Melt viscosity ................ 209
Methane .................... 34
Methyl acrylate .............. 190
Methylacrylonitrile ............ 190
Methylene free radicals ......... 36
Methyl free radical ............ 36
Methyl methacrylate .........185, 190
Methyl radicals ............... 263
α-Methylstyrene, radiation-induced
  polymerization of .......... 170
Molecular-weight distribution .... 113
Molecular weight of grafted side
  chains .................. 228

**N**

Negative ions ................ 35
Neutrons ................... 59
Nitrous oxide atmosphere, hydro-
  carbon-polymers in ......... 44
Nuclear reactor ............... 59

**O**

Olefinic groups in polybutadiene .. 57
Oxidation ................... 37
Oxygen reactions in irradiated
  polymers ................ 7

**P**

Peroxidation of polyurethane foam 215
Peroxides ................... 27
Peroxy radicals ............... 261
PET
  evolution of hydrogen from .... 132
  gelation of ................ 133
Phenolic antioxidant ........... 142

Photolytic degradation of cellulose
  triacetate ................ 240
Physical properties of poly(vinyl
  chloride)–styrene radiation
  graft copolymer ........... 203
Polybutadiene
  olefinic groups in ........... 57
  trans- and side vinyl ......... 66
cis-Polybutadiene ............. 61
trans-Polybutadiene ........... 57
Poly(1-butene) ............... 264
Polyene acids ................ 260
Polyenes ................... 37
Polyenyl free radical ........... 37
Polyenylic radicals ..........257, 261
Polyether ................... 113
Polyethylene ................ 258
  crosslinking of .............. 24
  radiation crosslinked ......... 139
  radiation crosslinking of ...... 44
  reactive intermediates in the
    radiation chemistry of .... 31
  single crystals .............. 7
  solution-crystallized .......... 259
  terephthalate, radiation chemis-
    try of ................ 127
Poly(ethylene oxide) ........... 113
Polyisobutylene ..............48, 263
Polymer radicals .............. 4
Polymer solutions, irradiation of .. 12
cis-1,4-Polymer, spectrum of a ... 59
Polymers
  reactive species in ........... 22
  in solution ................ 12
Polymeric macromolecules, irradia-
  tion of .................. 14
Polymerization
  of α-methyl styrene, radiation
    induced ............... 170
  of vinyl monomers, γ-radiation-
    induced ............... 184
Poly(methyl methacrylate) ...... 82
Polyolefins, free radicals in ...... 256
Polyox ..................... 113
Polypropylene ..............50, 261
Polystyrene ................. 82
  crosslinking in irradiated ...... 98
  ESR studies on irradiated ..... 83
  G-values for crosslinking in .... 97
  G-values for scission in ....... 97
  scission in irradiated ......... 98
  sol-gel studies on irradiated .... 82
Polyurethane foam
  flexible ................... 214
  grafting of vinyl monomer on .. 215
  peroxidation of ............. 125
  radiation-induced graft poly-
    merization of ........... 214
Poly(vinyl chloride)–styrene radiation graft copolymer ........ 203
Poly(vinyl chloride–vinyl acetate)
  copolymer ................ 82
Positive ions ................. 23

Postirradiation effects in wool
    grafting ................. 223
Preirradiation of poly(vinyl
    chloride) ................ 25
Product yields on dose, dependence
    of ..................... 128
Propane ..................... 34
Properties of crosslinked films .... 73
Properties improvement ........ ix
Proton affinity ................ 34
Proton transfer process .......... 24
Pulse radiolysis ..............13, 175
PVC–styrene, physical properties of 211

## R

Radiation
    chemistry of polyethylene
        terephthalate ........... 127
    crosslinked ionomers and poly-
        ethylenes .............. 139
    crosslinking
        of ethylene copolymers ...... 156
        of polyethylene ........... 44
    dose
        elastic modulus vs. ......... 144
        elongation at rupture vs. .... 144
        solubility vs. ............. 146
        tensile strength vs. ........ 143
    graft copolymer, styrene–
        poly(vinyl chloride) ...... 203
    grafting of vinyl monomers to
        wool ................. 221
    -induced
        polymerization of α-methyl-
            styrene ............. 170
        graft polymerization of poly-
            urethane foam ........ 214
        polymerization of vinyl
            monomers, gamma ..... 184
    -initiated transformations,
        mechanisms of .......... 22
    mechanisms in polymers ....... 1
    sensitivity ................ 16
    ultraviolet ................ 240
    and ionizing .............. 256
Radicals
    alkylic ................... 260
    allylic ................... 257
    dienylic .................. 260
    in irradiated elastomer ........ 8
    methyl ................... 263
    peroxy ................... 261
    polyenylic ..............257, 261
    polymer .................. 4
Radioactive isotopes .......... ix
Radioprotection .............. 12
Reaction rate vs. time .......... 191
Reaction rates of poly(vinyl chlo-
    ride)–styrene radiation graft
    copolymer ............... 203
Reactive intermediates in the radia-
    tion chemistry of polyethylene  31

Reactive species in polymers ..... 22
Reactivity transfer in biological
    material ................. 19
Recombination .............. 27
Recording dilatometer .......... 185
Reinforcement of polymer ....... 8
Resonance stabilization .......... 260
Rubberlike properties .......... 76
Rubber, synthetic ............. 57

## S

Santonox ................... 142
Santowhite powder ........... 142
Scission in irradiated polystyrene .. 98
Scission in polystyrene,
    G-values for ............. 97
Side vinyl group .............. 59
Side vinyl polybutadiene ........ 66
Sodium polybutadiene .......... 62
Softening temperatures, Vicat .... 158
Sol-gel studies on irradiated
    polystyrene ..............82, 93
Solids, ionization in ........... 2
Solubility vs. radiation dose ...... 146
Solution-crystallized polyethylene . 259
Solution viscosities ............ 250
Spectrum of a cis-1,4-polymer .... 59
Sponge, wettable ............. 214
Stress crack resistance, environ-
    mental .................. 74
Stress on creep of glassy polymers,
    effect of ................ 85
Styrene ..................172, 185
Styrene–poly(vinyl chloride)
    radiation graft copolymer .... 203
Sulfhydryl .................. 19
Super excited electrons .......... 3
Surlyn A ................... 141
Swelling effect in wool grafting .. 225
Synthetic rubber .............. 57

## T

Target dimension ............. 17
Temperature on creep of glassy
    polymers, effect of ......... 90
Tenite 3310 ................. 142
Tensile strength
    of PVC–styrene ............ 211
    vs. radiation dose ........... 143
Thermoluminescence .......... 10
Thiobisphenolic antioxidant ...... 142
Time vs. reaction rate .......... 191
Transformations, mechanisms of
    radiation-initiated .......... 22
Transient acceleration of creep
    rates of polymers .......... 79
Trapped electrons ............. 35
Trapped radicals .........26, 139, 215
Trienyl free radicals, kinetics of
    growth of ............... 42

## U

Ultraviolet
irradiation ................. 42
light ...................... 38
radiation ...............240, 256
sources ................. xi
spectroscopy at low temperatures 257
spectrum .................. 39
Unsaturated groups ............ 58
Unsaturation, vinylene .......... 6

## V

Van de Graaff generator ......... 81
Vicat softening temperatures ..... 158
Vinyl ....................... 61
decay ..................... 147
groups, decay of ............. 139
monomers
liquid ................... 170
gamma-radiation-induced
polymerization of ...... 184
on polyurethane foam, grafting of ................ 215
to wool, radiation grafting of . 221

*cis*-Vinylene .................... 60
*trans*-Vinylene .................47, 61
unsaturation ................. 32
extinction coefficients for .... 143
Vinylidine chloride ............. 190
*trans*-Vinyl polybutadiene ....... 66

## W

Weak links .................... 132
Wettable sponge .............. 214
Wool
electron accelerator grafting to.. 228
radiation grafting of vinyl
monomers to ........... 221
Wool grafting
air effect in ................. 225
ESR studies of ............. 233
dose rate effect in ........... 225
postirradiation effects in ....... 223
swelling effect in ............. 225

## X

Xenon ...................... 46

# Date Due

| FEB 1 0 '68 | | | |
|---|---|---|---|
| | | | |
| | | | |
| | | | |
| | | | |
| | | | |
| | | | |
| | | | |
| | | | |
| | | | |
| | | | |
| | | | |
| | | | |
| | | | |
| | | | |
| | | | |

mco 293-5